COMPASSIONATE LEADERSHIP

SUSTAINING WISDOM, HUMANITY
AND PRESENCE IN
HEALTH AND SOCIAL CARE

MICHAEL A. WEST

COMPASSIONATE LEADERSHIP

SUSTAINING WISDOM, HUMANITY AND PRESENCE IN HEALTH AND SOCIAL CARE

Michael A. West CBE

Professor of Organisational Psychology, Lancaster University, England

Senior Visiting Fellow, The King's Fund

Emeritus Professor, Aston University

The Swirling Leaf Press

The Swirling Leaf Press

www.swirlingleafpress.com
info@swirlingleafpress.com

Book design by Mash Chudasama
www.mash-design.com
mash-design

Cover photograph by Casey Horner
https://unsplash.com/@mischievous_penguins

Printed in the United Kingdom

First Edition Printed in 2021
ISBN 978-0-9957669-7-6

Dedicated to all those health and social care staff working during the covid-19 global pandemic, with gratitude for their courage, commitment, and compassion, and to all among them who gave their lives in caring for others.

Acknowledgments

Health Education and Improvement Wales (HEIW) have supported this project from its start just before the covid-19 pandemic and consistently since. Their commitment to developing a healthy and happy population in Wales is embodied in the organisation's vision and culture. This is translated into action by compassionate leaders such as Helen Thomas, Assistant Director of Leadership and Succession, who has provided support and encouragement in addition to being a joy to work with. Programme Manager Emily Millar has creatively and enthusiastically designed an award-winning leadership portal *https://nhswalesleadershipportal.heiw.wales/*, featuring many of the resources developed for this book. I am grateful also to Julie Rogers, Deputy Chief Executive for HEIW, and Alex Howells, Chief Executive for HEIW, who have enabled me to contribute to the health and social care leadership strategy for Wales. Thank you to my brilliant colleagues and friends at The King's Fund, Suzie Bailey, Director of Leadership and OD, and Jo Vigor, Assistant Director, for having the unfailing courage to pursue a challenging and positive vision of health and social care for the future.

And thank you to Gillian Hardy for my most profound learning about compassion.

June 2021

Contents

Chapter 5. Compassionate team leadership and psychological safety

Chapter 6. Compassionate leadership is effective leadership

Chapter 7. If it's not inclusive, it's not compassionate leadership

Chapter 8. Collective leadership

Chapter 9. Compassionate leadership across boundaries

Chapter 10. Compassionate leadership for quality improvement and innovation

Chapter 11. Leadership self-compassion

Chapter 1.

Compassion: a universal human value

It is the hands and hearts of health and social care staff that hold our communities together. They are the hands and hearts of people who have dedicated a large part of their precious, unique lives to caring for those around them. It is their wisdom, humanity and presence that has helped to hold our communities together through the most challenging of times. It was they who cared for our communities during the covid-19 crisis, thereby putting their own lives at risk, and continue to do so through the waves of the pandemic. They embody the universal human value of compassion. This book is about how they can best be supported in their mission to help and heal.

Summary

This chapter explores the concept of compassion and why we should seek to develop cultures of compassion in workplaces. The role of leadership in modelling and embodying compassion to develop such cultures is outlined. Compassionate leadership may be mistaken for a soft and ineffective approach to leading in health and social care, but more courage is required to lead compassionately than to lead using command and control. The chapter proposes that compassionate leadership requires maintaining a strong focus on performance while managing individual and team performance clearly and with compassion. Compassionate leadership involves clearly addressing misuses of power and abusive behaviour. It makes clear also that compassionate leadership is an institutional responsibility as well as an individual leadership style, and this requires organisations (including national health and social care bodies) to develop cultures of compassion through consistent leadership. The chapter also addresses how to deal compassionately with difficult behaviours that we encounter in the workplace.

Introduction

Compassion is a universal value because of two truths – the first is that we have all experienced compassion, no matter our cultural background, upbringing, or the different paths that our lives take. And second, compassion is universal because it is care that flows naturally from a deep part of ourselves, to those who need it, regardless of status, wealth, ethnicity, age or gender. Compassion binds us together, creates a sense of safety and interconnectedness and is a manifestation of love in an encompassing rather than exclusive sense. It nurtures a feeling of belonging to others beyond our immediate circles.

No country in the world has had enough resources to deal with the covid-19 crisis in the way they would wish to – all health systems have had to find creative responses to innovate, spread knowledge and collaborate, and to determine how best to respond. Most have recognised that compassion is at the heart of any effective response, and at the heart of health and social care. Most of us have recognised that we must promote understanding of our interconnectedness with each other – across professional boundaries, across hierarchies, across sectors, across communities and across nations. The learning from the pandemic urged us to seize the moment (every moment) and model and promote compassion within and across our health and social care organisations in an enduring way.

Why? Because connection and compassion are certain, unchanging and provide a safe refuge in the face of a major threat to our health and social care systems and our wider communities. And compassion enables us to cope with illness, pain, fear and uncertainty in unusual times. We must focus compassion on patients, communities and all those who provide health and social care services. Compassion, as chapter 3 describes, is the most powerful intervention that can be offered in healthcare, with effects more powerful than aspirin in the management of heart attacks and statins in the five-year risk of a cardiovascular event.

> Compassion is 'a sensitivity to suffering in self and others with a commitment to try to alleviate and prevent it'[1].

We are motivated to notice and become aware of the distress of the other and pay attention to this distress[2], while having an empathic insight into the needs of others[3]. These are basic human instincts.

It also implies having the motivation to help[2]. The 'commitment to alleviate/prevent suffering' requires courage and wisdom, ie, taking 'wise' action. Compassion involves 'the motivation to relieve the suffering of another'[3] and invokes the concept of cognitive empathy – 'stepping into someone else's shoes' – which helps to guide an appropriate response[4].

Compassion has facilitators and inhibitors. For example, it is easier to be compassionate to people we like than those we don't; those we think will appreciate us rather than people we think will not; and people who share our values rather than those who do not. Inhibitors of compassion in healthcare include poor working conditions, poor leadership, role confusion, role conflicts, and work overload. It is therefore important to identify both the inhibitors and facilitators of compassion in this context[5 9].

A story of compassion	Sharon's grandmother was a stroke victim. Perhaps that's why Sharon works in a job that requires her to listen to patients, find out what matters, what works well and then use what she has learned to identify and support best practice. At a listening event, Sharon meets Amber, who had a stroke at 19. Amber has her life ahead of her; she is courageous, resilient, resourceful and determined to lead a fulfilling life, despite instances of poor care – and Sharon learns from her what it means to be a stroke survivor and live life to the full after stroke. *http://www.patientvoices.org.uk*

Four elements of compassion

The increase in research and theorising about compassion and particularly compassion in workplaces has arisen in parallel with the global movements to nurture compassion across our communities and the planet more widely[10]. Compassion (in an organisational context) can be understood as having four elements: *attending, understanding, empathising and helping*[11].

In the context of an interaction between a healthcare professional and (for example) an elderly patient, compassion involves:

1. Paying attention to the other, being present and noticing their suffering - *attending*

2. Understanding what is causing the other's distress, by making an appraisal of the cause, ideally through a listening dialogue with that person to achieve a shared understanding - *understanding*

3. Having an empathic response, mirroring the other's feelings, having a felt relation with the other's distress without being overwhelmed by those feelings - *empathising*

4. Taking intelligent (thoughtful, wise and appropriate) action to help relieve the other's suffering – *helping*

Compassion is a means of connecting with others - those we love, those to whom we are neutral or indifferent and those who we find difficult, and establishing trust and warmth. It is a way of transcending boundaries and establishing our shared humanity with a commitment to help, support and nourish. When we become more aware, open, and curious about the world and those around us through attending (being present), seeking to understand, empathising and with a commitment to helping, life has meaning and richness. It enables us also to respond more wisely to personal challenges and to manage our anxieties, anger and pains with greater confidence and ease. It helps us to help make the world a better place – our relationships, our families, our workplaces, our communities, and our planet. Compassion and leading for compassion are the subjects of this book.

Compassionate workplaces and the role of compassionate leadership

How do we create the conditions within our workplaces – the organisational cultures – where compassion will be nurtured? Organisational culture is shaped by all of us but particularly by its leadership. It is the behaviour of leaders, top to bottom and end to end, individually and collectively, in healthcare organisations that powerfully determine whether care quality is the priority; all staff have clear objectives; there is enlightened people management; there are high levels of staff engagement; learning and quality improvement are embedded; and good team and inter-team working is endemic[12]. And leadership is potentially demonstrated by all in an organisation or community, not only those formally identified as leaders.

Research on climate and culture in health and social care internationally suggests that leadership cultures of command and control are less effective than more engaging and compassionate leadership styles and implies that compassionate and collective leadership approaches are likely to be most effective[13,14].

Compassionate leadership involves attending to, understanding, empathising with and helping those we lead.

> The purpose of compassionate leadership in health and social care is to help create the conditions where all of those in our communities are supported to live the best and most fulfilling lives they can.

To be compassionate as leaders in health and social care means being effective as a leader in pursuit of that vision by ensuring direction, alignment, and commitment. If leadership is not inclusive, it is not compassionate. That means leadership must include all, regardless of professional background, opinion, skin colour, sexuality, religion or gender. Including all is a core value of health and social care and including all is the nature of compassion.

Compassion implies sharing power and influence by encouraging collective leadership, where all feel they have leadership influence. And collective leadership requires leaders to work compassionately together to develop a climate of shared, interdependent leadership prioritising care for those in the communities overall, rather than just our own areas of responsibility.

Compassionate leadership embodies both a sensitivity to the challenges that colleagues in health and social care face and a commitment to help them respond effectively to those challenges and to thrive in the process of their work, through modelling the four elements of compassion. These themes are explored, explained and evidenced in this book, augmented by practical strategies and links.

Caring for the health and well-being of others is an intrinsically compassionate behaviour that is an expression of the core human value of compassion. Virtually all those who work in health and social care services have dedicated their lives to caring for others. Compassion is therefore a central value and motive in their lives and the extent to which their organisations mirror in practice that value of compassion will influence the value 'fit' between them and their organisations. The stronger that fit - the alignment of individual and organisational values - the higher the levels of their commitment, engagement and satisfaction[15]. Where organisations place more emphasis on financial performance, impression management or productivity, the value fit will be poorer, with an associated loss of staff motivation and satisfaction.

Compassion (in an organisational context) involves the same four elements of compassion but understood and applied in the context of leading others.

Attending: The first element of compassionate leadership is being present with, and attending to, those we lead. Leaders who attend will model being present with those they lead and 'listening with fascination'[16]. Listening is probably the most important skill of leadership[7] and involves taking the time to listen to the challenges, obstacles, frustrations and hurts of staff experience, as well as the successes and pleasures.

Understanding: The second component involves leaders appraising the situation those they lead are struggling with, to arrive at a measured understanding. Ideally, leaders arrive at their understanding through dialogue with those they lead, which may involve reconciling conflicting perspectives rather than imposing their own understanding. Sadly, in the context of highly pressured work situations, health and social care staff often feel they are not listened to and that their leaders do not understand the situations they face[17].

Empathising: The third component of compassionate leadership is empathising. Compassionate leadership requires being able to feel the distress or frustration of those we lead without being overwhelmed by the emotion and unable to help. Putting oneself in the other's shoes means taking their perspective which increases understanding of the sources and context of the difficulties they face[18].

Helping: The fourth and final component is taking thoughtful and intelligent action to help the other. Probably the most important task of leaders in healthcare is to help those they lead to deliver the high-quality, compassionate care they want to provide. Leadership, according to all definitions, includes helping and supporting others. The helping element can be seen as having four components: scope – breadth of resources offered; scale – the volume of resources; speed – the timeliness of the response; and specialisation – the extent to which the response meets the real needs of the other[19,20]. Helping means removing the obstacles that get in the way of people doing their work and providing the resources (staff, equipment and training, for example) for them to do so.

These four elements of compassionate leadership are particularly relevant in healthcare, where the workforce is composed of highly skilled and motivated professionals, intent on doing their jobs to the highest possible standard. They require support rather than direction and enabling rather than controlling interventions from leaders[21]. When leaders demonstrate compassion, they provide this support in a way that is consistent with the core value orientation of those they lead. But they also legitimate it as a valued and worthwhile way of behaving, thus encouraging those they lead to respond compassionately in the face of suffering[20,21].

Compassion during covid-19: Cardiff and Vale University Health Board

During the covid-19 pandemic, the Health Board's charity funded Staff Havens at the University Hospital of Wales (UHW), University Hospital Llandough (UHL) and the Dragon's Heart Hospital. These spaces offered staff a calm, quiet space away from their clinical area in order to wind down and relax during their breaks and provided a central hub on each site to receive donations for staff. During the covid-19 pandemic, the Health Board was overwhelmed by donations of gifts, food and drink from the public and other organisations, which were received and distributed to staff across all sites. The charity distributed over 70,000 meals to staff as part of their 'Spread the Love' campaign. In order to support staff, Dr Julie Highfield, a Consultant Clinical Psychologist developed factsheets with tips for staff to better manage their mental health. Examples included an end of shift well-being checklist, specific guidance for managers around grief and bereavement, and well-being tips for staff working at home.

The Health Board also implemented telephone psychological support for staff. The Health Board arranged suspension of parking restrictions at its sites so that staff could park in any available space regardless of whether they carried a permit. Further, the Capital, Estates and Facilities team arranged for 24-hour hot food provision to be implemented at the UHW restaurant, Y Gegin, and the restaurant at UHL. The team also installed shower facilities at both UHW and UHL so that staff could shower after their shift. The Health Board also provided an accommodation booking service for staff who needed somewhere to stay urgently following working in hospital, or if they had vulnerable family members meaning that they were unable to return home after caring for patients with covid-19.

The affective states of leaders influence the general mood of those they lead, a phenomenon known as mood linkage or emotional contagion[22-24]. Research shows that positive leader affect is associated with more positive affect among staff[25], enhanced team performance, and higher rates of prosocial behaviours[26,27].

Experiencing compassion from others shapes individuals' appraisals about themselves (eg, seeing themselves as more capable), their peers (eg, viewing them as kinder) and the kind of organisation of which they are a part[28]. When staff feel valued and cared for (ie, perceived organisational support), they tend to feel more satisfied in their jobs, and have increased affective commitment to their organisations. There is considerable evidence that this is true in health and social care organisations and is associated with high levels of patient or service user satisfaction, care quality and even organisational financial performance[18].

Research in healthcare has shown that learning and innovation are more likely to take place in a culture of compassionate leadership and psychological safety rather than in a culture dominated by fear and blame[29-31].

A culture of supportive teams with compassionate team leadership is linked with reduced levels of stress, errors, staff injuries, harassment, bullying and violence against staff, staff absenteeism and (in the acute sector) patient mortality[32,33].

Compassionate leadership is therefore at the heart of our efforts to nurture cultures that provide high-quality, continually improving and compassionate care for patients and service users[29,34].

Dispelling the myths of compassionate leadership

There are some myths that must be addressed to ensure leaders see the true value of compassionate leadership and implement strategies that enable and foster it. These myths are that compassionate leadership will mean:

- The loss of commitment to purpose and high-quality performance will result from always taking the easy, consensus way forward rather than putting patients and communities first

- Tough performance management and tough conversations won't be allowed

- Leaders will be unable to challenge the status quo and make the radical changes patients and communities need

- Teamwork and system working will be controlled by whoever has the most power and is most ruthless

- Compassionate leadership is focused on individuals so institutions will not change

Virtually all health and social care staff are committed to providing high-quality and compassionate care. They represent probably the most motivated and skilled workforce in the whole of industry. However, we impose on them a dominant command and control style that has the effect of silencing their voices, suppressing their ideas for new and better ways of delivering patient care and suffocating their intrinsic motivation and fundamental altruism. Released, their motivation and creativity will ensure commitment to purpose and performance. Their voices are needed to tell us how care can best be improved as the endless remote top-down plans often fail because they ignore the reality of day-to-day care.

Compassionate leadership means creating the conditions – through consistently listening, understanding, empathising and helping – to make it possible to also have tough performance management and tough conversations when needed. Staff often complain they only see their leaders when something goes wrong and that even if they do listen, nothing changes after the conversation. Compassionate leadership ensures a collective focus and a greater likelihood of collective responsibility for ensuring high-quality, compassionate care.

1. Maintaining a clear focus on performance

It is a myth that compassionate leadership will prevent leaders from effectively managing the performance of individuals, teams or organisations and ensuring the delivery of high-quality, continually improving and compassionate health and social care. Leadership compassion in health and social care is ultimately for the purpose of promoting the health and happiness of all those in our communities. That must be the overriding purpose for leaders. That is the reason they occupy a leadership position and must be their guiding vision.

Performance problems are often not addressed because leaders are anxious about upsetting staff. So-called 'wicked problems' are avoided or hidden. Compassionate leadership is fundamentally focused on performance in the interests of the people and communities served by our health and social care systems.

When Nelson Mandela was released from Robben Island Prison in 1990, the African National Congress celebrated his release partly because they now had a leader who could lead them against the apartheid regime and the Inkatha Freedom Party. Nelson Mandela went against many of his followers (hundreds of thousands) to strive for a power transition that would be based on negotiation and reconciliation. Against all the odds, he succeeded and ensured that South Africa avoided a civil war.

His compassion for his country transcended any need to placate or pander to his followers. That was the breadth and courage of his compassion for those in his country.

In the interests of compassion for our wider society, leaders in health and social care must keep a clear focus on the purpose of their leadership, identifying performance problems, and using the skills of compassionate leadership to ensure they are addressed.

The process is one of identifying problems, listening to those involved, finding an understanding of the causes, empathising and then finding ways to support staff to enable them to deliver high-quality and compassionate care.

2. Managing performance with compassion

It is a myth that performance cannot be managed with compassion – that compassionate leadership is just about being nice to followers. In fact, compassionate performance management is more effective than command and control, or punitive approaches to performance management.

Why is performance a problem? Most often it is because people have not agreed clear goals or objectives for their work. Or they may have too much work or too many competing goals, or may not have clear feedback or information about their job performance. Other reasons include working in poorly functioning teams with lack of role clarity, obstacles that get in the way (such as interpersonal conflicts, lack of collaboration and co-operation between departments) or because people don't have the relevant knowledge, skills, training or experience to do the work.

The skills of compassionate leadership are central to success in managing performance problems. Listening deeply to discover the underlying problems; exploring and discussing to fully understand those problems; having an empathic connecting response; and then finding ways to support the other person top perform effectively.

There are five useful steps in this process:

Step 1 - Identify the problem. This is the most important step because many leaders jump to conclusions about what the problem is and focus on 'solving' the wrong problem.

Step 2 - Assess and analyse the problem, ideally with the staff member or team. This involves gathering all necessary data and information that can help to clarify the problem. The more time spent clarifying the problem (ideally with the member of staff or team), the more likely it is that effective solutions will emerge naturally from the process. Compassion is about taking the time to truly understand in order to help.

Step 3 - Meet with the person to discuss the problem, based on the information gathered and if necessary, work through competing perspectives in a spirit of commitment to shared learning to arrive at a comprehensive and useful understanding.

Step 4 - Jointly devise and agree a solution. This is likely to involve setting clear measurable goals for the future.

Step 5 - Monitor performance by gathering relevant information and set a time for a review to determine progress.

Managing poor performance benefits from a compassionate coaching approach where people and teams have clear agreed objectives and feedback on performance is constantly provided (ideally in the form of data). Compassionate leaders must coach by agreeing clear objectives with those individuals and teams they lead (aligned around the vision of providing high-quality, compassionate services). There must be a strong emphasis on drawing attention to effective performance rather than only providing feedback when there is an apparent problem. Ultimately, compassionate leadership means having the courage to focus on difficulties and to have honest, open and necessarily difficult conversations in a compassionate way (attending, understanding, empathising and helping) in order to deliver for communities.

3. Compassion enabling radical innovation

It is a myth that compassion is 'soft and fluffy' and doesn't stimulate innovation because it is not focused on changing the status quo. But why is innovation/quality improvement so important in health and social care?

Only innovation can enable modern health and social care organisations and systems to meet the radically changing needs and expectations of the communities they serve. We have seen this repeatedly demonstrated during the covid-19 pandemic. While adequate financial support is a necessary precondition, more money on its own, without transformative change, will not be enough. To fulfil the vision for health and social care for our communities, we need leaders to ensure radical and sustained innovation.

Compassionate leadership is a fundamental enabling factor that creates a culture of improvement and radical innovation across health and social care. Compassionate leadership enhances the intrinsic motivation of health and social care staff and reinforces their fundamental altruism. It helps to promote a culture of learning, where risk-taking (within safe boundaries) is encouraged and where there is an acceptance that not all innovation will be successful – an orientation diametrically opposite to a culture characterised by blame, fear and bullying.

Compassion also creates psychological safety, such that staff feel confident in speaking out about errors, problems and uncertainties and feel empowered and supported to develop and implement ideas for new and improved ways of delivering services.

They also work more co-operatively and collaboratively in a compassionate culture, in a climate characterised by cohesion, optimism and a sense of efficacy. Compassionate leadership is an enabling condition for innovation because it ensures greater coherence between the values and behaviours within health and social care organisations and how they engage with patients and service users.

The evidence of the links between psychological safety, supportiveness, positivity, empathy, leadership (in effect, compassionate leadership) and innovation is deep and convincing. The research shows that compassionate leaders help to nurture the five fundamental elements of a culture for innovative and high-quality care:

- Inspiring vision and strategy

- Clear agreed and aligned goals at every level

- Positive inclusion and participation

- Enthusiastic team and cross-boundary working

- Support and autonomy for staff to innovate

4. Compassion versus power and abuse

It is a myth that compassionate leaders will be ignored or disempowered by people who misuse or abuse their power. Compassion is expressed by minimising power differentials and is the opposite of abuse or diminishing others.

Nevertheless, one of the most difficult challenges is dealing with a powerful person who misuses or abuses their power. Because compassionate leadership is focused on delivering high-quality care for people in our communities, abusers must be dealt with. Otherwise, they continue to undermine our collective ability to deliver that high-quality care.

Behaviours are more often a consequence of the situation people find themselves in rather than personality. We must ensure we fully understand the situation others find themselves in when their behaviour is problematic. Compassionate leadership requires attending to people and listening to their accounts to ensure a more comprehensive understanding of their work situation.

And it is important to ensure that people, whatever their level in the hierarchy, are given feedback about their behaviour and its consequences. Very often, those who misuse their power have not been given feedback about the effects of their behaviours and so are unaware of problems they may be causing. Compassionate leadership requires we gather data and provide clear feedback as a first step. Such feedback should be focused on providing information about behaviour and its consequences eg, '*I observe that in our team meetings, you express disagreements strongly and loudly with team members so that they often refrain from offering opinions or proposing new and improved ways of doing things. The feedback from our team survey suggests most do not feel safe in team meetings.*'

Compassionate leadership requires that we don't simply feedback once and hope all will be well. We must continue providing feedback (both positive and negative), consistent with a coaching model to maintain a focus on changing inappropriate behaviours. It is important to be clear when we see people misusing their power simply to get their own way.

It is valuable to provide feedback as close to the time when behaviours are observed, especially in relation to discrimination (based on gender or ethnic minority status for example), in relation to racist or sexist comments or in relation to aggression. This takes courage, clarity and practice.

Sometimes it is helpful to rehearse difficult conversations in advance to ensure that we are clear about the main points we wish to make. It is better to make three or four strong points in such a conversation than seven or eight which are a mix of strong and weak points.

It is not wise to act alone if you are feeding back to a person much more senior than you. Having a group of colleagues provide feedback together is far more powerful and less dangerous in such circumstances. For example, the compassionate leadership approach advocates that all leaders are assessed by those they lead in relation to the four behaviours of attending, understanding, empathising and helping. These assessments should take place at least annually and leaders encouraged to continue to develop their compassionate leadership. Feeding back from a group of people who work with a leader is a powerful way of ensuring a strong and consistent message. Such assessments and feedback should be part of the ways of working of every health and social care organisation.

This area is inherently difficult and some practical ways of having and managing difficult conversations are suggested later in this chapter.

More serious cases of bullying, sexual harassment, racism or the like should always be discussed with senior colleagues in the HR department or more senior leaders. Moreover, there are some individuals who may have narcissistic (or even psychopathic) tendencies who find it almost impossible to conceive that they may be doing harm or could be wrong. It is very difficult to provide guidance for such thankfully rare cases. Again, consulting HR professionals within our organisations is the wisest course in such circumstances.

5. Compassionate institutions

The final myth is that compassionate leadership refers to individuals behaving compassionately but this not being relevant to institutions and political leaders. The cultures of our health and social care service organisations are shaped partly by the behaviours of all who make up those organisations, particularly their leaders, but also by the cultures and leadership of national bodies that oversee them.

It is the responsibility of those organisations and their leaders (whose focus is on meeting the needs of the people and communities we serve) to make clear when other teams, organisations or national bodies are not modelling the four principles of compassionate leadership. The role of organisations and national bodies is to attend to those they partner with or oversee. It is to listen carefully, understand the problems faced (for example) by boards or trusts, to empathise and then - critically important - to find ways to support or help.

Whether it is hospital boards dealing with voluntary sector organisations, or national bodies working with patient and community representatives, or politicians working with national bodies, when the principles of compassionate leadership guide behaviour and relationships, the currents in the rivers are moving in the same direction. When the behaviours of institutions are inconsistent with the core values of our health and social care systems, they undermine our work to build cultures of high-quality, continually improving and compassionate care for those we serve in our communities.

Compassionate institutions model honest and respectful ways of working together as organisations and this must pervade the health and social care system of our nations. The cultures of all our organisations must reflect these compassionate principles of compassionate leadership to create strong compassionate cultures that are focused on providing high-quality and compassionate care for the people and communities we serve.

The same is true of politicians if we are to ensure that strong compassionate cultures characterise all our health and social care systems – top to bottom.

This is achievable in practice, but it requires that all leaders, at every level, recognise that compassion is expressed not only by individual leaders but also by the way institutions and organisations operate and behave with each other.

In summary, compassionate leadership involves a greater commitment to purpose and high-quality performance than existing approaches; compassionate leadership will focus more on effective performance management than less; and rather than an easy, consensus way forward, compassionate leadership requires putting patients, communities and staff well-being first; it means challenging the status quo and making the radical changes patients and communities need; and teamwork and system working will not be controlled by whoever has the most power and is most ruthless.

Northumbria Healthcare NHS Foundation Trust leading through covid-19

Vision and direction: Northumbria made the decision early in the spread of covid-19 that there should not be a trade-off between managing the epidemic and their commitment to high-quality, compassionate care for both patients and staff. For example, they did not want to shut patients' families out and so worked hard to enable contact. All wards were given iPads so patients' families could make contact and see their loved ones. Patients could make free telephone calls from the wards. And TV viewing was also free. There were helplines for families who could also email in photographs for staff to take to patients on the wards.

Listening to patients: All of this was built on the trust's extensive and pioneering work on patient experience, which saw 700 conversations a month with patients in real time. The learning was fed to staff teams within hours of the conversations taking place so they could address any issues and celebrate successes. It also helped them to be vigilant about areas where care quality and kindness might be lacking or diminishing.

Communicating with staff: Communication with staff was a key priority. Information was provided openly, honestly, and speedily. The chief executive wrote to staff weekly to update them via blogs on the internal Facebook pages, accessed by more than 7000 of the trust's 11000 staff. There was an emphasis on sharing positive stories about high-quality care, survival and recovery in the trust, contrasting with the gloomy and disempowering national news many were exposed to.

A new web-based platform was quickly developed and 'Corona voice' launched on 6 April 2020. Each week, staff were invited to reflect anonymously on their experiences. In a short online survey, they shared how motivated they felt, as well as their thoughts, concerns, or emotions. In the first three months they received more than 10,000 responses from the workforce. Each week the information is shared with the executive team helping the decision-making process.

Staff felt they were heard and their concerns were responded to and it led to big improvements in relationships between staff and managers. "Very early on, we became aware that staff experience was worse for those who remained at home – many felt isolated, lonely and guilty as they felt they weren't doing their bit to support colleagues. We were able to increase our contact with this group of staff to establish and maintain regular support. More than 1,300 welfare calls have been made to date – sometimes just to listen, sometimes to address financial or safeguarding concerns, and for others to direct them to more specialist forms of emotional support through occupational health and psychology. Our well-being website has been well-utilised by many of our colleagues, while the guide we wrote for our managers on leading teams through covid-19, was directly informed by some of the challenges and frustrations expressed by our workforce." Annie Laverty, Chief Experience Officer at Northumbria Healthcare NHS Foundation Trust.

Safety: The organisation adopted a proactive stance rather than waiting for national guidance when they ran short of PPE. They built a factory to manufacture the needed equipment at scale and pace and have produced over 2.2 million gowns and are offering supplies to other trusts across the country.

There was a strong emphasis on staff safety with a comprehensive approach to infection control. Sinks were installed at the entrance to every hospital so patients could be encouraged by the many volunteers present to wash their hands and wear masks.

Staff safety has been reinforced through stronger partnerships with Northumbria police, developed over recent years to prevent violence and aggression towards staff, particularly in Emergency Departments. A zero-tolerance policy has led to a stronger and clearer response to all such incidents.

There was quick escalation to provide team level support, hot debriefing, and referral routes to specialised psychological support when teams were under high levels of stress. These responses focused on normalising the difficulties for staff, challenging stigma and encouraging staff to reach out for support.

Sustaining belonging: Free food, parking and accommodation (where necessary) were provided for staff so that they would feel cared for. People were acknowledged constantly for their contributions whatever part of the organisation they were working in. For example, the CEO visited the mortuary staff who had been under huge levels of pressure, to acknowledge their contribution, as well as many other non-clinical areas.

At Christmas 2020, they sent all staff 'brown paper packages tied up with string' labelled 'From Northumbria with Love' containing well-being gifts and local produce. All staff also received a £50 bonus in January 2021. Staff were supported with financial difficulties via the trust's Community Bank (established prior to the pandemic and with 500 members) which has enabled staff to take out loans as needed.

Belonging was bolstered by the 'Who have you noticed this week' programme that asked staff to recognise publicly those who had made a difference to their well-being at work. The hundreds of nominations were published weekly, resulting in staff feeling powerfully appreciated by the organisation.

Teams and teamworking: Teams and teamworking were vital to the organisation before and during covid-19. "Teamwork got us through this. We must build back stronger and keep those teams strong." The trust continues to provide time and space for hour-long meetings for teams to reflect on difficulties they faced and to discuss how to improve things. Teams then implement their changes with support from the business team.

It is no surprise then that, based on staff survey data, Northumbria Healthcare NHS Foundation Trust is the best in England for health and well-being, morale and equality, diversity and inclusion.

https://www.health.org.uk/news-and-comment/ blogs/supporting-staff-wellbeing-during-covid-19-a-northumbrian-experience

A question raised consistently by many leaders in health and social care is how they can compassionately manage 'difficult people' or 'difficult behaviours'. It is important to address this issue clearly here before proceeding to explore compassionate leadership in more depth.

Managing difficult behaviour

Compassionate leadership in health and social care requires that we maintain a clear focus on the vision of the work – to promote the health and happiness of all in our communities. That requires also that we continually remind those we lead of the purpose and contribution of their work. Because such leadership is focused on a higher purpose to help all those in our communities, it makes the need to deal with difficult or toxic behaviour at work both more obvious and more clearly justified than might be the case in some other settings. Toxic or difficult behaviour undermines team effectiveness and therefore detracts from our ability to deliver high-quality, compassionate care.

What do we mean by difficult people? It is not the people that are difficult but their behaviour. They might be aggressive, passively aggressive, constantly cynical, sarcastic, bullying, not displaying conscientiousness, discriminating against minority ethnic staff or women, or being narcissistic (never recognising let alone willing to admit their mistakes for example). Our focus should be on not accepting the behaviours rather than not accepting the individual.

Compassionate leadership requires we take an evidence-based approach to dealing with difficulties – that means enriching our understanding of human behaviour and needs at work so that we can be more supportive and effective. A key principle is that behaviour is much more likely to be due to the situation people are in rather than to personality.

Toxic behaviours in teams are more likely to be a result of team members not having agreed clear team goals, not having clear roles in the team, not collecting accurate data on team performance, failing to meet regularly to review performance, or not providing warm and compassionate support for each other. Another common problem is chronic excessive workload which means team members are unable to complete their work effectively. These are more common explanations for difficult behaviour than 'personality problems.'

The first principle of compassionate leadership is therefore spending time with team members to better identify and understand the problems they face. This is achieved, as described earlier, by listening deeply, using reflective and active listening skills, and by gathering as much information as possible to enable an understanding of a team member's work or non-work situation (where the latter may be relevant).

It is compassionate (ie, with a focus on helping) to provide feedback to people whose behaviour is causing difficulty. Often, those around them have not given feedback so they may not be aware of their behaviour and its consequences. Failing to give feedback helps neither the individual nor the team they are a part of. And it fails the wider mission of health and social care in communities.

Giving clear and honest feedback about behaviour and its consequences is simply good leadership and management and this is relevant to both desirable and undesirable behaviours. In some cases, because people have never been given clear feedback, they have developed strategies and patterns which have become their history. They are no longer aware that people are a little afraid of them because this is how they have always behaved – and it has been reinforced.

The courage of compassionate leadership is evident when we give clear feedback. This applies to all difficult behaviours including aggression, dominating, bullying, discrimination, constant cynicism, passive aggression (being angry or withdrawn but not saying why), unpleasant 'humour', discrimination or sexual harassment.

Serious abuse (racism, sexual harassment, homophobia, religious intolerance) are HR issues and must be dealt with through formal, fair and clear processes. If such behaviour is tolerated, it will be perpetuated.

Compassionate leadership also requires we empathise with the other both in terms of how their behaviour is impacting on them (they probably elicit negative responses from many people) and in relation to the pain of receiving negative feedback.

Compassion involves helping. That includes giving feedback, setting agreed objectives with the person in relation to future behaviour, and continuing to give feedback and monitoring progress towards those objectives. Such coaching helps the individual to transform their behaviours over time.

Ultimately, if damaging behaviour does not steadily decline, it becomes a performance management issue and compassionate leadership would involve ensuring that either the behaviour is eliminated, or the person is required to leave the team or organisation. Because such damaging behaviours undermine team effectiveness and team member well-being, they cannot be tolerated and therefore the person must be 'performance managed' out of the team.

Compassionate leadership of difficult behaviours requires us to have difficult conversations courageously. There are several steps that may help in this.

1. **Think positively about the conversation:** See the meeting as a positive way of improving individual and team performance and helpful for the person you are giving feedback to. It will be a constructive conversation about their development.

2. **Stay present and calm:** The more we are present, grounded and calm, the better difficult conversations go. Mindfulness is a powerful practice to help with this. Come back to being present rather than anxious or angry – and 'listen with fascination'.

3. **Plan the conversation:** It helps to prepare a few bullet points before your conversation – not a list of 20 infractions going back years, but two or three recent and clear issues. Your language should be simple, clear, direct and descriptive. It should describe behaviour and consequences and not make personality attributions (you are an aggressive person).

4. **Understand the other's perspective:** Take the time to listen to and deeply understand the other person's perspective on the issues and ensure you have demonstrated your understanding to them before proceeding or disagreeing.

5. **Be compassionate:** Your standpoint must be compassion. Being disliked by colleagues, feeling under pressure, hearing negative feedback, or being clearly confronted with bad news can be painful. It is important to demonstrate compassion in these circumstances without diluting clear feedback in any way. It is about being impersonal in a sense but showing compassion by keeping the higher purpose of health and social care to the fore while appreciating the difficulties the other person is facing.

6. **Let there be space and silence for listening and reflecting:** By listening deeply and quietly, the other person can explain themselves clearly and feel understood. Allowing space for silence while you process what they say is helpful too – often people will add more in those spaces. Those spaces offer time to be present and mindful also of thoughts, emotions and the other person.

7. **Document and record:** For difficult performance issues, it is necessary to document instances both for use in conversations and should formal performance management be necessary. It is also important to follow the correct procedures laid down in the organisation's HR policies and practices.

Conclusion

The only way to respond to the challenges that face us in health and social care is through radical innovation – transformational change – underpinned by a transformed approach to leadership. That can only come through releasing staff from the rigidities of bureaucracies, command and control hierarchies and relentless top-down scrutiny and control. And the evidence from research is clear that compassionate leadership is the vital cultural element for innovation in organisations.

> Compassionate leadership creates the conditions where the collective good – the needs of patients and communities, and staff well-being and development – are prioritised over individual agendas (regardless of status), aggression, or undermining.

Such leadership creates the conditions where it is possible to identify and challenge inappropriate use of power, hierarchy or control over resources that are inconsistent with the values and vision of our health services. The only way to respond to the challenges that face us in health and social care is through radical innovation – transformational change.

As Don Berwick (Institute for Healthcare Improvement, USA), Prerana Issar (NHS Chief People Officer) and Sam Allen (CEO of Sussex Partnership NHS Trust) commented in a King's Fund event, that compassionate leadership requires courage. The courage to listen to tough messages from those we lead. The courage to explore their understanding of the challenges they face and to have our own interpretations challenged and rejected. The courage to feel how draining it is to work a 70-hour week, to not have time to go to the toilet on a shift, to have no access to food and drink on a night shift, or to be on the receiving end of violence or abuse from members of the public. And the courage to accept that practicing compassionate leadership will first and foremost address the most apparently intractable workplace challenges such as excessive workload, staff shortages and ever-increasing demand.

> Compassionate leadership requires courage, resilience and belief – it requires a commitment by each person as a leader (and all staff should be considered leaders in health and social care) to be the best that they can be.

It begins with self-compassion so that by attending to oneself, understanding the challenges we face in our own work (and life more generally), empathising or caring for ourselves, and then taking wise action to help ourselves, we are able to stay close to the core values that give our lives and work meaning – compassion, wisdom, courage, justice – we are able to have deeper, more authentic and more effective interactions with all those we work with and offer care for. Putting such leadership into action demonstrates not the myths, but the magic of compassionate leadership.

Resources

Exercises/Discussion questions (to reflect on or discuss with a colleague)

Compassion and compassionate leadership

1. Think of an example of compassion others have shown to you and identify the four elements of compassion in their behaviour.

2. Think of an example of compassion you have shown to another person (ideally a neutral person or someone you had found difficult). Identify the four elements and reflect on the consequences of your compassion (for you and the other person).

3. Think of an example of compassion at work that has moved you recently. How did it make a difference and what can you learn from it?

4. Which of the four elements of compassion come to you more easily? Which might you focus on developing more? Look at the resources and videos and plan for how you can best accomplish that.

5. To what extent are each of the four compassionate leadership behaviours generally modelled by those in your team/organisation?

6. What are the barriers to you modelling each of the compassionate leadership behaviours and how can they be overcome?

7. How can you as a leader better model compassionate leadership? What goals would you commit to setting for yourself to develop your compassionate leadership? For example, this might include having two days a week where you deliberately practise 'listening with fascination' in interactions and/or practising reflective listening to establish shared understanding.

8. Where should leaders focus their help for those they lead to ensure high-quality compassionate care for patients and for staff?

Managing performance

1. Think of a situation you currently face or have faced in the past involving addressing performance issues. What did you learn from this? How could you manage this situation more effectively, considering the guidance here?

2. Think of a situation you currently face or have faced in the past where your team needed to develop new and improved ways of doing things at pace. What did you learn from this about leadership? How could you manage this situation more effectively, considering the guidance here?

3. Think of a situation you currently face or have faced in the past involving addressing an abusive, aggressive or dominating individual. What did you learn from this about leadership? How could you manage this situation more effectively, considering the guidance here?

4. Think of a situation you currently face or have faced in the past involving a difficulty with the culture or leadership of another organisation. What did you learn from this? How could you manage this situation more effectively, considering the guidance here?

Questionnaires

Compassionate leadership can be measured using the following items, based on four dimensions of compassion: attending, understanding, empathising and helping. These can be used by team members or could be adapted as a self-report measure for leaders.

Attending

This person

... listens carefully to others when exploring problems

... pays close attention to you when listening

... is very attentive when you are telling them about difficulties

... gives you their full attention when you are describing challenges you face

Understanding

... is helpful in understanding the reasons for difficulties we face

... does not impose their understanding of the cause of difficulties we face

... takes time to understand carefully the causes of problems

... works together with us to come to an understanding of problems

Empathising

... is genuinely warm and empathic

... is emotionally in touch with others' feelings when they are upset

... is sensitive to what others are feeling

... genuinely cares about others' difficulties

Helping

... helps people practically with problems they face

... takes effective action to help others with the problems they face

... deals effectively with problems in order to help others

... is genuinely committed to making a difference in helping others

A shorter scale capturing the same core dimensions:

This person ...

... gives you their full attention when you are describing challenges you face

... works together with us to come to an understanding of problems

... genuinely cares about others' difficulties

... takes effective action to help others with the problems they face

Response scale:

Never	Rarely	Frequently	Almost always	Always
1	2	3	4	5

Guidance on using these questionnaires is provided in Appendix 1.

Websites

1. The Compassionate Mind Foundation
    Founded as an international charity in 2006 by Paul Gilbert and
    colleagues including Drs Deborah Lee, Mary Welford, Chris Irons, Ken
    Goss, Ian Lowens, Chris Gillespie, Mrs Diane Woollands, Mrs Jean
    Gilbert and other supporters, the foundation promotes an evolution
    and neuroscience-informed approach to compassion, which now
    forms the basis of a psychotherapy (Compassion Focused Therapy)
    and Compassionate Mind Training. The last 10 years have seen an
    expanding evidence base for both the therapy and Compassionate Mind
    Training for the alleviation of mental health difficulties and promoting
    well-being. It is now being used internationally in hospitals, prisons,
    schools and businesses. One of the greatest challenges facing
    humanity is how to stimulate compassionate ways of thinking and
    problem-solving for the benefit of all.
    https://www.compassionatemind.co.uk/

This pdf from the Compassionate Mind Foundation offers guidance to help develop qualities of inner compassion focusing on valuing compassion, empathy, sympathy, forgiveness, acceptance and tolerance. It also helps in developing feelings of warmth and growth, and taking responsibility and training to strengthen compassion.
https://www.getselfhelp.co.uk/docs/GILBERT-COMPASSION-HANDOUT.pdf

2. The Compassion Institute
   The institute offers an 8-week Compassion Cultivation Training programme, developed at Stanford University, with insights and techniques from psychology, neuroscience and contemplative (meditation) practice. The course integrates evidence-based meditation techniques, interactive discussions, and lectures as well as real-world exercises to put learning into practice.
   https://www.compassioninstitute.com/the-program/compassion-cultivation-training/

3. The International Compassion Community
   The community provides an online space for those working in health and care with daily guided meditations (live), webinars, question and answer sessions.
   https://ccmm.care/

4. Compassion in Politics
   A cross-party organisation working to put compassion, inclusion and co-operation at the heart of politics. From their website: "Compassion has the power to change politics for good. From inequality and racial discrimination to homelessness, divisions over how covid-19 has been handled to refugees dying at sea - imagine how these issues would be tackled if compassion was the main motivation of decision-makers. Yet compassion has been edged out of the political debate, replaced by a politics of fear, anger and divisions, and a narrative which emphasises individual success over collective well-being and happiness. Through a new kind of politics and with a new set of values at the heart of decision-making we can create a nation that cares for one another, improves everyone's lives, and protects our natural world."
   https://www.compassioninpolitics.com

5. The King's Fund
   The King's Fund, a leading UK health and social care charity and think-tank, has a website with a range of blogs, videos, webinars and reports that address compassionate leadership.
   https://www.kingsfund.org.uk/

The King's Fund publication on compassionate leadership and innovation in healthcare.
https://www.kingsfund.org.uk/publications/caring-change

A King's Fund blog post on why compassionate leadership matters so much during the covid-19 crisis.
https://www.kingsfund.org.uk/blog/2020/03/covid-19-crisis-compassionate-leadership

6. Hult Ashridge Business Education: Compassion makes teams stronger
   A website with a blog and other resources by Dr Amy Bradley on compassion at work.
   https://www.hult.edu/en/executive-education/insights/compassion-makes-teams-stronger/

7. A Roffey Park paper on compassionate leadership and why organisations need such leadership.
   https://www.roffeypark.ac.uk/wp-content/uploads/2020/07/Compassionate-Leadership-Booklet.pdf

8. A recent publication (2021) exploring the importance of healthcare worker well-being, patient safety and organisational change, edited by Montgomery, A., van der Doef, M., Panagopoulou, E., Leiter, M. P. Connecting Healthcare Worker Well-Being, Patient Safety and Organisational Change. Aligning Perspectives on Health, Safety and Well-Being. *Springer, Cham.* See also within this edition a chapter on Compassion and Collective Leadership for Culture of High-Quality Care, by Michael West.
   https://link.springer.com/book/10.1007/978-3-030-60998-6

9. Harvard Business Review: Handling difficult conversations
   https://hbr.org/2015/01/how-to-handle-difficult-conversations-at-work

10. Amy Gallo writes for Harvard Business Review on how to manage a toxic employee.
    https://hbr.org/2016/10/how-to-manage-a-toxic-employee

11. The US Society for Human Resource Management provide resources for dealing with difficult people.
    https://www.shrm.org/hr-today/news/hr-magazine/0217/pages/how-do-you-deal-with-difficult-people.aspx

12. A call for compassionate performance management and a best practice guide from the Fair Ombudsman of the Australian Government.
    https://www.hrreview.co.uk/analysis/analysis-wellbeing/murray-furlong-call-compassionate-performance-management/95838

Videos

A video from the Oxford Mindfulness Centre featuring Christina Feldman leading a meditation on rediscovering compassion. Christina Feldman is a leading teacher in the insight meditation community, offering retreats internationally. She is a contributing faculty member in several postgraduate mindfulness programs, including the University of Exeter in the United Kingdom and Radboud University in the Netherlands.
(7 minutes 41 secs)
https://www.youtube.com/watch?v=pnKVJaEL6Ec

A video of Paul Gilbert drawing on his research and others' to provide a powerful, compelling and comprehensive overview of the evolution of compassion and its role in our happiness. He explores the science of compassion and how we can put this into practice to create happier lives - for ourselves and others around us. This talk was filmed at an Action for Happiness event in London on 18 April 2017.
(1 hour 17 minutes)
https://www.youtube.com/watch?v=e2skAMI8c-4

A wide range of inspiring videos from the Compassionate Mind Foundation.
https://www.compassionatemind.co.uk/resources/videos

Thoughts about compassion accompanied with quotations from Chögyam Trungpa, Karen Armstrong, Christina Feldman, Pema Chödrön, Albert Schweitzer and Rachel Joy Scott. (3 minutes 35 secs)
https://www.youtube.com/watch?v=5qpoFTC5C50

A short video outlining the key components of compassionate leadership.
(16 minutes)
https://www.youtube.com/watch?v=0RXthT32vcY

A King's Fund webinar on compassionate leadership with Don Berwick, Institute for Healthcare Improvement, USA; Prerana Issar, NHS Chief People Officer; Sam Allen, CEO of Sussex Partnership NHS Trust, a mental health and learning disability organisation; chaired by Michael West. (1 hour)
https://www.kingsfund.org.uk/audio-video/compassionate-inclusive-leadership-event

The King's Fund: The core value of compassion and centrality of compassionate leadership in health and social care. (7 minutes)
https://www.youtube.com/watch?v=RrPmMwg9X8s

A more extended discussion of the role of compassionate leadership, teamworking and reflection in health and social care. (1 hour)
https://vimeo.com/manage/502557741/general

A brief explanation of the importance of compassionate and collective leadership from Michael West at The King's Fund. (7 minutes 10 secs)
https://www.kingsfund.org.uk/audio-video/michael-west-leadership

Three steps to having difficult but necessary conversations – a TEDx video featuring Adar Cohen, a conflict resolution expert. (15 minutes 45 secs)
https://ideas.ted.com/3-steps-to-having-difficult-but-necessaryconversations/

Compassion in politics: Podcast with Michael West discussing the pandemic and recovery from it with a new approach to leadership. (18 minutes 26 secs)
https://directory.libsyn.com/episode/index/show/compinpolitics/id/14152574

Chapter 2.

A crisis of leadership in health and social care

Summary

This chapter outlines the pressures on health and social care staff and argues that existing approaches to leadership in health and social care have largely failed, though there are outstanding examples of success. Instead, compassionate leadership is now essential given the challenging context that existed even before the tidal wave of the pandemic broke upon health and social care services. Research evidence about vacancies, absenteeism, turnover, intention to quit, stress levels and the consequences of stress in relation to health and patient safety is summarised. The causes of staff stress are also identified using research evidence.

Introduction

Even before the covid-19 pandemic, in January 2020, the health and social care sector was facing the biggest crisis in staffing since the introduction of the welfare state in 1948[1]. In particular, there was a crisis related to vacancies, sickness absence, staff turnover and stress levels. This has damaging consequences for staff health, performance and patient/service user safety. The causes of these difficulties include staffing levels; workload and work schedules; moral distress; bullying, harassment and violence; discrimination and pay. Collectively, these problems reveal a crisis of leadership.

> We can find hope and inspiration from the evidence which shows that compassionate leadership results in better staff well-being and commitment, improved care quality and fairer, more transparent and kinder workplaces.

The elements of the crisis

Vacancies

Before the pandemic, there were over 100,000 staff vacancies in the NHS in England, representing one in 11 of all posts[2]; Health and Social Care Northern Ireland (HSCNI) reported approximately 7,500 vacancies, representing one in eight posts[3]. There was no official national data on vacancy rates in Wales, but responses from health boards and trusts to a

British Medical Association (BMA) Cymru Wales freedom of information request revealed a 6.8% vacancy rate[4]. In Scotland, as of June 2019 there were 5,124 whole time equivalent (WTE) vacant posts among clinical staff, representing a 6.4% vacancy rate[5].

One of the greatest challenges was in nursing, with 41,000 nurse vacancies in England[2]. By September 2019, the NHS in England had a nursing vacancy rate of 12%, a rise of 1% from September 2017[6]. Data from the NHS in Scotland showed 3,607 nurse and midwife posts were vacant out of a total of 60,812 WTEs[7]. Analysis by the Royal College of Nursing (RCN) Wales in 2019 suggested that there were around 1,651 nursing vacancies in the Welsh NHS[8]. And there were 2,488 nursing, healthcare assistant and nursing assistant vacancies (12.4%) across health and social care in Northern Ireland in 2020[9]. There has been a 35% reduction in health visitors in England's NHS, from 10,309 WTE in October 2015 to 6,693 WTE in April 2020 (this reduction is partly a consequence of the move of some health visiting roles into local government)[10]. This has resulted in health visitors in some areas of England now being accountable for caseloads of over 750 children[11].

The King's Fund has identified a large and growing gap between capacity and demand in district nursing services: a significant increase in activity over recent years, both in terms of the number of patients and the complexity of care; a decline in staffing levels, particularly in senior 'district nurse' posts; an increasingly task-focused approach to care and lack of continuity of care. Inevitably, this has had a negative impact on staff well-being, with unmanageable caseloads being common and some leaving the service as a result. The researchers heard of staff being 'broken', 'exhausted' and 'on their knees'[12].

These issues extended into social care. The adult social care sector was also under huge pressure even before the pandemic and facing many of the same issues as the NHS. There are 1.65 million jobs (1.16 million WTE) in adult social care in England and vacancies were running at 7.8% (122,000 vacancies) before the pandemic (this has come down to around 6.6%). The registered nurse vacancy rate in adult social care was 12%. There were 36,000 registered nurses working in adult social care in July 2020 (a decrease of 15,500 over the previous eight years). Around 17% of nurses in social care were on zero-hours contracts, known to be associated with higher rates of stress and turnover among staff[13]. In Wales, there are an estimated 1,600 registered nurses working in care homes; in Scotland, there were around 6,650 nurses working in the social services sector at the end of 2016, representing just under 10% of the nursing workforce. Care homes for adults employ 64% of this total and 27% are employed by nurse agencies. In all four UK countries there are high levels of vacancies for nursing in social care[14].

Sickness absence

Prior to the pandemic, sickness absence (a key human indicator of organisational performance) in the NHS in England was at 3.4%, twice the rate of that in the private sector (1.7%)[15]. It was even higher in Northern Ireland (5.3%), Scotland (5.3%), and Wales (5.6%)[16-18].

In the 2019 NHS Staff Survey in England, which covers secondary care, of the 187,000 nurses and midwives who responded, some 44% indicated that they had been unwell as a result of work-related stress in the previous twelve months. This is the highest percentage reporting this in the last five years. Over half reported attending work in the last three months despite not feeling well enough to perform their duties[19].

While doctors are less likely than other healthcare workers to take time off due to sickness (a rate of 1.3% for hospital doctors compared with 4.2% for all NHS hospital staff[20]), attending work while unwell (presenteeism) may be much more prevalent. The medical and dental staff group in Wales also had the lowest rate of sickness absence, at 1.9%[17]. 42% of doctors in England and 47% in Wales report having recently attended work despite not feeling well enough to perform their duties[21,22]. Previous research has shown that staff attending work while sick are unlikely to be able to perform effectively, while also potentially passing on their illness to colleagues or patients[23,24].

Turnover and intention to quit

Over a quarter of midwives and nurses working in secondary care organisations in England are considering leaving the organisations in which they work[19]. The RCN Employment Survey 2019 suggested even more (37%) across the UK were seeking a new job, and of these, over a third were looking for a different job in the NHS and nearly a quarter for a job outside the NHS[25]. The survey also showed that before the pandemic, many were considering working abroad. There has also been an increase in NHS nurses from other EU countries quitting following the Brexit referendum[25]. Data reveal that around one in four nurses and health visitors in England leave the NHS within three years of joining[26].

According to analysis by the Health Foundation and Nursing Standard, 24% of nursing students and 21% of midwifery students in England are leaving their courses early or suspending their studies – nurses and midwives that the health and social care system can ill afford to lose[27].

A UK-wide RCN survey of 42,000 of its members during May and June 2020 revealed that one third were considering leaving nursing by the end of the year. Some 44% indicated that the way nursing staff had been treated during the pandemic made them consider leaving the profession. This was higher among minority ethnic group staff (54%) than among white staff (42%)[28].

A Royal College of Midwives (RCM) survey of 2,000 midwives in 2016 showed that 66% had considered leaving the profession entirely in the previous six months. The main reasons were dissatisfaction with staffing levels (60%), being unable to provide the quality of care required (52%), high workload (46%), and poor working conditions (37%)[29]. A Nursing and Midwifery Council survey in 2019 confirmed the pattern of these findings, indicating that among the most common reasons for intending to quit midwifery were working conditions such as staffing and workload (44%) and disillusionment with the quality of care provided to patients (27%)[30].

In adult social care in England, recent analysis by Skills for Care suggests that the turnover of staff in 2019 was 30.8% (around 440,000 leavers per year)[13]. According to the analysis, there are an estimated 36,000 registered nurse jobs in the adult social care sector in England. Most of these jobs were in care homes in the independent sector (33,000) and around 1,600 employed by independent sector non-residential care providers. Registered nurses were one of the only job roles in adult social care to see a significant decrease (15,500, or 30%) since 2012/13[13].

In 2019, just under half of doctors working in hospitals and other secondary care organisations in England were considering leaving the organisations in which they worked (47%)[19]. Nearly one in five (17%) were considering leaving the NHS altogether[19], and the same patterns were seen across the UK[22,31]. The ninth National GP Worklife Survey in England, published in 2019[32], reported the lowest levels of job satisfaction among GPs and revealed the highest levels of stress since the survey began in 1998; it also showed that 35% of GPs were intending to quit direct patient care within the next five years[32]. In Scotland, 26% of GPs said they were unlikely to be working in general practice in five years' time, citing unsustainable workloads and unmanageable stress levels as the main reasons[33].

Stress levels

Previous research in the most careful study conducted in the last 25 years has shown that 50% more staff in the NHS report debilitating levels of stress compared with general working population[34].

The 2018 General Medical Council (GMC) National Training Survey employed an internationally used and validated measure of burnout (Copenhagen Burnout Inventory). This showed that nearly one in four UK doctors in training, and one in five trainers were burnt out to a high or very high degree because of their work. Nearly one in five said they didn't have energy for family and friends (spending quality time with loved ones is a key determinant of well-being)[35].

GPs in the UK had the highest levels of stress in a survey across 11 countries according to a Commonwealth Fund survey, which revealed that 59% had high stress levels compared (for example) with 18% in the Netherlands[36].

In the annual NHS Staff Survey in 2019, covering all staff in England working in secondary care, 41% of staff overall reported being unwell because of stress in the previous year[19]. The percentages were 37% of doctors; 44% of nurses and 51% of midwives. A Royal College of Nursing Employment Survey in 2019 found the percentages of staff agreeing with the statement 'I feel I am under too much pressure' were 66% in NHS trusts, 64% in the independent care sector, and 64% amongst nurses working in primary care[25].

Over a third of doctors working in secondary care in the other nations also indicated that they had been unwell as a result of work-related stress in the previous year; 36% of doctors in the 2015 Health and Social Care Northern Ireland (HSCNI) Staff Survey[31] and 34% of doctors in the NHS Wales Staff Survey 2018[22].

Drawing on the annual Labour Force Survey covering the whole of the UK, the Health and Safety Executive (2019) has shown that health and social care staff consistently report higher rates of work-related stress, depression and anxiety than those in most other sectors[37]. National staff survey findings in England, Northern Ireland and Wales indicate that each year, between 34% and 44% report being unwell due to work stress during the previous year[19,22,31]. Such stress is likely to be chronic, as measures of work stress repeated over time among health and social care staff are highly consistent[4].

Consequences of the crisis

There are substantial consequences for staff health in terms of the behavioural, physiological and psychological impact of work stress and strain, particularly in health and social care. The consequences for organisations are considerable, including low work ability, sickness absence, intention to quit, and early retirement. There are also effects on productivity, performance, organisational citizenship behaviour, engagement and, inevitably, care quality and patient experience[38,39].

1. Behavioural

Cognitive and emotional outcomes of work stress include negative effects on concentration, mood disturbance, depression, anxiety, health complaints and work performance. Strain leads to more errors on cognitive tasks including deterioration in memory, reaction time, accuracy and task performance[40].

2. Physiological

Chronic work stressors are linked to hypertension, cardiovascular disorders and recurrent cardiovascular events[40]. Cognitive and emotional outcomes include negative effects on concentration, depression, anxiety, stress-related addiction and work performance[41,42]. Other outcomes associated with chronic stress include diabetes, recurring musculoskeletal pain, musculoskeletal injury, sleep problems, gastrointestinal problems, poorer functioning of the immune system, cancers, chronic fatigue syndrome, eating disorders, early ageing and early mortality[42-47].

A 2015 meta-analysis of 228 studies assessing ten workplace stressors and health outcomes found that high job demands raised the odds of diagnosed illness by 35% and that long work hours increased mortality by almost 20%[48].

3. Patient safety

Long working hours and shift work impact on doctors' and nurses' personal safety, increasing the likelihood of occupational accidents and needle-stick injuries[49].

> Work periods of over eight hours carry an increased risk of accidents, that accumulates, with twice the risk of an accident at around 12 hours compared with eight hours of work.

This imperils both patients and staff[50]. Excessive workload affects patient safety, productivity, efficiency and staff mental health and well-being.

This has implications for staff health and patient safety. Strain is associated with more medical errors amongst healthcare workers[51] and there is now considerable evidence that stress and strain impair doctors' and nurses' decision-making, productivity and patient safety (including medical errors)[52]. In one study, researchers found that doctors with high levels of burnout had between 45% and 63% higher odds of making a major medical error in the following three months, compared with those who had low levels[53]. Another study from the University of Washington suggested that doctors experiencing high levels of stress were four times more likely to provide substandard patient care[54]. And a study of 7,905 surgeons by the Mayo Clinic found that highly stressed surgeons were three times more likely to make a major surgical error than those with low stress levels[55]. A UK survey of 681 doctors working in emergency medicine suggested that compassion fatigue (one symptom of burnout or stress) was associated with reducing care quality standards in a way that could harm patients[56].

The same is true in nursing. One study of nurses in intensive care units revealed that high stress levels were associated with significantly higher patient mortality[57]. A survey of more than 61,000 nurses and 130,000 patients in Europe and the US found that positive work environments (managerial support for nursing, nurse participation in hospital affairs, doctor–nurse relations and promotion of care quality) and lower ratios of patients to nurses were associated with lower nurse burnout, better care quality, and higher levels of patient satisfaction[58].

4. Psychological

Psychological burnout, first described by Maslach and Leiter (1997)[56], refers to three sub-dimensions of strain – emotional exhaustion, depersonalisation (becoming hardened and treating patients as objects), and a sense of ineffectiveness[57]. Burnout is associated with sleep deprivation[56], medical errors[52,59], poor quality of care[31,51], and low patient satisfaction[21].

Longitudinal analyses of data from the NHS Staff Survey in England have consistently shown associations between staff reports of stressful and unsupportive work environments and poorer patient satisfaction, quality of patient care and financial performance[1-5,46] and, in the acute sector, increased patient mortality[47].

> Better staff well-being is linked to positive patient outcomes within NHS organisations.

What is it that leaders are failing to adequately address that is leading to the damage we see amongst health and social care staff?

Causes of staff stress

1. Staffing

Midwives are under unsustainable pressure and this has been increasing over time. The RCM stated in 2017 that midwife shortages, rising levels of complexity in pregnancy and financial constraints in the NHS were increasing demands on England's maternity workforce and services[60]. Complexity has increased with the women requiring maternity care typically being older and with more underlying health conditions. There was a reported shortage of 3,500 midwives in England in 2017. A 2016 RCM UK-wide survey of those who had left midwifery in the preceding two years or who were intending to leave in the next two years found three key causal issues: lack of staffing, size of workload and not having enough time to provide high-quality and safe care[61]. Similar concerns about staffing levels are reported amongst almost all staff groups in health and social care, resulting in the recent development of long-term workforce strategies in Northern Ireland, Scotland and Wales. As of the time of writing (June 2021) there is no such plan published in England for health and social care.

An RCN survey conducted in 2020 showed that four in ten respondents said staffing levels had worsened during the pandemic and this was particularly problematic in the independent and social care sectors[28]. Nearly two thirds (62%) indicated that patient needs had become more complex during the pandemic.

Work pressure

The Nursing and Midwifery Council surveyed 1,626 nurses of the 15,600 who left their register across the UK between November 2018 and June 2019[30]. As in previous years, the top three reasons for leaving were retirement (52.7%), too much pressure resulting in stress and poor mental health (26.4%) and a change in personal circumstances (24.5%). Other reasons included disillusionment with the quality of care provided to patients (16%), staffing levels (15%) and concerns about workload (12%).

The UK-wide RCN 2019 Employment Survey[59] asked respondents to react to the item 'I feel I am under too much pressure'. Across all sectors, high proportions of the 8,307 nurse and midwife respondents agreed with the statement, with the highest proportions amongst NHS trusts/boards (66.1%), followed by the independent care sector (63.5%) and general practice (54.2%) – and the lowest proportion (hospices) still at nearly half (46.2%). Levels of demand were already at their highest in a decade even prior to the covid-19 pandemic. A further UK-wide survey conducted by the RCN in 2020 revealed that over half of respondents were concerned about their physical and mental health and nine out of ten were concerned about the well-being of those in the profession generally[28].

The research evidence points clearly to chronic excessive workload as the key factor influencing stress, staff shortages, absenteeism, turnover, long working hours, and moral distress.

> Put simply, among many staff working in health and social care, work demands consistently exceed their resources to meet those demands.

Doctors cite unacceptable working and training conditions which damage their performance at work[4]. They report feeling undervalued in the workplace; isolated from seniors, teams and colleagues; unsupported in their roles; fearful of making a mistake and being blamed or prosecuted; overwhelmed by their workloads and feeling that they have little control over their work lives. Analysis of data from the GMC National Training Surveys shows that, where doctors reported heavy workloads and a lack of supportive environment, there was often a negative impact on well-being and effectiveness[4]. They also report facing a significant increase in the volume of patients and the complexity of their health needs and demands, without a corresponding growth in support. This is associated with the loss of mechanisms that had supported them in the past, such as strong team structures and communities for hospital doctors.

Working in primary care can expose doctors to stressors that differ from those in secondary care. Some GPs say their working environment can be lonely, with long hours spent seeing many patients without the opportunity to talk with colleagues[4]. Further stressors can include unsustainable patient volumes, the added demand of scheduling an average of only ten minutes with each patient, and inadequate time to catch up with other tasks. The findings of research on the retention of GPs are congruent with studies of hospital doctors in the UK. Poor working conditions (high workload, low job autonomy, long hours, low social support, work-life conflict) and poor mental health (high burnout, symptoms of depression and anxiety) are associated with an increased intention to leave medicine[4].

What we know about recovery from work stress

An international review of the research literature on recovery from stress in work shows that the following activities can help to *enable recovery*[62]:

- Psychological detachment from work – activities that help us to disengage completely from work

- Relaxation – meditation, yoga

- Mastery – success or achievement from a challenging task such as cooking, sport, creative tasks, gardening

- Control – it is important we have relatively high control over what to do and when to do it in non-work time. Filling up time with chores (activities that are depleting) does not help

- Some intuitive and empirically supported findings:
  - Work breaks (especially proper lunch breaks without chores) help a great deal

  - Vacations (though effects fade within a week or two)

  - Physical activities/exercise are highly beneficial

  - Natural environments enable recovery in order of effect sizes:
    i. 'Blue' environments – sea, lakes, rivers etc, are most beneficial followed by...

    ii. 'Green' environments – forests, hills, fields

    iii. Urban green (parks)

    iv. Least beneficial are urban non-green environments (even here recovery is better with architectural variety and low building height)

  - And a general finding that biodiversity is beneficial ie, the more species around the better we feel (birds, insects, animals, butterflies, etc).

An important 'inverse recovery law':
Those whose work is most stressful are least likely to engage in optimal recovery activities.

2. Work schedules

In Northern Ireland, 27% of doctors in the HSCNI 2015 Staff Survey reported working additional paid hours and 93% worked additional unpaid hours, with 39% of all respondents working more than five additional unpaid hours per week[31]. Working additional hours is strongly associated with levels of stress and workplace injury[4]. In England, the figures from the 2018 NHS Staff Survey were 43% working additional paid hours and 81% working additional unpaid hours[21]. These figures are significant in accounting for some of the most serious effects on doctors' mental health. Recent GMC National Training Surveys showed that nearly half of UK doctors in training worked beyond their rostered hours (England 48.5%, Northern Ireland 50.5%, Scotland 46.9%, Wales 51%), while one in five said that their working pattern had left them short of sleep[4].

In England, the figures from the 2019 NHS Staff Survey suggest 41.7% of nurses worked additional paid hours and over two thirds worked additional unpaid hours[19]. In Northern Ireland, the figures were 53% and 77% respectively[31]. For midwives in England, the figures are even higher – 46.3% and 79.6% respectively. Many nurses (23% according to the RCN Employment Survey) do additional bank or agency work in order to top up their earnings[25].

Excessive workload and the need to work additional hours are major factors determining levels of work stress[34]. Long working hours and shift work impact on nurses' and midwives' personal safety, increasing the likelihood of occupational accidents[63]. There is also a significant impact on work/home life balance, which is a powerful cause of stress for nurses and midwives.

Excessive workload affects patient safety, productivity, efficiency and the mental health and well-being of staff. Burnout and poorer well-being are associated with poorer quality and safety of care, higher absenteeism, and higher turnover rates[64]. Minority ethnic group nursing staff are much more likely than other staff to work seven or more additional hours per week and to take on extra paid work[25,28]. One factor behind this is that these staff are often less able to increase their salaries via promotion because of discrimination.

A UK-wide RCN survey of its members conducted in May and June 2020 showed that one third of respondents were working longer hours than they did before the pandemic. Minority ethnic group staff were less likely than white staff to be paid for working additional hours (39% compared to 48%). Some 56% of respondents felt staff morale had worsened during the pandemic[28].

3. Moral distress

"I put added stress on myself by beating myself up about the fact that could I have done something about it. That was the overwhelming feeling - what could I have done differently?" Midwife[65]

"...walking back into that room with that dead baby in my arms and telling the parents [...], that was just the worst thing I've truly ever done. And that woman's scream will live with me forever." Midwife[65]

Health and social care staff are at risk of 'moral distress' in situations where they are prevented from providing the quality of care they feel they should be providing (because of, for example, excessive workload or a lack of resources)[66].

Moral distress is associated with higher staff turnover, burnout and dissatisfaction[67]. Being forced to go against their moral compass undermines professionals' feelings of integrity, their sense of self-worth and their well-being.

This has been particularly acute during the pandemic when there have been shortages of beds, the need to discharge patients quickly to create capacity, rampant infection in some care homes, and a shortage of services for critically ill patients. Added to this, many staff have a pervasive fear of being held responsible for poor care and being accused of negligence[68,69].

Over two thirds of nursing staff across the UK working in independent care sector homes (73.1%), and NHS bank staff (66.7%) say they are too busy to provide the level of care they would like. In NHS organisations the figure is 63.5% and in general practice 46.6%[25]. Again, though there is much variation across settings, the experience of moral distress amongst staff is pervasive. It also affects student nurses, with nearly two thirds (64.4%) saying they are too busy to provide the level of care they would like[70-72].

4. Bullying, harassment and violence

In the NHS, staff also refer to lack of voice and influence, fear and blame cultures, bullying and harassment, and discrimination[4,21,22,31]:

- In England some 40% of healthcare assistants are assaulted each year, primarily by patients, their relatives or other members of the public.

- 23-36% of doctors reported being bullied, harassed or abused by members of the public, patients or their carers (England, Northern Ireland, Wales). In Scotland, 33% reported emotional verbal abuse from members of the public.

- 9-16% of doctors reported being bullied by managers and 14-22% reported being bullied by other colleagues (England, Northern Ireland and Scotland).

- In Wales, 19% of doctors reported being bullied by managers and colleagues combined.

In England, over a quarter of nurses and midwives report having experienced physical violence from patients, their relatives or carers in the previous year, and 40% have been subjected to harassment, bullying or abuse. On top of that, over 20% of nurses, midwives and healthcare assistants have experienced harassment, bullying or abuse from colleagues in the previous year[19]. In Wales, 20% of staff overall report having been bullied by a colleague or manager in the previous year and 32% by a patient, service user or another member of the public[22]. In Northern Ireland, the figures are 22% (bullying by staff) and 25% (bullying by patients, members of the public) respectively[31].

Aside from patients and other members of the public, the main perpetrators are colleagues in a more senior position. Darbyshire et al. suggest that bullying and incivility are "a part of the fabric of almost every nurse's and health professional's lives"[73]. Bullying can cause distress and depression, leading to up to 25% of those bullied leaving their jobs or the profession. Factors contributing to bullying include hierarchical management cultures and staff not feeling empowered[74].

5. Discrimination

The evidence on the experience of discrimination at work, particularly amongst staff from black and minority ethnic (BME) backgrounds, is stark. This is reviewed in more depth in chapter 7. The 2019 NHS Staff Survey in England showed high levels of discrimination from patients, their relatives or carers in the previous 12 months (18.3% of BME staff and 4.6% of white staff reported such discrimination), and from managers/team leaders or colleagues (14.5% among BME staff and 6.4% amongst white staff)[19]. The proportion of cases of discrimination experienced by BME staff that were based on ethnicity has also risen over the last five years from 77.8% to 82%. Discrimination has substantial influences on workplace stress and physical health[75].

For doctors in training, gender discrimination (among those experiencing discrimination at work) has risen from 33.1% to 43.5%[76]. The level of discrimination experienced by doctors on the grounds of ethnicity has risen over the last five years from 52% to the current 57.7%[8].

6. Pay

Many staff are dissatisfied with their pay, with 61% of nurses who responded to an RCN UK-wide survey (n=7,720) considering their pay/grade to be inappropriate[59]. Nurses across all pay scales report financial challenges, with more than half (56%) of the 7,720 nurses responding to the 2019 RCN survey saying they had to cut back on food and travel costs, 23% had taken an additional job, 21% struggled to pay their gas and electricity bills, and 11% had been late with mortgage and rent payments[25]. Nursing is a gendered profession and yet research published last year showed that men are still advantaged in terms of pay and opportunities for promotion and development across some pay grades in the UK[77].

Conclusion

All the foregoing makes it clear there has been a general crisis of leadership across health and social care. Many leaders are committed to the maxim that 'our people are our most important asset' yet this review of the evidence makes it clear that this is simply not the case in practice. Of course, there are many good and outstanding examples of teams and organisations in health and social care where staff well-being is not so neglected or abused. However, most leaders in health and social care organisations would be deluding themselves and those they serve if they do not accept responsibility for the crisis of leadership these data reveal.

This is not a plea for hair-shirting self-condemnation among leaders.

> Rather it is a clarion call for a different approach based on the core value of compassion in health and social care. The case for compassionate leadership is clearly made by this review.

Sustaining cultures of high-quality compassionate care requires compassionate leadership at every level and in interactions between all parts of the system – from national leaders to local teams. Compassionate leadership in practice means leaders 'listening with fascination' to those they lead, arriving at a shared (rather than imposed) understanding of the challenges they face, empathising with and caring for them, and then taking action to help or support them. Such leadership will help us begin to address the problems health and social care services face.

Resources

Exercises/Discussion questions (to reflect on or discuss with a colleague)

1. What are the levels of vacancies, sickness absence and staff turnover in your organisation (or your area of the organisation)? How do these compare with the national averages given in this chapter?

2. What are the main sources of stress you see in your work or the work of those you lead?

3. What are the underlying causes of these sources of stress and what role can you and other leaders play in reducing or eliminating them?

4. What can be done to reduce or eliminate those sources of stress?

5. How could staff be better attracted to coming to work in your organisation?

6. What could be done, thinking radically, about how best to retain staff working in your organisation (or your part of the organisation)?

Questionnaires

A standard *measure of strain or burnout* is the work-related burnout scale from the Copenhagen Burnout Inventory[78] (used in the General Medical Council Training Survey), with the following seven items:

1. Is your work emotionally exhausting?

2. Do you feel burnt out because of your work?

3. Does your work frustrate you?

4. Do you feel worn out at the end of the working day?

5. Are you exhausted in the morning at the thought of another day at work?

6. Do you feel that every working hour is tiring for you?

7. Do you have enough energy for family and friends during leisure time?

Guidance on using this questionnaire is provided in Appendix 1.

Websites

1. The NHS England website to support staff during the pandemic
    This has had more than 700,000 visits in its first year and includes
    support phone lines, free apps, text messaging support, 20 short
    guides to help support staff with skills and new ways to improve their
    experience of work. The guides cover topics such as personal resilience,
    support for line managers and how to run a '10 min Pause Space'.
    https://people.nhs.uk/

2. The Practitioner Health Programme
    This programme offers a range of support for the multi-disciplinary
    healthcare team, including resources specifically for NHS nurses dealing
    with work-related stress.
    *https://www.practitionerhealth.nhs.uk/wellbeing-and-mental-health-
    for-nurses*

3. Skills for Care
    An independent charity experienced in supporting workforce
    development and working as a delivery partner for the Department of
    Health and Social Care. They offer a guide on dealing with stress for
    those working in social care.
    *https://www.skillsforcare.org.uk/About/News/News-Archive/Tackling-
    stress-in-adult-social-care-this-Mental-Health-Awareness-Week.aspx*

4. A warning that the pandemic will only add to the stress faced by health
    and social care workers in the long term.
    https://www.nature.com/articles/s41591-020-0878-4

Videos

Social Work Scotland, Iriss and the Scottish Social Services Council have
worked in partnership to draw together helpful resources for social service
practitioners and their organisations to support them to think about and
promote well-being and resilience.
https://www.iriss.org.uk/resources/reports/resilience-resources

An American Medical Association video with well-being experts from three
health systems sharing how they supported clinicians' wellness during the
covid-19 pandemic. They were: Nigel Girgrah, MD, PhD, Chief Wellness Officer
at Ochsner Health, an AMA Health System Program Partner; Amy Locke, MD,
Co-Director of the Resiliency Center at the University of Utah Health in Salt
Lake City; and Bryant Adibe, MD, System Vice president and Chief Wellness
Officer at Rush University System for Health in Chicago. (18 minutes)
*https://www.ama-assn.org/practice-management/physician-health/5-
factors-contributing-physician-stress-during-pandemic*

Chapter 3.

Compassion in health and social care: the evidence

Summary

Compassion is fundamental in health and social care, but it is far more important even than is often imagined. This chapter describes the importance of compassion as protective of health and life. This summary is based partly on the reviews published in the book *Compassionomics*[1] by Stephen Trzeciak and Anthony Mazzarelli, two physician researchers at Cooper University Health Care in New Jersey. They gathered evidence from hundreds of studies to show how compassion leads to better outcomes for patients and lower rates of burnout for practitioners. This chapter explores the evidence they review and additional material on the protective effects of closeness, the health outcomes of compassion, the effects of compassion on patient experience, barriers to compassion, developing compassion and the effects of being compassionate on the well-being of health and social care staff.

Introduction

Connection and closeness are protective. There is a strong link between human connection (closeness, rather than number of connections) and risk of death from all causes[2-5]. Having good relationships is associated with 50% higher odds of survival over time, revealing how fundamental belonging and connection are to us humans. We are the species Elliot Aronson, a leading social psychologist, called 'the social animal' because connection and belonging are core to our existence.

Indeed, loneliness is deeply damaging to human well-being and is associated with higher mortality than obesity and high blood pressure and comparable in terms of mortality to smoking and alcohol abuse[6]. Being lonely was associated with 26% higher odds of early death in one study[3] and 50% higher odds in another study[5].

For those who are already ill, connection and a sense of belonging are protective. Heart attack patients who reported lacking emotional support had three times higher odds of death[7]. The corollary is also true. A study with 406 volunteers monitored their stress, conflict and social support over a two-week period. They were then exposed to the cold virus, following which they were quarantined to determine who developed symptoms and what factors appeared to protect those who did not. The study showed that those with high stress and conflict in the previous two weeks were more likely to develop the infection. Social support, in contrast, protected against infection. Thirty-two per cent of the protective effect of social support was attributable to the number of hugs the volunteers had had in the previous 14 days[8]! Caring hugs not only feel good, but they seem to also boost our immunity.

Compassion leads to better health outcomes

Many of the studies of compassion in healthcare employ a relatively rigorous study design called the randomised control trial (RCT). This is a research design that attempts to eliminate or reduce potential biases that arise when testing the effectiveness of treatments. The participants are randomly assigned to one of two or more groups, each of which is subject to a different treatment. The outcomes from these different groups are then compared. The experimental group receives the treatment being assessed (for example compassionate care), while the other (the control group) receives an alternative treatment such as the standard treatment or a placebo.

One such RCT of low back pain compared conventional physical therapy with what happens when the same treatment is provided, but with an enhanced therapeutic alliance (the therapist is asked to show more compassion). The additional compassion treatment group reported more than double the pain relief[9]. Another similar study showed these effects persisted for six months[10].

RCTs were also used by researchers from Harvard Medical School and Massachusetts General Hospital in Boston to determine whether additional compassion ('special care') shown by anaesthetists prior to surgery had an impact on patient care and outcomes. Half of the patients were assigned an extra visit from the anaesthetist prior to surgery, with the explicit purpose of building rapport through showing compassion to patients. 'Special care' was associated with a 50% lower requirement for opiates post-surgery and patients had a significantly lower length of stay following surgery. They also compared the effects of this 'special care' with the effect of a powerful sedative just prior to surgery and found that in comparing extra compassion from anaesthetists with sedatives, patients were calm but not drowsy prior to surgery (whereas the sedatives group was drowsy but not calm). The compassion intervention had more than double the effects of phenobarbitone in achieving adequate sedation[11,12].

In another study[13] involving surgical nurses in a similar enhanced compassion treatment, patients in the compassion arm of the study had 50% lower scores on pain ratings on the first day following surgery.

A US National Institute of Health review of 34 studies[14] showed a positive association between psychological and emotional support from clinicians and favourable clinical outcomes in recovery from crisis (such as major surgery or heart attack).

What about chronic conditions? A study of 49 physicians[15] in consultations with nearly 900 people with diabetes categorised the physicians into low, medium and high emphasis on compassion. Those treated by the physicians with a high compassion emphasis had (on average) 80% higher optimal blood sugar control. Another study in Italy involving 242 doctors and 21,000 patients with diabetes[16] found that high compassion was associated with 41% lower odds of complications.

Other studies reveal how compassion is a powerful intervention in the treatment of HIV[17]. In a sample of 1,700 HIV patients, where the clinician treating the patient showed high compassion, there was 33% higher adherence by patients to their antiretroviral therapy and 20% higher odds of no detectable virus in the blood. Patients reported how powerful it was to feel known as a person and this was related subsequently to a much stronger (39%) belief that their medicines were helping them to live longer. In another study at the University of Virginia involving 435 patients and 45 physicians, compassion was assessed by recording and analysing the interactions between them. The results showed that the patients with physicians showing high compassion had more than double the odds of believing they could successfully adhere to their life-long antiretroviral medication regime (a measure of treatment self-efficacy)[18].

The effects extend also to survival rates following an early diagnosis of terminal lung cancer[19]. An RCT compared normal early cancer diagnosis treatment of 97 patients with this treatment plus early compassionate palliative care. The study was designed to examine the impact on quality of life but revealed the surprising finding that, those randomly assigned to receive early compassionate palliative care versus standard care survived 30% longer. A study in Germany of cancer patients showed that high patient ratings of their physicians' compassion were related to lower levels of depression and improved psychological quality of life[20].

Powerful effects have also been demonstrated in primary care. A UK study of GPs showed that GP compassion during a patient visit, on average, was associated with improved patient well-being at least one month after the surgery visit[21]. And positive communications from GPs intended to boost patients' expectations of recovery had a powerful impact, but only when the GP was warm and compassionate[22].

A University of Pennsylvania study of cultures of compassion in 13 long-term nursing home facilities revealed that patient outcomes were better in compassionate cultures. The nursing home residents had a better quality of life, fewer Emergency Department admissions and better patient and family experience. And there was an impact on staff, who themselves experienced less stress and absenteeism[23].

So far, this review has focused on physical health and pain. What of mental health? Here, the results are equally compelling based on the many studies of the impact of therapist compassion and rapport. In cases where there are several studies focusing on a topic, it is possible to conduct meta-analyses - collating the overall findings by combining and analysing the data from multiple published studies. A meta-analysis of the psychology literature on 21 RCTs involving 1,285 participants showed significant impacts of compassion in reducing patients' depression, anxiety and distress, and improving their well-being[24].

Compassion and patient experience

Not surprisingly, patients want and like receiving compassionate care. The top three qualities patients want are carers who listen, who are compassionate and who explain well[25].

A Harvard Medical School study of patient satisfaction revealed no differences in patient satisfaction based on the time they had to wait to see a clinician. But clinician compassion accounted for 65% of the variation in patient satisfaction[26]. Despite this, the opposite of compassion is particularly prevalent and damaging in some health and social care settings. One study of 1,400 US adults revealed that 64% had experienced rudeness or unkindness in their most recent visit to a healthcare setting[27].

Several studies suggest that patient perceptions of lack of compassion among doctors is the deciding determinant of their overall assessment of their treatment and their decision about whether to complain or sue[28-33].

> Compassion increases our sense of connection, trust and psychological safety[34,35].

Compassion is also sometimes expressed by touch, which itself mediates outcomes. One study examined hand-holding by a trusted other. This revealed coordination of heart rates, breathing and even EEG (brain wave) patterns[36] between the people holding each other's hands. Another study showed that wound healing was 17% quicker[37] when people had the support of their marital partners, compared with a manipulation focused on marital conflict (encouraging the couple to reflect on a conflict situation between them).

A study in the US of anxiety in patients showed that every compassion statement by a physician reduced patient anxiety by an average of 4.2% (so three statements reduced anxiety by 12.6%, and so on)[35].

Moreover, when caregivers are compassionate, this appears to motivate patients to take more responsibility for their healthcare. One meta-analysis of 127 studies showed that patient-centred communication (compassion) was associated with 62% higher odds of patient adherence to the treatment they had been prescribed[38].

Compassion also appears to enable and empower patients.

One study of 3,000 patients suggested that, if their physicians were brusque, patients did not feel fully empowered to understand, cope with and manage their illness[39].

A study that examined concordance or agreement between 22 GPs and 370 patients (ie, do the patient and doctor report the same health problems and treatments after an encounter?) found that patient/doctor concordance was associated with 34% higher odds of patient adherence to prescribed medications[40]. And a large-scale study of 9,377 patients with diabetes showed that, when they trusted and felt a better connection with their clinicians, they were much more likely to adhere to their medication regime[41]. A similar study of emotional support provided by healthcare providers among 881 women with breast cancer showed such support was associated with better adherence to tamoxifen (their treatment medication). Indeed, more compassion was associated with 12% higher adherence for as long as four years later[42]!

The research evidence suggests that compassion not only accounts for 65% of the variance in patient satisfaction, but is also associated with more than 50% fewer referrals and readmissions, and with quicker recovery[26].

In conclusion, the data suggest that compassion increases trust in the caregiver-patient relationship. It increases patients' feelings of safety and reduces their anxiety. It also appears to affect communication, understanding and patient commitment to their treatment. Patients adhere to their treatment regimens (resulting in better healthcare outcomes), receive more effective treatment (including fewer referrals and readmissions), have a stronger sense of control and thus feel more empowered to better manage their illness or disease.

Effects of being compassionate on the caregiver

A systematic review shows that most studies find an inverse relationship between compassion and burnout.

> The more clinicians and carers are compassionate, the less likely they are to experience burnout subsequently.

Moreover, being compassionate appears to make us happier. Neuroscience studies suggest that the most potent activator of brain circuits associated with happiness is compassion, or helping others[43,44].

More sophisticated physiological and psychological studies suggest that compassion affects clinicians in a range of positive ways, including improved clinician well-being and lowered stress. These studies also showed that compassion has positive effects on receivers' autonomic nervous systems[45,46], as indicated by lower respiration and heart rates.

The importance of caregivers showing compassion to each other has been revealed in recent years, partly as a result of the pioneering efforts of Kenneth Schwartz. He was a 40-year-old (non-smoking) healthcare lawyer who developed lung cancer and died less than a year after diagnosis. Because compassionate care was so important in his experience, he became convinced that caregivers should also benefit from compassion. He established 'Schwartz Rounds' where caregivers come together (with lunch) and share emotional experiences that have been powerful during their work. These events, conducted in a compassionate and supportive way, have spread around the world and demonstrated profoundly positive outcomes. Research evaluations in the UK (and other countries) have demonstrated the benefits of attending these events[47]. They include lower stress levels and improved well-being.

Sadly, seventeen out of eighteen published studies show compassion declines during clinical training[48]. Is this because compassion is both too expensive and time-consuming to be sustained?

Does compassion cost more?

'There are so many demands on the system and healthcare professionals are under such pressure that compassion is a costly luxury that our systems cannot afford.' Is this true? Research suggests not. The size of the effects of compassion is greater than the effects of aspirin in the prevention of heart attacks, and of statins in the five-year risk of a cardiovascular event[1,49,50].

And it is associated with fewer medication errors. In the HIV study described earlier, doctors who got to know the patient as a person had 41% higher odds of prescribing the right medication.

A study of cost data for 3,000 US hospitals showed that better patient experience is associated with lower healthcare spending per episode of care. The difference of 5.6% between high and low patient satisfaction for hospitals is an enormous figure both organisationally and particularly when accumulated nationally[51].

In another US study of compassion among GPs, the data showed that patients were less likely to have unnecessary healthcare interventions and (accordingly) they had lower medical bill charges (51% lower) when their GP was caring[52]. Less compassion by the GP caregiver was associated with more referrals to specialists and more diagnostic tests.

A Canadian study of GPs[53] that involved audiotaping interactions between them and their patients showed that the proportion of patients who received more compassionate, patient-centred care referred to a specialist, was 51% lower than among those who did not have such compassionate interactions. Moreover, they had less diagnostic testing (40% lower). Where patients said there was common ground between them and their caregiver, referrals were 59% lower and there was 84% less diagnostic testing.

An RCT in Canada, reported in the prestigious medical journal The Lancet, focused on homeless people arriving at an Emergency Department. These patients were randomly assigned to usual treatment versus usual treatment plus extra compassion. The outcome measure was the number of return visits to the Emergency Department over the next 30 days. The results showed people in the compassion treatment group were 33% less likely to have a return visit in that period[54].

Medical errors cost every healthcare system huge amounts of money. In the US, the annual cost of errors is between $735 billion and $980 billion[55] – more than 6 times the cost of running the entire UK National Health Service per year. In 2018-19, according to NHS Resolution (the body that deals with negligence claims for the NHS in England), the NHS paid £2.4bn in clinical negligence claims, which equates to about 2% of the NHS budget[56]. NHS Resolution has a reserve of £83.4bn for such claims (second only to £131bn for nuclear decommissioning in public sector financial liabilities)[56]. All the more important then for leaders to recognise that research evidence shows compassion makes a big difference to the likelihood of medical errors and to patients' decisions to pursue litigation.

> Treating healthcare staff compassionately has a large impact on patient safety.

The Mayo Clinic conducted a three-year study of 380 of their own physicians and found an association between how stressed they were and the incidence of major medical errors[57]. Physicians were asked to report any major medical errors they had made, every three months for the three years of their training. They were also regularly assessed on two measures of stress – emotional exhaustion and 'depersonalisation' (a measure of the extent to which they felt less able to treat patients as people). High depersonalisation was associated with 45% higher odds of making a major error in the following three months; high emotional exhaustion was associated with 54% higher odds. A subsequent replication study (the same procedure but with a new sample of 184 doctors) found similar results[58], with depersonalisation associated with 50% higher odds of an error and emotional exhaustion with 63% higher odds. A study of 7,905 surgeons by the Mayo Clinic showed that highly stressed surgeons, were three times more likely to make a major error in the subsequent three months[59].

Another study of 115 doctors conducted by the University of Washington[59] found that those with high depersonalisation were more than four times as likely to report they had provided substandard care to patients. The data is overwhelming, and not just in relation to doctors. A Swiss study of Intensive Care Units (ICUs) found that emotional exhaustion among 1,425 nurses and physicians was associated with higher ICU patient mortality[60]. Emergency doctors in the UK with higher emotional exhaustion and depersonalisation reported that they reduced quality standards in a way that could harm patients (one third suffering with fatigue reported this at least monthly)[61].

Obstacles to compassion

So, what stops us from being compassionate in health and social care? The main reason staff say they aren't always compassionate with patients, service users or their colleagues is because they don't have time. When people feel 'time poverty' as opposed to 'time affluence', they are much less likely to show compassion. Time pressures profoundly reduce time affluence and therefore compassion. One study suggested that 56% of healthcare providers don't think they have time for compassion[62] because they must focus on reducing costs, dealing with administration, clinical audit, rules and regulations and other administrative tasks.

Time pressures are indeed a powerful factor. One famous social psychology study from 1973[63] involved priests in training preparing a short teaching on the Christian biblical parable of the Good Samaritan, who shows pity to a stranger lying beaten by the roadside. On their way to give their talks in the seminar, one third of them were told they were late. All encountered a dishevelled man lying in a doorway moaning in pain. Those who thought they were late were six times less likely to stop and help than those who thought they were early, and 4.5 times less likely than those who were told they were on time.

> And yet, the evidence we have is that compassion does not to take more time. It does not seem to affect caregiver encounter length or, at least if it does, not by much.

In an RCT of patients with a new cancer diagnosis[64], the researchers examined the effects of compassion on patient anxiety by comparing a standard consultation with an enhanced compassion consultation. The latter treatment involved the clinician simply using this script: 'I know this is a tough experience to go through and I want you to know that I am here with you. Some of the things that I say to you today may be difficult to understand, so I want you to feel comfortable in stopping me if something I say is confusing or doesn't make sense. We are here together, and we will go through this together.' At the end of the consultation, they would say: 'I know this is a tough time for you and I want to emphasise again that we are in this together. I will be with you each step along the way'. The total time for this compassion intervention was 40 seconds. The RCT revealed that patients who experienced enhanced compassion had significantly lower anxiety.

Another study[35] found that the number of compassionate statements made by hospital clinicians was not related to overall encounter length. More compassion did not mean more visits from patients subsequently. Similar results have also been in found in primary care[65]. GPs trained in emotion handling had higher compassion ratings from patients and those patients were not only less distressed after their visits, but the effects persisted for months. And the consultations were not that much longer (on average, only 54 seconds longer). Taking all the evidence together, compassion appears to take on average 40 seconds longer[64-69]. This is a tiny investment compared to all the benefits to care quality, patient satisfaction, care costs, carer well-being and even mortality.

Some research suggests that one solution to time poverty is to give some time away[70]. A series of experiments compared different conditions – spending time helping others, wasting time, spending time on oneself, and gaining an unexpected windfall of free time. Helping had a larger boost on people's sense of time affluence than the other three conditions, perhaps because of the elevated sense of purpose and self-efficacy.

Can compassion be learned?

The University of Houston researcher, author and TED speaker, Brené Brown, argues that compassion is a commitment, not something we have, or we don't have – it's something we choose to practise[71]. It does require acting, but what is called 'deep acting', which appears to be less emotionally exhausting than 'surface acting'[72].

A study by Barbara Fredrickson and colleagues of training in loving kindness meditation as an intervention at work suggested a profound impact on participants' lives[73]. The study was conducted at the Compuware Corporation, a large business software and information technology services company in Detroit, Michigan. They compared the experiences of 67 members of staff who began a practice of loving kindness meditation with 72 colleagues in a waitlist control group (they would learn when the experiment was over). The meditation training involved six 60-minute group sessions. In the first session, participants practised a meditation directing love and compassion toward themselves; in the second, they added loved ones; and during subsequent sessions, the meditation built from self, to loved ones, to acquaintances, to strangers, and finally, to all living beings. They were asked to practise the meditation daily. Results showed that the meditation practice produced increases in positive emotions, mindfulness, purpose in life, social support, life satisfaction and decreased illness and depressive symptoms.

In a study of brain activity among advanced practitioners of loving kindness meditation (Tibetan Buddhist monks), researchers found very high levels of gamma waves, associated with synchronous brain activity across many different areas, typical in an 'aha moment' of powerful insight[74,75]. Moreover, these unusual patterns of activity were present not only during meditation practice but also during normal waking as well as during sleep, suggesting permanent alterations in brain wave activity as a result of the practice of loving kindness meditation[76].

This is consistent with research from Tania Singer's laboratory at the Max Plank Institute in Germany showing changes in brain wave activity after only six hours of compassion meditation training[43,44], and with research from the University of Wisconsin-Madison showing changes in brain wave activity after a two-week compassion training course[77].

This evidence suggests therefore that compassion training can lead to neurophysiological changes, but what about behaviour? A study with doctors showed that patients of those who were trained to increase levels of compassion reported an increase in levels of their doctors' compassion[62]. And a meta-analysis of 18 RCTs of compassion training involving over 1,000 people showed that compassion training is effective in producing substantial increases in compassion[78]. Similar results emerge from studies of compassion training for medical students[79,80] and for nurses and nursing students[81-84]. A meta-analysis of compassion training for physicians found that 80% of the most rigorous studies demonstrated that compassion training increased physician compassion[49]. And compassion training is associated with better outcomes for patients, according to a meta-analysis of RCTs on compassion training[50,85].

Those most likely to benefit from compassion training in healthcare are those who believe it will help – what Carol Dweck from the University of Stanford calls a 'growth mindset'. Dweck found that those who believe compassion can be developed put more effort into being compassionate than those who hold a fixed mindset[86]. Healthcare practitioners must want to develop their compassion, and to be able to offer it freely, rather than compassion being mandated as part of their responsibilities[87]. The implication is that we must help healthcare practitioners to understand why compassionate care is so important, in order for them to want to be compassionate.

> Enlightened healthcare practice is based on believing that every patient deserves compassion.

Compassion as an antidote to burnout

In the UK, between 35% and 50% of doctors and nurses have high levels of burnout, while in the US, 50% of physicians are burned out[88-90]. Burned out physicians are twice as likely to make a major medical error in the subsequent month[91].

Most studies show an inverse relationship between compassion and burnout amongst healthcare professionals[92]. It is relevant that neurophysiological studies show that the most potent activator of brain circuits associated with happiness is compassion[75].

A large study of 1,000 medical students suggested those with high levels of compassion had lower burnout and better quality of life[93]. Another study of 7,500 physicians revealed that those with the lowest compassion satisfaction (enjoying a sense of compassion) were more burned out and distressed and had higher levels of sickness absence[94]. Compassion may be a buffer against stress. For example, among doctors working in A&E[61], those who were able to maintain compassion for patients were more satisfied with their work.

All of this raises the question about direction of effects. Does burnout reduce compassion or vice versa? The weight of evidence clearly suggests the protective effects of compassion. In one study, an eight-week training programme in compassion was associated with reductions in physician burnout and increased well-being[95]. An RCT conducted at Emory University in the US found similar effects with 132 medical students randomly assigned to a ten-week compassion training programme having increased compassion and reduced depression and burnout[96].

These effects appear to be consistent whatever the level of seniority in medicine. A study of Chief Medical Officers of large hospitals or health systems who were under severe pressure revealed that compassion was the main factor affecting their well-being and preventing burnout[97].

And those who train medical students on their placements have a big impact in transmitting the value of compassion. Supervisors who model compassion and teach compassion are 2.6 times more likely to be role models[98]. If mentors role model lack of compassion, there is a cultural transmission that can damage both trainees' well-being and patient care[48]. The leadership literature generally has consistently demonstrated that attending, understanding, empathising and helping, the four behavioural elements of compassion, are also the core behaviours of effective leadership.

Conclusion

Compassion makes a profound difference to outcomes for patients, service users and to clinicians. It costs less and empowers patients and service users, and it protects the well-being of those providing care. And it is something that can be learned and practised. The evidence must also inform training and education courses for health and social care professionals.

> It is clear then that compassion may be the most important intervention overall in health and social care.

Our challenge is to create the conditions in our health and social care organisations that enable professionals to provide the high-quality and compassionate care we all wish for. Those conditions constitute the organisational culture and all of us have the opportunity and responsibility to shape the culture, in every interaction we have in our workplaces, every day. Whatever our level of seniority in the organisation, our compassionate leadership is key, therefore, to creating the conditions for compassionate care in service of our communities.

Resources

Exercises/Discussion questions (to reflect on or discuss with a colleague)

1. How can the evidence of the link between compassion and health outcomes for patients and positive patient experience be communicated effectively throughout your team/organisation? How can you involve patients in that process?

2. Why does compassion affect health outcomes and to what extent do team members/staff appreciate that? How can that appreciation be strengthened?

3. How can you ensure that staff are aware of the link between showing compassion in the delivery of care and better caregiver well-being/ lower levels of burnout?

4. Does your finance director and the finance team know about the effects of caregiver compassion on healthcare costs? How can you make them aware of the evidence?

5. What are the barriers in your team/organisation to compassionate care and how can they be overcome?

6. What strategy should be put in place to develop compassionate care across the organisation – for patients and for staff?

7. How can we support the development of our senior leaders to ensure they all model compassion in their leadership?

Questionnaires

Measuring compassionate healthcare with the 12-item Schwartz Center Compassionate Care Scale[99]

Did the clinician...

1. Express sensitivity, caring and compassion for your situation?

2. Strive to understand your emotional needs?

3. Consider the effect of your illness on you, your family and the people most important to you?

4. Listen attentively to you?

5. Convey information to you in a way that is understandable?

6. Gain your trust?

7. Always involve you in decisions about your treatment?

8. Comfortably discuss sensitive, emotional, or psychological issues?

9. Treat you as a person, not a disease?

10. Show respect for you, your family and those important to you?

11. Communicate results in a timely and sensitive manner?

12. Spend enough time with you?

Guidance on using this questionnaire is provided in Appendix 1.

Websites

1. Health Education and Improvement Wales: Compassionate Leadership Principles for Health and Social Care in Wales
   This website sets out the leadership principles for Health and Social Care in Wales. It commits the system to ensuring that, by 2030, leadership will be distributed. The strategy outlines a shared vision that everyone across health and social care in Wales will model and practise compassionate and collective leadership, in order to ensure high-quality, continually improving and compassionate care for the people of Wales.
   https://nhswalesleadershipportal.heiw.wales/leadership-principles

2. The Social Care Institute for Excellence (SCIE)
   The SCIE in the UK has published the principles for ensuring that warmth and kindness are practised to bring dignity in social care. The Institute explains that people feel their dignity is respected when the care they receive is delivered with human warmth and empathy. They are not objects, burdens, numbers or aliens. They are us, cared for with kindness. Their website offers interactive case examples to help the reader consider their own compassionate responses to specific situations.
   https://www.scie.org.uk/dignity/care/warmth-and-kindness

3. The Health Foundation: Compassion, Dignity and Respect in healthcare
   The Health Foundation, an independent charity committed to bringing about better health and healthcare for people in the UK, published a report in 2014 on Compassion, Dignity and Respect in healthcare. The report offers some definitions of compassion in care:

   'Compassion comes from that moment when we can see the world through somebody else's eyes.'
   'Compassion is about treating patients with dignity, respect and empathy.'

'I think it's particularly powerful when we are feeling vulnerable, in physical or psychological pain, or when we are afraid.'

'The consistent theme is that it's always the smallest things that make the greatest differences.'

'You hear so many stories nowadays of people being treated as a number.'

'Compassion isn't just about talking to the patients – it's making them feel safe in a nice, clean environment, where they can feel at home.'

'I think that the most valuable gift that we can give each other, and give the patients, is the gift of time.'

https://www.health.org.uk/video/compassion-dignity-and-respect-in-health-care

4. In this blog, Dr Clare Price-Dowd from the NHS Leadership Academy talks about her personal experience of compassionate nursing and discusses why it's so important in the NHS.
https://www.nursinginpractice.com/views/what-does-compassion-mean-to-me/

Videos

A TEDx talk by Dr Stephen Trzeciak about the research and findings in *Compassionomics* and how his 12-year-old son asked a question that sparked his awakening and changed his life's work. (15 minutes)
https://www.youtube.com/watch?v=pNkb6R5whXE&feature=emb_rel_pause

Another TEDx talk by Dr Stephen Trzeciak about the research and findings in *Compassionomics* and how 40 seconds of compassion could save a life. (15 minutes)
https://www.youtube.com/watch?v=elW69hyPUuI

A fuller talk by Dr Stephen Trzeciak about the research and findings in *Compassionomics*, in a Grand Round at his own institution, Cooper Medical School Rowan University. (55 minutes)
https://www.youtube.com/watch?v=g-cDC-M_3UM

The Compassionate Leadership interview by Chris Whitehead with Dr Stephen Trzeciak, covering key questions about the findings from his research and what inspired Dr Stephen Trzeciak. (37 minutes)
https://www.compassionate-leadership.co.uk/podcast/episode/20179444/stephen-trzeciak-compassionomics-the-evidence-base-for-compassion

Chapter 4.

Compassionate cultures in health and social care

Summary

This chapter focuses on cultures of compassion in health and social care, identifying both the barriers and enablers of compassionate cultures. It outlines practical ways in which leaders can put into practice the four elements of compassionate leadership – attending, understanding, empathising and helping. The chapter explains how to develop compassion in interactions with colleagues, how to nurture and sustain compassionate climates in teams and departments, and how to develop compassionate organisational and institutional cultures. The resources section provides guidance on recruiting for compassion and describes a measure of compassionate culture already widely used in health and social care services.

Introduction

The aim of health and social care services is to deliver high-quality, compassionate care and promote the health, well-being and happiness of all in our communities. These aspirations are not easily achieved in a context characterised by high levels of stress, complexity and workload, and where the possibilities of errors are many[1]. Health and social care are a demanding setting for staff at the best of times, let alone in managing the health consequences of a pandemic. As we saw in chapter 2, the most detailed study of NHS staff stress showed that 26.8% of staff suffer damaging levels of stress, compared with 17.8% of the general working population[2]. Half as many more staff experience stress compared with the rest of the working population. Health professionals, especially nurses, have among the highest rates of work-related stress, depression or anxiety every year[3].

Caring for the health and well-being of others is an intrinsically compassionate behaviour. The people who work in health and social care have decided to dedicate a large part of their precious lives to caring for others. Theirs is a vocation that implies a core value of compassion. The extent to which their organisations also value compassion will influence the value 'fit' between health and social care workers and their organisations. The stronger the alignment of individual and organisational values, the higher the levels of staff members' commitment, engagement and satisfaction. Creating, nurturing and sustaining cultures of compassion is therefore at the heart of our ability to provide high-quality and compassionate health and social care for those in our communities.

Successive studies have demonstrated that the culture of organisations is key in creating the conditions where staff can fulfil their purpose of delivering safe, high-quality, continually improving and compassionate care and which thereby have an impact on their ability to cope with work-related stress[4]. Culture is the combination of *the values and beliefs that characterise organisations as transmitted by the socialisation experiences newcomers have, the decisions made by management, and the stories and myths people tell and re-tell about their organisations*[5]. Staff are committed and engaged when their core values are mirrored by their organisation's values, prioritising above all high-quality, compassionate care. Consequently, their commitment and engagement will be higher[6] and they will be more likely to be compassionate in their interactions with patients and colleagues.

But what factors influence the culture of organisations? Culture is a consequence of all our interactions in our workplaces, but leadership plays a powerful role in transmitting the core values and beliefs of organisations[7]. Every interaction by every leader, every day, shapes the culture of the organisation. Therefore, to the extent that leaders consistently model compassion in their behaviour, the organisation will develop a culture of compassion. These norms and expectations, in turn, are communicated to staff creating the expectation that they should behave with compassion in all interactions (with patients and colleagues) at work. But there are obstacles to compassion in many health and social care organisations.

Barriers to and enablers of compassion

Barriers to compassion

The 'shackles of routine and ritual' are compassion inhibitors and have been blamed for constraining compassion by hindering flexible, patient-centred and creative delivery of care[8]. The complexity of health and social care environments with the demands of regulation, governance protocols and political conflicts can lead to a focus on chasing targets and to cultures of fear and blame. Other barriers to compassion include the fear of making errors, time pressures, excessive and sometimes defensive bureaucracy, bullying, stress, depression, burnout, rapid change, excessive workloads, inadequate staffing levels, job insecurity, difficult patients and families, and complex clinical situations[3,9-15].

The emphasis across health and social care systems is on cost-efficiency, processes, driving performance with targets, and 'high-volume' care which creates ever heavier workloads, more complex task variety and increased managerial pressure. Stressed leaders themselves often pass their stress downwards. When leaders in health and social care become preoccupied with non-patient centred tasks and targets, this can diminish staff motivation and performance. Moreover, this shift from person to ritualised task, and from people to diseases and bed capacity, can lead to the dehumanisation of patients and the disengagement of leaders and staff[14].

Enablers of compassion

In contrast, compassionate cultures can be nurtured by leaders behaving with compassion. While much of the research on emotions in organisations has focused on the personal impact of an individual's emotions, emotions have influence beyond the individual. For example, the emotional states of individual group members can influence the general mood of the whole team, a phenomenon known as mood linkage or emotional contagion[16-18]. Similarly, the moods and emotions of leaders, given their positions of power and influence within organisations, can influence the moods and behaviours of those with whom they work. Research shows that positive leader affect is associated with more positive affect among staff, enhanced team performance, and higher rates of prosocial behaviours[19-21].

The language used and stories told at work, and the feelings that leaders model and endorse in their members, can also help to create compassionate cultures across the organisation[22]. Leaders set an important tone for this by noticing suffering at work themselves and valuing such compassionate awareness in others[23]. Organisational cultures of compassion can be developed therefore where there is collective noticing or acknowledging of pain within a system that values such noticing[24,25]. Similarly, staff can collectively feel concern and show their concern through what they say and model in their behaviour at work.

> Compassion spirals out; those receiving compassion are more likely to be caring and supportive towards others.

And this also replenishes the emotional resources that caregivers need, especially in a caring environment, and helps cushion them from stress and burnout[16]. The positive ripples of compassion can also affect witnesses and by-standers (beyond patients and carers), who may experience feelings of pride about the way people in the organisation behave, encouraging people to act more for the common good[25].

Experiencing compassion from others shapes individuals' views of themselves (eg, seeing oneself as more capable), their peers (eg, viewing them as kinder) and their work organisations[25]. When staff feel valued and cared for (ie, perceived organisational support), they tend to feel more satisfied in their jobs, and have increased commitment to their organisations. This is true in the NHS and is associated with high levels of patient satisfaction, care quality and financial performance of healthcare organisations[26].

This sense of being valued and worthy is not a state that is a given in work organisations, rather, it is something that is either created, or destroyed, by the way that people interact with one another at work and show kindness and appreciation[27].

Being on the receiving end of compassion in the workplace has beneficial effects, both for staff and the organisation. It can lead to people experiencing more positive emotions such as gratitude, pride, and inspiration, and can lead to upward emotional spirals that can enhance emotional well-being[28]. It can help communicate dignity and worth, and help people feel better psychologically and connected with others. The theory of positivity resonance explains how moments of connectivity (eg, moments of interpersonal compassion) benefit people through a natural synchronisation of bodies and brains in ways that foster health and well-being[28]. We connect deeply physiologically in a compassionate interaction.

Drawing on this knowledge of compassionate cultures and what inhibits and enables them, guidelines are given below on how all can lead compassionate cultures and on how to apply compassionate leadership in our work with individuals, teams and whole organisations in health and social care.

Leading compassionate cultures

Through our leadership, we can help develop compassionate cultures through how we attend, understand, empathise and help[29].

Attending:

- Pausing and noticing suffering at work (our own and others').

- Inquiring - asking about suffering, difficulties and challenges is crucial for awakening compassion.

- 'Listening with fascination' to all those we interact with and lead.

- Recognising and addressing time pressure, chronic work overload and performance demands that distract us from noticing suffering at work.

- Policies, rules and norms of conduct can orient us unconsciously towards punishment, rather than curiosity about what is happening with others.

- Leadership presence and mindfulness are vital for creating climates of compassion.

Understanding:

- Suffering is often masked by missed deadlines, errors or difficult and ambiguous work situations that trigger blame instead of compassion. Leaders can learn to be curious about the causes of difficult or ambiguous work situations as a way of cultivating more generous interpretations.

- Leaders can practise cultivating the positive default assumption that others are good, capable and worthy of compassion – offering them the benefit of the doubt.

- Leaders can withhold blame by steering conversations about errors or failure towards learning.

- We can practise imbuing all others with dignity and worth no matter what their role, position or difference from us.

- We can learn to develop our ability to be present with suffering as a form of being authentically with others, without necessarily having to find immediate solutions or balms.

Empathising:

- Learning to be present in the moment is a powerful leadership strategy. This involves an awareness of our own and others' experience and of interpersonal processes, moment-by-moment. It helps us to remain calm and steady in the face of suffering – our own as well as others.

- We can cultivate the capacity for attunement with those we work with, which involves being aware of the other person while simultaneously staying in touch with our own senses and experiences. Through this, we can heighten the sense of interconnection.

- We can develop empathic listening, the capacity to tune into feelings of concern, as we hear others' perspectives and experiences. This allows us to be present with those we lead and work with, without necessarily needing to fix, solve or intervene.

- Being empathic as a leader at work helps us to 'feel our way forward' together and motivates a compassionate response.

- Identifying with others leads to empathy and a higher likelihood of compassionate action. Feeling similar to the other contributes to identification, which is especially important when we are working with people from professional or demographic backgrounds different to our own.

- Physical and psychological presence, conveyed through eye contact (more important especially because of mask use during the covid-19 pandemic), verbal tone, posture and facial expressions heighten identification, connection, trust and a sense of psychological safety.

Helping:

- Compassionate acting involves spontaneity and improvisation (because every situation is unique) and 'listening with fascination'. Understanding and empathising allow us to initiate an in-the-moment response to the other, which is directed by what is most useful to those who are suffering.

- Skilful compassion involves taking tangible actions that address the roots of suffering rather than superficial actions taken as being easy ways out, platitudes or providing irrelevant 'solutions'. But the breadth of skilful compassion can also include the powerful act of simply listening and understanding, and the empowerment that this can convey to another. So whilst not strictly tangible, the act of acknowledging and understanding a problem, can in some instances be enough to provide the other with a reminder of their own agency and strength.

- Compassionate leadership requires creating flexible time for others to cope with suffering, buffering people from task overload, monitoring and checking in, providing resources that will alleviate suffering and designing rituals that convey support (even things as simple as taking the time to listen, or making someone a cup of tea/coffee). Compassionate leadership also involves continually directing the organisation's (everyone's) attention to the biggest challenges it faces, such as chronic excessive workload, staff shortages, toxic conflicts and bureaucratic sclerosis, to develop new and improved ways of working.

- Compassionate action is hindered by legalistic and bureaucratic approaches that deny human connection. Corrosive politics, toxic interactions, consistent underperformance and other forms of conflict at work are sources of suffering that must be addressed. They require 'fierce compassion.'

- Compassion is reduced when people fear that they will be viewed as weak or vulnerable for giving or receiving compassion.

- Finally, compassionate leadership involves stressing the importance of integrity and privacy in dealing with suffering and with personal issues in work-life.

Nurturing compassion across levels

Compassion is a human quality and it is humans that constitute relationships, teams, organisations and even networked systems (such as the wider health and social care system). Therefore, we can and should plan to develop compassionate relationships, teams, organisations and systems in health and social care. This is essential for creating cultures of high-quality and compassionate care for the people of the communities we serve. Detailed below are strategies for developing compassion at each of these levels.

Individuals

The culture of the organisations we work in is the most powerful influence on behaviour in our organisations. In order to develop cultures of high-quality and compassionate care, we must ensure we develop high-quality and compassionate relationships. How can we shape culture? Every interaction by every individual, every day, shapes the culture of our organisations. How positive we are, how kind, humourous, cynical, aggressive, supportive, civil, respectful – the ripples of our interactions spread out and affect others in their subsequent interactions.

We know that when nurses have been spoken to sharply by, for example, a supervisor, this affects their subsequent interactions with patients over the course of the day. When people are asked (as part of a research study) to do something kind for another person at work each day for two weeks, this has a large impact on their own well-being during and after that period. Moreover, those who benefit from the initial acts of kindness go on to undertake acts of kindness to others, so the ripples spread out[30]. Humans are social animals and we 'catch' emotions from each other – a sort of emotional contagion. And all of this affects performance positively[31-33].

> Positive emotions help us to be resilient and creative and to make better decisions and identify more with others.

When we are subject to incivility, aggression or exclusion, this has a large effect on our well-being, performance and ability to be compassionate towards others[34]. Seeking to ensure that our interactions are supportive, positive and kind is, therefore, the most powerful way in which we can build compassionate cultures within the organisations we are a part of.

Compassion at the individual level manifests as:

- Colleagues being present with each other, attending to the other and 'listening with fascination'

- Seeking to understand the challenges colleagues face through a dialogue with them

- Empathising or caring for colleagues without being overwhelmed by the feelings this evokes

- Helping or supporting colleagues so that their challenges are overcome or their distress is relieved.

Teams

How do we develop compassionate teams? This is a responsibility of all team members because cultivating compassion is an additive process - one that is created (or destroyed) through continuing exchanges and interactions between each team member.

The most important skill we bring to teams is our knowledge and practice of how to work collaboratively rather than our technical knowledge and proficiency. These include:

- Ensuring our teams have a clear shared purpose and objectives

- Ensuring we monitor performance by gathering helpful feedback

- Making sure everyone is clear about their and each other's roles

- Providing support to team colleagues when they need help

- Looking after each other's well-being by building cohesion and modelling compassion

- Communicating effectively, sufficiently and frequently

- Coming together to reflect and review so we ensure effective performance[35].

Compassionate teams in health and social care have a clear statement of the purpose of the team's work – an inspirational set of words encompassing a purpose that everyone is committed to and that provides a compass or direction.

Compassionate teams ensure that the overall purpose is translated into four or five clear goals that they prioritise. Having too many goals and being overwhelmed by tasks is inherently punitive for health and social care staff, so managing the workload to avoid it being chronically excessive is vital to creating the conditions for compassionate teamwork. They also gather feedback (data) to help them appraise their progress in relation to the team goals.

Such teams minimise hierarchy in the process of making decisions or setting direction. Shared or collective leadership is characteristic of effective and compassionate teams in every sector, not only in health and social care. This does not mean rampant and inefficient democracy where every decision must be backed in a vote. Shared leadership is evident where all voices are valued. And leadership seamlessly shifts between situations and discussions from the hierarchical leader to whoever has the most relevant expertise for the task in hand. Hierarchical leaders will still make necessary decisions in a crisis, but the whole team will be likely to review decisions after the crisis is over so that it can learn.

Compassionate cultures: Mental Health Hub Team, NHS 24, Scotland

In Scotland, NHS 24 provides a range of services via phone and internet to the people of Scotland to access care and support. The Mental Health Hub was newly established as a team within NHS 24 in February 2019.
The team is successful, engaged and supportive of each other. The service itself was developing and, in response to the pandemic, it changed from a 4-day service only operating Thursday-Sunday from 6pm to 2am, to one providing support 24/7.

There was a noticeably greater demand for the service as lockdown was clearly taking a toll on people's mental health. The anxiety, uncertainty, instability, illness and bereavement from the virus was greatly affecting the general public's well-being. The hub was quickly expanded in order to respond to this need, with new Psychological Well-being Practitioners (PWPs), Mental Health Nurse Practitioners (MHNPs) and Senior Charge Nurses (SCNs) recruited.

Many team members had never worked day shifts or full night shifts, which was a significant change in their personal circumstances and required them to adapt. Discussions and one-to-ones with staff members ensured they were willing and happy with rota changes. Compromises were made to honour some long-standing commitments or difficulties people had in changing their rotas.

"It was almost like a war cry - you dropped everything and would do whatever was necessary. People just went, 'What do you need and when?' Everyone in the NHS was pulling together so we felt like we were doing our job. Even though we weren't on the 'frontline' dealing with covid-19 patients we were always doing an important job that couldn't just be put on hold."

The team reports that team morale and support has not faltered through this testing time. If anything, it has brought them closer together and made them look out for one another more, as they now know there are a lot more challenges in people's lives.

"The prospect of more restrictions is less daunting since I have been part of this team because I know that no matter what, there is always a supportive environment available to me."

SCNs and MHNPs keep an eye out for staff throughout shifts and, if they notice them having a difficult call, they check in with them and send them on a 'walk away' to clear their heads. They are always checked up on during debriefs and even on the team member's next shift, to ensure that the call or experience they had on the phone with a patient has not affected their own well-being or that they have not been thinking about it outside of work. The 45-minute debrief they have at the end of every shift is particularly effective in ensuring this. The team discusses openly and in confidence any tricky or interesting calls they have had, as well as any learning points. They practise mindfulness every Sunday and leave the debrief on a positive note.

"The debrief is incredibly useful for self-regulation which is essential during these times where our emotional resilience can be tested. It allows us time to reflect on our practice and learn from our experience. I particularly value when our MHNP SCNs join because it gives us an opportunity to draw on their years of experience and to learn and share together." - PWP

"We cover shifts when people are in quarantine and make sure to check in on one another regularly. We have never had to shut the service since going 24/7 and our lights never go off. We will continue to do whatever it takes to support each other and the mental health of the Scottish general public."

https://www.imatter.scot/team-stories/nhs24/nhs-24-mental-health-hub-covid-story-an-expanding-service/

In compassionate teams, leaders facilitate rather than direct, ensuring all voices are heard and valued and that there is a positive and supportive climate in the team.

Leadership is focused primarily on ensuring clear direction, alignment of efforts around that purpose and a climate of psychological safety that fosters trust, motivation and commitment. Such teams also blur professional boundaries in a way that values each member's contributions, does not create fault lines and prevents the formation of competitive silos between professional groups. Mutual respect, valuing and support across professional boundaries are hallmarks of compassionate teams.

Compassionate team members demonstrate a commitment to mutual support, building cohesion, modelling trust and demonstrating humility (rather than arrogance or directiveness). Frequent positive contact is essential to creating compassionate teams because it helps to reinforce trust and build understanding. Such contact is also necessary for effective communication about purpose, goals and team processes. Compassion involves attending (being present), understanding, empathising and helping. These are facilitated or enabled by (ideally) frequent face-to-face contacts.

During the covid-19 crisis, this has been more difficult, but some teams have incorporated additional coffee/tea/cake time into their remote/virtual meetings to ensure informal contacts and warm interactions are maintained, thereby reinforcing a sense of psychological safety in the team.

We are hard-wired to sense information from tiny signals in each other's faces and postures, tones of voice, and eyes, and much of this richness is lost when we are not able to be together. Meetings are important for encouraging positive contact and so we must compensate in virtual meetings by giving more positive signals or cues and interacting warmly.

Compassionate teams bring compassion to their interactions with other teams in their organisation (or outside the organisation) with whom they work in the provision of health and social care. Compassionate teams demonstrate enthusiastic and supportive inter-team and cross-boundary working by:

- Ensuring there is a clear, inspiring shared purpose among the teams that need to work together to provide health and social care

- Having clear long-term goals for what they are seeking to achieve together

- Having frequent positive contact (ideally face-to-face)

- Identifying, surfacing and resolving conflicts quickly, transparently, fairly, ethically and courageously

- Focusing attention on how they can help the other teams they work with to ensure high-quality and compassionate care for patients, service users and communities.

At team level, compassion manifests in team members as:

- Paying attention to the climate and processes of the team as a whole, 'listening with fascination' to how the whole team, as a team feels

- Seeking to understand the challenges and difficulties the team is facing (such as some chronic interpersonal tensions, for example) and ensuring a dialogue involving the whole team to promote shared understanding

- Sensing the emotional climate of the team (eg, when it is experiencing a high workload that is causing anxiety, stress or frustration)

- Encouraging the team to act to address difficulties or distresses to ensure it can be the best it can be and function effectively in the interests of the communities it serves.

In summary, the hallmarks of compassionate teams include that:

- They focus on effectiveness by clarifying the vision and direction of their work, aligning their efforts around that vision and developing high levels of trust and motivation

- They are inclusive, valuing all team members equally in relation to knowledge, skills and experience; professional background; ethnicity, sexuality, gender identity and age; opinions and perspectives

- They model shared team leadership and everyone having authority and influence

- They are also focused on collaborating and supporting across boundaries with other teams and sectors, not simply their own areas of responsibility, ensuring a commitment to providing high-quality health and social care[35,36].

Organisations

To what extent are our organisations compassionate? Organisations (hospitals, care homes, learning disabilities services, primary care practices, clinical commissioning groups) are simply human communities. They happen to have a focus (delivering health and social care to others), but they are simply a form of human community.

Communities develop different cultures that may include, for example, clear vision and purpose; lack of consensus and cohesion; high levels of fear and anxiety; strong, kind, supportive relationships; isolation and alienation; an orientation of welcoming newcomers; and co-operative and warm relationships. So do organisations.

What are the cultures, then, of compassionate organisations in health and social care?

- They have a clear, inspiring vision of promoting the health and well-being of those they serve and those within the organisation.

- They have a limited number of clear goals at every level (every team and department within the organisation) aligned around the vision.

- They have enlightened approaches to people management, ensuring well-being, engagement, positivity and care. Leadership strives to be authentic, open and honest, showing humility (a commitment to learning to improve their leadership, for example), optimism, appreciativeness and compassion.

- They have a strong commitment to learning, innovation, positive diversity, universal inclusion and reflection, all within the context of psychologically safe climates. Leadership is predominantly collective rather than command and control or excessively hierarchical.

- They have strong and supportive team and inter-team relationships[4,37,38].

How would we know a compassionate organisation? Compassion is manifested in purpose, climate, processes and outcomes:

A. Purpose

Compassionate organisations have a focus on making a profound and positive difference to the well-being of those in their communities and to the well-being of their staff both now and in the future. These are not simply words on the website but are woven into the genetic structure of the organisation and translated into a few clear, challenging goals, providing alignment around direction for all.

B. Climate

In compassionate organisations, the climate is one of positivity and engagement. Staff describe their workplaces as warm, fun, supportive, kind, respectful, caring, positively challenging and engaging, inclusive and honest. Conflicts are dealt with openly, ethically and quickly so they do not linger. Colleagues listen to each other, are understanding and empathic, and help each other when the going is tough. There is a strong emphasis on everyone's growth, development and learning.

C. Processes

Organisational processes reflect a commitment to the development of a compassionate culture. For example, new staff are recruited and selected using values-based approaches with compassion at the heart. People's performance evaluations are values-based with commitment to attending, understanding, empathising and helping at the heart of the evaluations. Such evaluations are part of developmental orientations that support the development of compassion (eg, compassionate leadership and compassionate teamworking training). Education and development reinforce values-based approaches encouraging continuous development of positive and compassionate cultures in the fundamental interests of delivering high-quality and compassionate care for the people and communities the organisation serves. And organisations mirror these values back in enlightened HR policies including, for example, contract types that reflect the organisation's commitment to caring for the well-being of its staff and their continued professional development and growth.

Compassionate cultures: Berkshire Healthcare NHS Foundation Trust

Berkshire Healthcare is a community and mental health trust, employing 4,500 staff who operate from multiple sites, as well as out in people's homes and in various community settings. They are rated as 'Outstanding' by the Care Quality Commission.

Consultant Clinical Psychologist Dr Deborah Lee led the development and implementation of a Compassionate Leadership Programme across the trust. Compassion has been her driving force in transforming care for people and in helping to create a culture of compassion. Deborah led the training of more than half the staff in compassion cultivation training and this programme is the largest compassionate leadership programme in England to date.

The Compassionate Leadership Programme draws on the science of human nature and the principles of Compassionate

Mind Training (Paul Gilbert and the Compassionate Mind Foundation). The aim is to support Berkshire Healthcare to nurture and maintain a consistently compassionate culture by creating a safe work environment for all, helping colleagues develop self-compassion, and fostering good compassionate relations with team members and colleagues. The Compassionate Leadership Programme focuses on the development of self-compassion by teaching skills of:

- Self-awareness

- Education about the science of human nature and teamworking

- The practice of compassion-based exercises

- Team compassion, developed by teaching skills of:

  - Self-awareness and team awareness

  - Courageous engagement in team behaviour and emotional environments

  - Using greater good solution-focused thinking shaped by compassion

  - Using bottom-up problem solving and creativity

  - Developing inter-team compassion focused behaviours through team pledges.

Compassion and self-compassion have increased for most staff following their participation in the Compassionate Leadership Programme. Workloads emerged as a barrier to compassion, along with the perception of a competing culture, which for some reduced opportunities to build stronger relationships. Other barriers included team fragmentation, competitive cultures, workload and organisational pressures. Team cohesion and supportive team and organisational cultures were key to change because they helped people to make use of the shared language and tools from the programme.

https://www.berkshirehealthcare.nhs.uk/about-us/

An inspiring and moving video from Dr Deborah Lee – Everyone Needs Compassion (17 mins)
https://vimeo.com/256389115

Institutional compassion is also focused externally in the relationships the organisation has with other organisations. For example, Health Education and Improvement Wales (HEIW) has committed to support the development of compassionate and inclusive leadership for all leaders in health and social care in Wales for the next ten years (see case example below). HEIW is committed to modelling this approach in its relationships with other organisations.

HEIW will have frequent (ideally face-to-face) interactions with boards and trusts to enable them to attend and 'listen with fascination' to their experience. They will try to understand the challenges faced by boards and trusts, not by imposing an understanding but through dialogue with them. Such dialogue may be contentious if there are sharp disagreements, but they will have a constructive dialogue that delivers a more profound and comprehensive understanding, because both organisations fundamentally share the same vision – of providing high-quality, compassionate health and social care.

HEIW will show empathy, considering the distress or difficulty the other organisations may face (such as during the covid-19 crisis). This then gives HEIW the motivation for the fourth element of compassionate relationships - helping and supporting the other organisations to be the best they can be, overcoming challenges and delivering high-quality, compassionate care for the people of Wales.

And, of course, the same principles apply to boards and trusts in their work with HEIW, with each other and with all organisations that care for the well-being of the people of Wales.

Health Education and Improvement Wales' (HEIW) Compassionate Leadership Principles	After extensive consultation across health and social care, HEIW has established seven compassionate leadership principles. These overarching principles underpin the ambition that, by 2030, leaders throughout the health and social care system in Wales will display collective and compassionate leadership.
	The principles affirm that compassionate leaders across health and social care in Wales will:
	1. Enable safe, trusting and engaging systems and cultures
	2. Strengthen respect, voice, influence and choice
	3. Improve equality, inclusion and diversity, consciously removing barriers and boundaries

4. Create environments where collective leadership thrives

5. Establish the conditions for its workforce to reflect, learn, continually improve and innovate

6. Develop supportive and effective team and inter-team working

7. Manage behaviour positively, openly, courageously and ethically.

https://nhswalesleadershipportal.heiw.wales/

D. Outcomes

Compassionate organisations in health and social care deliver the outcomes they and their communities wish for. This is likely to include, among others:

- Improving health and well-being and quality of life of all in the community

- High-quality and compassionate care – safe, clinically effective, appropriate, compassionately delivered and meeting patients' needs

- Effective involvement of patients, services and communities and other organisations that provide care in the genuine co-design and/or co-ownership of services

- High levels of patient, service user and community satisfaction with services generally

- High levels of staff well-being and low levels of stress, sickness absence, staff turnover, vacancies, and intention to quit

- Effective and efficient use of financial and other resources

- Positive impacts on the environment.

Conclusion

There is a large and convincing evidence base for the beneficial effects of compassion on patient outcomes and the well-being of health and social care professionals. Neglect, incivility, bullying and harassment have quite opposite effects. Helping organisations to develop compassionate and collective cultures or ways of working enables health and social care professionals, their teams and organisations to deal effectively with the challenges they face – both now as we deal with the consequences of a pandemic and in the future.

> All healthcare leaders must practise the skills of compassion in order to create the cultures that health and social care services need for the future.

Where organisations are founded on values and cultures of compassion, they foster individual, team, inter-organisational, and community well-being characterised by fairness, trust, thriving and well-being. They effectively create the conditions for staff well-being, effective organisational performance and thereby better serve the well-being needs of the patients and communities they serve.

Resources

Exercises/Discussion questions (to reflect on or discuss with a colleague)

1. Explain the five main reasons why compassion must be the core value in health and social care services.

2. What are the main barriers to sustaining compassionate cultures in health and social care?

3. Why is compassion important in the integration of health and social care services locally and nationally?

4. How can compassion be more effectively developed among individuals in your organisation?

5. How compassionate and effective is your team? What do you need to do to develop compassionate and effective teamwork in your team?

6. What do you need to do to develop or contribute to compassionate and effective teamwork across the organisation?

7. How compassionate is your organisation? What do we need to do in order to develop a compassionate organisation? How can we begin and sustain that process into the long-term future?

8. How compassionate is the wider health and social care system? What do we need to address to develop a compassionate health and social care system? How can we begin and sustain that process into the long-term future?

9. How can we ensure the communities we serve, the voluntary sector, the entire public sector, families and patients are involved in the genuine co-design and co-ownership of a compassionate health and social care sector that is a model for the world?

Questionnaires

Measuring compassion at the organisational level involves assessing particularly the behaviour of leaders and managers, but also the behaviour of staff generally.

The Culture Assessment Tool (CAT) – a copyrighted instrument developed by AffinaOD (*www.affinaod.com*) in co-operation with The King's Fund assesses the extent to which the culture of an organisation is characterised (among other things) by compassion: between staff and patients, between staff, and between managers (or leaders) and staff.

The Culture Assessment Tool	Score (1-5)*
Support *The following statements relate to levels of support provided by managers and leaders in your workplace. How strongly do you agree or disagree with the following statements?*	
1. Managers and leaders encourage warm, supportive relationships among staff	
2. Managers and leaders recognise and celebrate good performance	
3. Managers and leaders deal effectively with problems that get in the way of our work	
4. My manager listens carefully to staff to find out how to support them effectively	
5. My manager is very compassionate towards staff when they face problems	
6. My manager is highly empathic in their dealings with members of staff	
Compassion *The following statements relate to levels of compassion shown to and demonstrated by people in your workplace. How strongly do you agree or disagree with the following statements?*	
7. People here are very compassionate towards colleagues when they face problems	
8. People here give good support to colleagues who are distressed	
9. People here are very compassionate in the way they behave towards patients/service users	
10. People here take effective action to help patients/service users in distress	

* Response scale:
Strongly disagree = 1, Disagree = 2, Somewhat agree = 3,
Agree = 4, Strongly agree = 5

Guidance on using this questionnaire is provided in Appendix 1.

Websites

1. The Center for Positive Organisations (CPO)
    The CPO was established nearly 20 years ago, pioneering a new field
    of inquiry at Michigan Ross - Positive Organisational Scholarship - that
    sought to understand the characteristics, practices and principles that
    create a thriving organisation. It has helped create a global movement
    to promote effective workplaces where people thrive.
    https://positiveorgs.bus.umich.edu/about/

2. Developing a positive culture in health and social care – practical
    open-source tools and resources from NHS England/Improvement
    and The King's Fund.
    https://webarchive.nationalarchives.gov.uk/20210107182025/
    https://improvement.nhs.uk/resources/culture-leadership/
    *https://www.kingsfund.org.uk/sites/default/files/media/Suzie_*
    Bailey%20pres.pdf

Videos

This talk features Jane Dutton and Monica Worline, authors of
*Awakening compassion at work: The quiet power that elevates people and
organisations.* (23 mins 44 secs)
https://www.youtube.com/watch?v=I8qfdwDUARs

Compassion in health and care in Wales – a video from The Health
Foundation (4 minutes 15 secs)
https://www.youtube.com/watch?v=HVF0273iHus

Barbara Fredrickson on the importance of positivity in work-life and
organisations (8 mins 44 secs)
https://www.thepositiveencourager.global/barbara-fredricksons-
approach-to-doing-positive-work/

A selection of videos on improving teamwork by Michael West can be
found by using the search term 'teamwork Michael West' in an internet
search engine.

Further resources: Recruiting and selecting for compassion

Compassion-based recruitment - recruiting and selecting for compassion - is a method of attracting and selecting staff whose personal values and behaviours align with the organisation's core value of compassion. It is an approach to recruitment and selection that ensures the values and behaviour of candidates indicate a strong orientation of compassion towards others. The recruitment process also communicates the commitment of the organisation to a core value of compassion at an early stage. Compassion-based recruitment therefore seeks to ensure that staff have not only the right skills, but the right value of compassion to deliver high-quality patient care and experience.

Assessing for compassion signals a core value of the organisation to applicants – compassion is an important competency here. This forms part of the socialisation process and is the first signal to the prospective staff before they enter the organisation. One way of doing this is to embed a psychometric scale into assessment and selection methods by using a multi-rater feedback methodology (asking the candidate to gather ratings from diverse perspectives). For new candidates, this may be difficult. You may wish to use a 'realistic job preview' as part of selection procedures and observe the behaviours of the prospective staff throughout, scoring them on a scale of 1 – 5.

Compassion can be measured using the questionnaire in chapter 1, based on four elements of compassion: attending, understanding, empathising and helping. These can be used by co-workers or could be adapted as a self-report measure.

During recruitment, those responsible for making decisions can explore compassion amongst potential recruits in several ways, such as:

- Pre-screening assessments

- Interviewing techniques such as structured interviews, role play or responses to scenarios

- Assessment centre approaches

- Psychometric instruments

- Situational judgement tests.

In practice, this might involve adding to the interview a number of questions such as those shown below.

Example of compassion-based interview questions

1. To test for support and compassion towards patients – tell us about a time when you worked with a patient in distress. How did you go about the process? (Criteria - attending, understanding, empathising and helping)

2. To test for support and compassion towards colleagues – tell us about a time when you worked with a colleague who was angry with you. How did you go about managing the situation effectively? (Criteria - attending, understanding, empathising and helping)

3. To test for commitment to compassion in teamworking and collaboration – tell us about how you feel you work particularly well with colleagues who are under pressure in teams and the way you make a contribution. (Criteria - building cohesion, support, optimism and efficacy)

4. To test for commitment to compassion in working with those in other professions – tell us about a time you worked with someone from another professional group and there was some tension or conflict. How did you deal with this? (Criteria - listening, understanding, empathising, helping, building cohesion and support)

5. Give an example of a time when you encouraged and enabled collaboration between your team and another team or department. (Criteria - working effectively across boundaries and prioritising patient care overall, not just within team performance).

- Compassion-based approaches to recruitment work best if implemented effectively and comprehensively. This means ensuring that much of the questioning in an interview, for example, is focused on compassion issues and plays a big role in determining selection.

- Organisations should provide training to enable leaders to conduct effective compassion-based recruitment. The more objective the approach to selection, the better, so where good psychometric measures of compassion exist, it makes sense to use them.

- Structured interviews are much more effective than unstructured interviews, as are work sample tests. Using scenarios to test for compassion is also helpful – 'How would you react in this situation?'

- Recruitment is just one part of the whole employment journey, so it must form part of an holistic approach that ensures compassion is embedded in all areas of employment practice, from supportive contracting, training and appraisals, through to organisational development.

- When interviewing/observing, it is important that more than one person is present in the interview to rule out any unconscious biases that may be influencing the way a person is being assessed.

Chapter 5.

Compassionate team leadership and psychological safety

Summary

This chapter focuses on the teams that make up health and social care organisations and that, which are the most important determinant of our daily work-life experience. It describes the research literature, showing how teams affect mental health and well-being of staff, determine care quality, and how they should be constant sources of innovation. These outcomes depend on the quality of teamworking and, particularly, on whether there is a team climate of psychological safety. The influences on such climates include a clear shared vision, values and goals; support for reflection, learning and innovation; frequent and positive contact between team members; team members valuing diversity, difference (eg, of opinion) and positive conflict; and relationships based on mutual support, compassion and humility. The role of compassionate leadership in creating these conditions is detailed throughout this chapter.

Introduction

Our daily work lives are shaped primarily by our experiences in the teams of which we are a part. Culture is translated into work-life experience through our interactions with those with whom we work most closely and most frequently. Shaping culture to ensure high-quality, compassionate care and support for both those who use services and those who deliver them, therefore, requires a strong beam of attention on teamworking. Teams are the means by which we deliver care and meet the purposes of health and social care organisations. Compassionate cultures, focused on care and support, are characterised by compassionate teamwork. And such teamwork is associated with the outcomes we want from our health and social care organisations – better quality of life and health for service users, and better quality of work-life and workplace health for staff.

Teamworking in health and social care is a taken-for-granted good. Teams of people must work interdependently to provide high-quality, compassionate care for patients. They must combine their varied skills, expertise and experience to deliver the best possible care. Uni-professional, lone practitioner working cannot deliver the care patients need to the same extent as multi-professional teamworking.

This chapter explores this taken-for-granted assumption and argues that, though teamworking is vital for high-quality healthcare, the quality of teamworking in this sector is often poor. Such poor teamworking leads to errors that harm both staff and patients; injuries to staff; poor staff well-being; lower levels of patient satisfaction; poorer quality of care; and higher patient mortality. This chapter details how compassionate teamworking, compassionate team leadership, and team-based working as an organisational form can be developed within and across organisations by creating climates of psychological safety. This must be enabled by sustained compassionate leadership.

Why teamworking?

The need for belonging reflects our human desire to feel and be connected to others – to feel included, valued, respected and supported in teams and organisations, and to care and be cared for in those contexts[1]. There is abundant evidence to show that support from colleagues enables people to thrive in their work, helps them cope with difficult work experiences, and buffers them from the wider organisational factors that cause irritation and stress[2]. Exclusion, discrimination, bullying, incivility and chronic conflict have the opposite effect[3]. The support of health and social care colleagues for each other in teams has been movingly evident during the pandemic, enabling most to cope successfully in very challenging times.

> To enable health and social care staff to deliver high-quality, compassionate care and to flourish, all must work together to create positive, supportive, compassionate and inclusive workplaces.

Belonging requires an organisational commitment to the delivery of high-quality and compassionate care that reinforces the sense of vocation of health and social care staff. The quality of teamworking and a culture of inclusiveness and supportiveness of teams are central to the sense of belonging of those working in health and social care.

An effective team is a group of usually no more than 8–10 people, who work together to pursue a limited number (5–6) of clear, shared goals. The team is provided with data or information that ensures helpful feedback in relation to their progress in achieving their goals or objectives. Team members are clear about their roles in the team. The team climate is characterised by positive emotions and a sense of psychological safety[4].

Teams with these characteristics ensure greater role clarity for team members, provide higher levels of social support, and buffer members from the negative and depleting effects of wider organisational demands. Good team leadership also ensures connection and compassion across boundaries so that healthcare staff work together across professions (including social care) to deliver high-quality care[5,6]. Where there are larger numbers of team members (as is typical on wards and in general practices), it becomes more difficult to manage team processes and communication, and so clear protocols and the concept of 'teams within teams'[4] are required.

In modern health and social care services, the skills of 'teaming' that enable people to work in multiple teams or with a variety of team members who may be different across shifts are vital[7], but it is also necessary for well-being and effectiveness to have stable membership of a home team. Dropping in and out of teams, or rarely being part of a team with the same team members, undermines the sense of connection, community and belonging[6].

Working in teams is vital for health and social care quality but there is also good evidence that those working in supportive 'real teams' with good team leadership, have significantly lower levels of stress than dysfunctional or 'pseudo teams' in health and social care[8].

> 'Real teams' fulfil the very minimum of requirements of having clear, shared objectives and meeting regularly to review performance and how it can be improved[8].

The more people working in 'real teams' in a healthcare organisation, the lower the levels of stress, errors, injuries, harassment, bullying and violence against staff, staff absenteeism and (in the acute sector) patient mortality; and the higher the levels of patient satisfaction[8]. Data from primary care over many years has shown similar results; that quality of teamwork determines care quality and staff well-being[4].

Teamworking in health and social care can easily be assumed to be functioning adequately with blithe reflections such as 'we are all one big team here'. But we know that the quality of teamworking and inter-teamworking in health and social care in the UK is often poor[4,9]. The basic mechanisms of effective teamworking are often not in place in our organisations, even though there is extensive international research that consistently identifies what is required to have effective teams in health and social care. Successive inquiries into failings in healthcare nationally and internationally identify culture and teamwork as fundamental to success.

Data from the NHS Staff Surveys across England suggests that in the acute sector, only around 40% of staff work in 'real teams'[10]. The data from staff surveys across the four UK countries suggests that between 50% and 60% of staff work in 'pseudo teams' in health and social care, which either do not have clear, shared objectives, or do not meet regularly to review performance and how it can be improved.

Effective teams are 'real teams' that also have climates of psychological safety, shared team leadership, take time to review and improve, and work co-operatively across boundaries with other teams and departments[11].

Psychological safety in a team refers to everyone feeling included, cared for and valued; a strong sense of interpersonal trust and mutual respect; team members feeling comfortable being themselves; and team members not fearing they will be ridiculed, humiliated or judged by their colleagues. This is described and explored in more detail below.

Shared leadership in effective teams is characterised by team members valuing all contributions regardless of profession, 'or place', in the status hierarchy. Shared leadership ensures that leadership moves between individuals (even though there may be a hierarchical leader) dependent on expertise in relation to tasks, rather than hierarchical position[12]. Effective team leadership ensures that there is regular, protected time for collective reviews of team functioning and performance.

Inter-teamworking is as important as quality of intra-teamworking in the delivery of health and social care. Effective teamwork involves co-operating and supporting other teams to ensure effective delivery of overall high-quality and compassionate care, rather than just the team's own area of responsibility[8].

These elements of effective teamwork apply in primary care, secondary care, community care and social care. There is much to be done in all these settings to ensure that health and social care staff work in effective teams. Training in the basic skills of teamworking and team leadership is required at all levels. There is compelling evidence of the value of team training for health and social care professionals, showing that it is effective for both students and practising clinicians[13]. Moreover, high-fidelity, expensive team training appears to be no more effective than low-fidelity, inexpensive team training.

The evidence suggests we must find new ways to enable staff to work as part of effective and supportive (ideally multidisciplinary) 'home' teams. This will be challenging, but compassionate leaders who respond positively to this challenge can make a profound difference to staff well-being, as well as to productivity and care quality.

Good practice would see all health and social care staff belonging to a stable 'home team' (where possible, multidisciplinary) that enables:

- Involvement in quality improvement initiatives

- A sense of belonging and social support

- A space to discuss challenges, difficulties and frustrations

- Opportunity for appreciation and recognition

- Clarification of roles and responsibilities

- Peer coaching and mentoring

- Professional development

- Leadership development and teamwork training.

During the pandemic, some teams have become more stable entities, so staff have felt more part of a 'home team'. Camaraderie, daily briefings, huddles and regular time to discuss the work have dramatically improved teamwork. Some teams have had a clear sense of purpose and have built cohesion and a sense of team compassion and support. Check-ins and huddles with the whole team, and having protected time to have lunch/ coffee breaks together, have helped build belonging, cohesion and support.

"Switching off telephones at lunch and going out for lunch together – initially this was shocking. But the positive outcomes were incredible and everyone was so well rested. The leader in the team absolutely made sure this happened. It's not all about the patient, it's about the staff too."

The pandemic has stimulated an extraordinary acceleration of more integrated ways of working in health and social care in some settings, with a significant improvement in the quality of inter-teamworking across boundaries. Staff have overcome communication challenges, adapting and developing new roles, and breaking down barriers to work across primary, secondary and social care.

Improved teamwork is just one of the outcomes of the blurring of hierarchical and professional boundaries – a contrast to operating in silos. Organisational and professional identities have been relinquished or relaxed as staff have transferred from acute settings to work in community settings when necessary. Additionally, cross-boundary working has become the new normal in some areas, with collaboration between primary care, secondary care and social care and a range of volunteer and community groups. Ways of working have been transformed in a matter of days and in ways that were unimaginable just a few months before. All of this is a testament to enlightened multidisciplinary team and inter-teamworking.

Multidisciplinary team (MDT) working is known to promote improved care and safety. When diverse professional groups (such as general practitioners, health visitors, district nurses, midwives, physiotherapists, pharmacists, counsellors and practice nurses within primary healthcare teams, and psychiatrists, social workers, occupational therapists, psychologists and community psychiatric nurses in community mental health teams) work well together, alternative and competing perspectives are carefully discussed, leading to better quality decisions about care. Primary healthcare teams that include many different professional groups have been shown to deliver higher quality patient care and implement more innovations in patient care[14].

Face-to-face MDT working should be the first choice. Such teams need stability of membership to become cohesive, time for reflection on work challenges, accessible space to meet, and ways of involving all team members. Social interactions such as shared tea/coffee breaks, meals and celebrations also build a sense of cohesion and psychological safety[6]. Alongside this, health and social care staff must have the skills to work in multiple teams – what Amy Edmondson calls 'teaming'. This is not complex; it is simply the transfer of basic teamworking skills to the multiple teams that staff may be required to work in over the course of a week. These skills include ensuring clear team and individual goals, clear roles, good communication, and regular check-ins and reviews[7].

The Academy of Medical Royal Colleges, based on consultation with other professionals in the NHS, articulated in 2020 some of the key principles of MDT working and identified multiple case studies of success across the UK. These include the following:

- The importance of celebrating diversity and difference and resisting protectionism and silo working, which together require creating a supportive culture, promoting respect for the contribution of others, and resolving conflict effectively.

- How inter-professional education and training can enhance professional identity formation and teamworking skills at the outset of health and social care careers.

- The ongoing role of continuing professional development (CPD), supervision, mentoring and appraisal in stimulating a culture of shared learning and a supportive and self-reflective environment.

Health and social care staff need training and ongoing support, including through protected time for teams to reflect together, to continuously develop their MDT and compassionate team leadership skills from the beginning of their undergraduate education onwards. These are not complex or difficult skills to learn, and several programmes for developing effective teamworking in health and social care have been developed in the US, the UK and other settings[15].

> There are clear links between the quality of teamworking, quality of patient care, patient satisfaction and staff well-being[16,17].

Health and social care professionals must work together to develop and sustain inter-professional relationships to address difficulties in working across primary, community, secondary and social care.

Compassionate health and social care working arrangements must develop, prioritise and sustain effective teamworking, make provision for it (for example, by ensuring high-quality support for team leaders) and provide areas where regular team meetings can take place. Teams that regularly take time out to review and improve their performance are far more effective and innovative – such timeouts increase productivity by an average of between 35% and 40% and substantially improve the health and well-being of staff[18].

Before considering how compassionate leadership can help develop climates of psychological safety, the chapter now details the evidence of the links between teamworking and outcomes for staff, patients, service users and organisations. It describes the research at three levels: individual, team and organisational.

Individual level outcomes

Healthcare is a stressful sector to work within[15,19]. The service delivery and organisation of caring for people in society incurs damage to the very people who provide that care. Does teamworking make a difference? Research suggests that teamworking is associated with lower stress levels among healthcare workers as a result of greater role clarity, social support and being buffered by their teams from negative organisational factors[19]. Moreover, a meta-analysis of 35 studies of the implementation of teamworking in healthcare found an overall positive effect on staff satisfaction and well-being[20]. The effects in healthcare were significantly larger than those found in 23 studies in non-healthcare environments. The research suggests that this is dependent on the quality of team functioning.

In a study of 400 healthcare teams, researchers found that quality of team functioning was associated with lower team member stress levels[14]. Team functioning was measured as clarity of team objectives, levels of participation of team members in decision-making, emphasis on quality of task performance, and support for innovation within the teams. Another study gathered data from 65,142 hospital staff in the NHS in England and found that those working in well-structured teams had the highest levels of job satisfaction[21]. Again, levels of social support and role clarity appeared to account for these differences.

Team level outcomes

Does effective teamworking lead to better patient care and patient outcomes? A review of the literature suggests that teamworking in healthcare is associated positively with a range of patient outcomes[9]. This review echoed the conclusions of the earlier review in that good teamworking reduced errors in patient care and improved quality[22]. A review of teamworking in intensive care settings concluded that working in teams can significantly reduce the level of errors and promote learning and quality improvement in intensive care units[23]. But quality of teamworking matters. There is also evidence that poor teamworking leads to medical errors, while good teamworking prevents them. Researchers have found that medical errors were often a result of poor teamworking and status hierarchies[24]. Such hierarchies are associated with reluctance on the part of lower status team members to challenge the decisions of more senior team members, even when they believe those decisions to be wrong. In an analysis of 193 critical prescribing incidents, one third were attributed to team-related problems such as hierarchies, failure to challenge prescribing etiquette, ignoring hospital regulations and neglecting best practices in the interests of team relationships[25].

Teamworking in healthcare should not be a taken-for-granted good; it is the quality of teamworking that counts in ensuring high-quality care. Research also shows that quality of teamworking predicts the extent to which teams develop and implement innovation in healthcare - introducing new and improved treatments for patients and new and improved methods of delivering care. In another study of two samples of healthcare teams (66 and 95 teams respectively), MDTs produced higher quality innovation than less diverse teams, but only when the teams functioned effectively[26]. Effective teamworking included clear team objectives, high levels of team member participation in decision-making, commitment to high-quality work, and practical support for innovation. A study of community health teams over a six-year period in Sweden showed that, where teamworking was introduced, regions reported reductions in emergency visits[27]. Again, quality of teamworking was important, and accessibility and continuity of care were particularly important factors.

Organisational level outcomes

Research has examined the extent of team-based working in organisations and explored its relationships with outcomes such as patient satisfaction, quality of care, efficiency of use of resources, innovation, staff engagement and well-being and (in the acute sector) patient mortality. A study of the links between human resource management (HRM) practices in hospitals[28] found that the extent and quality of teamworking had a significant negative relationship with patient mortality - the more widespread and the better the teamworking, the lower the levels of patient mortality. Where more than 60% of staff reported working in 'real teams', mortality was 5% lower than expected, and this result held after controlling for the number of doctors per 100 beds, GP facilities per 100,000 population, and local health and socio-economic profiles.

An analysis of the NHS England Staff Survey data over eight years suggested that the quality of teamworking in healthcare organisations (across primary care, mental healthcare, ambulance services and acute care) was associated with better patient satisfaction, quality of patient care, efficiency of use of resources, lower staff absenteeism, lower staff turnover and better financial performance[29,30]. Studies of teamworking in primary care in the US suggest that high intensity collaboration in multidisciplinary teams is associated with reduced patient hospitalisation and physician visits[31]. Overall, the research suggests that teamworking and team-based working in healthcare have positive outcomes for staff, patients and organisations. But a consistent finding is that the quality of teamworking is important and that, in healthcare, there is a need to clarify both what is meant by the concept of 'team' and what constitutes effective team functioning or teamworking. Calling a group of people who work in healthcare a team is not a guarantee that their combined efforts will prove beneficial for patients (or their well-being), as the research above confirms.

To ensure effective, high-quality, continually improving and compassionate care, we must shape the environment appropriately for health and social care staff. What should we be aiming at? All the evidence and staff experience points to the need to develop and sustain psychologically safe environments.

Compassionate team leadership for psychological safety

Psychological safety is a 'shared belief held by members of a team that the team is safe for interpersonal risk-taking[11].' It describes a team climate characterised by inclusivity, interpersonal trust and mutual respect in which people are comfortable being themselves and expressing their views. Such psychological safety is vital for effectiveness in health and social care, and compassionate leadership (attending, understanding, empathising and helping) helps to create psychological safety. A related concept is 'participative safety', which refers to encouraging people's involvement in decision-making in a non-threatening work context[32].

It is in teams that psychological safety, or threat and blame, are manifested. Teamwork is fundamental to the effective delivery of health and social care, and effective teamwork delivers higher quality care, better staff well-being, higher levels of patient satisfaction, higher levels of innovation, and in the acute sector it is associated with lower levels of avoidable patient mortality[33]. Effective teams have clear direction and clear roles, climates of psychological safety and shared team leadership, take time to review and improve, and work co-operatively across boundaries with other teams and departments[4]. Psychological safety in a team refers to everyone feeling included, cared for and valued; a strong sense of interpersonal trust and mutual respect; team members feeling comfortable being themselves; and team members not fearing they will be ridiculed, humiliated or judged by their colleagues.

The reality sometimes presents a sharp contrast to effective, psychologically safe teams. Many health and social care staff report feeling unfairly treated or threatened by blame. They want environments that emphasise support, compassion and learning. The context of healthcare often undermines compassion with its 'shackles of routine and ritual' hindering flexible, individualised and creative delivery of patient-centred care. Other barriers are the fear of making errors in the contexts of time pressure, excessive and sometimes defensive bureaucracy, bullying, rapid change, chronic work overload, poor levels of staffing, difficult patients and families, and complex clinical situations.

How then do we create psychological safety in teams? The following figure describes the key elements that can nurture such a climate.

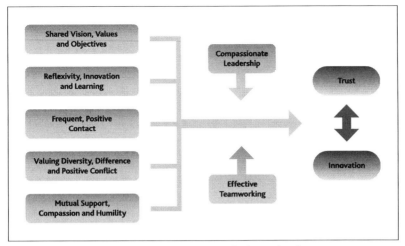

Figure 1: The key elements that nurture Psychological Safety

Shared vision, values and objectives

Compassionate leadership is focused on ensuring a clear, shared vision of working to provide high-quality care and support for those we serve. When a team has a clear, shared vision of its purpose, team members are united around an inspiring direction for their work. Social psychologists have demonstrated the importance of such shared purposes for preventing fractures or fault lines in relationships within teams (fault lines can be created for example, by all nurses in the MDT being female or by all junior grades being minority ethnic group staff)[34,35].

> ## Compassionate leadership embodies the values of compassion, humanity, courage and wisdom.

Having clear, shared values is also helpful to ensure that team members have agreed how they should work together by committing, for example, to mutual respect, to valuing all members' contributions, and to compassion, honesty and support. One way of achieving this agreement is to ask teams to agree on 'five things we must always do and five things we must never do'. Such an agreement can be refreshed annually.

Equally important to creating a sense of purpose and structure is translating the vision into a limited number of clear, agreed and challenging goals or objectives. This means no more than four to six challenging goals or objectives aligned to the vision of the team and that are agreed by team members rather than imposed by hierarchical leaders. Teams will have confidence and focus when they have regular, accurate and valid data that provides feedback on progress in relation to their goals[36,37]. Overall, vision, values and clear objectives help create a strong sense of team identity or belonging.

Effective and safe teams can reinforce a sense of pride in the team's performance and nurture team identity through rituals, celebrations, humour and narrative so that people feel proud of who they work for and with. This includes directing attention to how their work makes a positive difference in patients and society. They can also model 'sympathetic joy', where team members take pleasure from the successes of others around them, rather than feeling envious or critical.

Reflexivity, learning and innovation

Compassionate leadership will help create psychologically safe teams by encouraging team members to:

- Share learning, including about errors and near misses

- Avoid unnecessary blaming

- Improve the quality of their work through regular reviews of working methods

- Develop and implement ideas to improve quality

- Support others in implementing ideas for new and improved ways of working.

Compassionate leadership involves helping teams review and learn both from successes and difficulties or errors. Such leadership should help team members process negative emotions – pain and grief – where necessary, not simply emphasising the positive (Schwartz Rounds have proved a powerful way of legitimating such learning – see chapter resources). When team members regularly take time out together to review objectives, strategies and processes ('team reflection' or 'team reflexivity'), they collectively learn and improve at work while ensuring team member personal well-being[38-41].

Moreover, considerable research evidence shows that such teams are both much more productive and innovative than teams that just continue to spin the hamster wheel. Indeed, one meta-analysis of 49 research studies (as described earlier in the chapter) suggests such teams are between 35% and 40% more productive[18]. Reflection or reflexivity can be achieved through the regular scheduling of team away days, meetings, 'after action reviews', debriefs, etc. This ensures clear shared direction, early detection of problems and corrective action via innovation.

Research in the NHS has shown that learning and innovation occurs in the context of psychological safety, rather than in blame cultures.

Such innovation is vital for high-quality, continually improving and compassionate care. Following failures in healthcare organisations, a succession of reports[42] have advocated embedding learning and quality improvement throughout health and social care. To sustain psychological safety in teams, team members must be compassionate in their interactions with each other and they must commit to[4]:

- Paying attention ('listening with fascination') to each other

- Developing mutual understanding

- Being empathising and caring

- Practically supporting each other.

In safe team environments, there are higher levels of learning and innovation[11,43,44]. Blaming cultures, in contrast, are fearful, inhibit compassion and prevent learning.

Creating the conditions for innovation requires giving frontline teams the freedom (from heavy handed hierarchical or bureaucratic control) to experiment, discover and apply new and improved ways of delivering care[44,45]. Releasing the capacity for innovation means supporting team members and giving them discretion, control and freedom for service improvement[46]. There is consistent evidence from healthcare teams over nearly forty years that identifies the key characteristics of innovative healthcare teams:

- An inspiring vision and clear, agreed, shared, challenging objectives

- High levels of participative safety

- Commitment to excellence

- Practical support for new and improved ways of working

- Inspiring and compassionate leadership

- Diversity of team membership (eg, multidisciplinary, ethnicity, experience).

Such characteristics are fostered by compassionate leadership that promotes continued learning and development for all team members. This is enacted by ensuring that all:

- Have freedom to work autonomously where appropriate

- Can participate in challenging projects and development opportunities

- Are enabled to lead in their work

- Can respond successfully to challenges

- Are provided with the necessary support and resources (emotional, as well as practical) to achieve this.

It involves leaders ensuring conditions that develop and empower team members by enabling their continued growth and development and their ability to function autonomously, both of which are fundamental to human health and well-being.

Self-managing nursing teams: Buurtzorg, the Netherlands	Buurtzorg Nederland is a not-for-profit social enterprise providing a range of long-term personal, social and clinical care to people in their own homes. It was founded in 2006 with a single team of four nurses. By 2016, there were 850 self-managing teams and 10,000 nursing staff, supported by just 45 administrative staff and 15 regional coaches. It was founded with the aim of connecting to the intrinsic motivation of nurses, who would be the carriers of its vision of high-quality, continually improving and compassionate care.
	The Buurtzorg model has two defining features. The first is its holistic approach to care, with one or two staff working with each individual and their informal carers to access all the resources available in their social networks and neighbourhoods, to support that individual to be independent.
	The model's second key feature is its flat organisational structure and the autonomy held by its nursing staff. Small, non-hierarchical, self-managing teams of nurses and nursing assistants make their own operational and clinical decisions, based on a consensus model of decision-making. The teams are responsible for recruitment, organising and delivering care, and managing their own performance. They are supported by a small centralised back office.

Staff receive training on self-management and the Buurtzorg approach to care. All teams have access to ongoing developmental support from Buurtzorg coaches, whose focus is on enabling teams to learn to work constructively together. There is a strong emphasis on inter-team sharing of innovative practice through the Buurtzorg online platform and regular inter-team events.

Buurtzorg has won 'best employer of the year' in the Netherlands, and has achieved the highest service user satisfaction ratings for any community care organisation in the country. Their staff sickness rates are less than half of those of other community care organisations in the Netherlands. The organisation sees trust, flexibility and autonomy as the backbone of its success, set in the context of humanistic, person-centred care. For more information, see: *https://www.kingsfund.org.uk/blog/2019/09/buurtzorg-model-of-care*

In Northern Ireland, the Buurtzorg model has been adopted and adapted to ensure that district nurses work in partnership with patients, carers, families and their communities to achieve better health and well-being outcomes. Through the development of a Neighbourhood District Nursing Model, district nursing teams are empowered and resourced to manage and direct patient care for the populations they serve. This approach encourages a population health focus where district nurses lead the assessment, planning and co-ordination of care in self-managed nursing teams.

https://www.health-ni.gov.uk/publications/district-nursing-framework-2018-2026

Frequent, positive contact

Compassionate leadership in teams involves being present with those we lead and helping them be present with each other. A half century of research on meeting the human need to belong and on overcoming intergroup hostility has reinforced the importance of building trust and of people having frequent positive contact with each other[1,34]. Team members feel safer with each other when they meet, interact, chat, share coffee or lunch together and simply engage. Face-to-face contact is the richest form of human contact and is superior to more impoverished forms, such as email, telephone or video conferences. The latter have become ubiquitous following the covid-19 pandemic, and experience suggests a need to compensate for the lack of in situ face-to-face contact through what can be described as 'social grooming' (asking questions such as 'How was your weekend?' or 'How was the birthday celebration?').

Reliance on technology means important social cues are filtered out of communications: an apologetic tone may be lost in an email communication; a warm smile as a joke is made is not seen during a teleconference and a shared exasperation with a third-party may not be appreciated in the text of a shared document. The loss of face-to-face connection can lead to reduced politeness and informal social chatting. It can also lead to intolerance, aggression, conflict and 'flaming' (sending angry email messages) in virtual teams[47,48].

Research shows that physical proximity is associated with greater liking[49] and better communication. On the other hand, the greater the extent of virtual teamworking, the lower the levels of liking, friendship and cohesiveness in teams[49]. Communicating frequently and in face-to-face meetings develops team trust and effective performance[50].

Valuing diversity, difference and positive conflict

If leadership in teams is not inclusive, it is not compassionate. Teams composed of people with differing professional and demographic backgrounds, and diverse knowledge, skills, experience and abilities, are more likely to develop and implement quality improvements (or new and improved ways of doing things). This is because they bring usefully differing perspectives on issues to the group[51]. But, generally, high diversity leads to team innovation only when the team feels psychologically safe.

A study of 100 primary healthcare teams[14] found higher levels of innovation when more professional groups were represented in the team. The challenge is to create diversity within healthcare teams without threatening their shared view of their task and their ability to communicate and work effectively together. It also requires team members to manage conflict constructively and positively.

Why is this? The variation and divergence of views in diverse teams offers multiple perspectives, and that can lead to either destructive or constructive conflict. If conflict is managed in the interests of effective decision-making and task performance (eg, the delivery of high-quality and compassionate care) rather than on the basis of motivation, because of conflicts of interest, interpersonal resentments or the desire to win or prevail, it will improve performance and quality[16,52-56].

Team members learn to get on, collaborate, integrate their skills and discover safety through the effective management of diversity and conflict. Where the team is homogeneous, there are strong pressures for conformity. Where the team is diverse, there are pressures to manage diversity in ways that ensure constructive and creative approaches to conflict. Team members must see task conflict as a positive – to be worked through and resolved in a climate of mutual respect and support.

Chronic interpersonal conflict is almost always destructive and prevents teams from delivering high-quality, compassionate care. Chronic interpersonal conflicts must therefore be compassionately confronted and prevented within teams, and this is a responsibility of all team members[55].

We only discover a solid sense of safety through the effective management of potentially threatening environments. Managing conflict compassionately, constructively, creatively and positively in teams ensures high levels of interpersonal and team safety[55].

> Compassionate leaders must therefore focus on ensuring equity and positively and overtly valuing diversity (such as race, disability, religion or belief, age, gender, sexual orientation, and professional background).

This can be facilitated by modelling careful listening to others' contributions ('listening with fascination') and ensuring everyone's opinions are valued (including those of all staff and patients). In psychologically safe environments, all team members feel included and valued, not simply those who are in some majority[56].

Team members must work together to ensure that everyone feels comfortable to be honest and open. They must also challenge aggressive or intimidating behaviours and deal effectively with bullying, harassment or discrimination. Such teams are in effect promoting social justice and morality, ensuring fairness and honesty and challenging unethical practices or social injustices.

Mutual support, compassion and humility

The need for belonging reflects our desire to feel and be connected to others - to feel valued, respected and supported in teams and organisations and to care and be cared for in those contexts[1]. It is met by working in nurturing teams and in cultures and climates that reinforce the sense of relatedness.

Health and social care jobs are stressful occupations for obvious reasons. What helps people manage that stress is the support, camaraderie, good humour and compassion of colleagues. The support of colleagues buffers people from the stresses they experience at work, helping them be clear about their work roles, helping them cope with difficult work experiences, and buffering them from the wider organisational factors that cause irritation and stress[34]. The support of team members therefore reduces the risk of poor mental health and well-being among health and social care staff such as burnout, anxiety, depression and work-related stress[57-59].

Exclusion, discrimination, bullying and harassment, ridicule, aggressive humour and chronic conflict have the opposite effect. These negative aspects of social interaction cause stress, physical ill-health, mental health problems and undermine the sense of connectedness that people need to stay well and be effective in their work roles. Chronic interpersonal conflicts corrode professional, supportive, civil, communal and compassionate relationships at work[55].

The experience of mutual support and concern builds a sense of belonging and safety. To create the conditions that enable health and social care staff to deliver high-quality care, flourish and stay well, all team members must work together to create positive, supportive, compassionate and cohesive teams in the workplace. That also means supporting each other at work emotionally, practically and professionally. Indeed, the factor that makes compassion more powerful and mutually fulfilling than empathy alone is the intent to help the other. When team members ask each other 'How can I help you?' it communicates a commitment to mutual support and a deeper sense of mutual affective concern and genuine compassion.

Humility is an important trait for both leaders and team members in influencing team psychological safety[60].

When team members value each other relationships are likely to be more harmonious. Moreover, everyone's contributions are likely to be valued, respected and supported. Those with humility realise they can benefit from the expertise of others, especially those who have less power than them. Such humility is not based on a desire simply to please others, but on a genuine valuing of others' contributions.

Compassionate leaders also promote mutual support across boundaries, encouraging people to build trust, respect and co-operation across teams, departments and organisations by fostering the idea of 'teams of teams'. Teams, departments and leaders within healthcare organisations must collaborate to provide seamless, coherent, integrated and efficient patient care. Where there are chronic inter-team conflicts, patient care suffers. Such compassionate leadership involves describing and emphasising shared visions; building a sense of long-term continuity and stability in cross-boundary relationships; ensuring frequent contact with these other teams; surfacing and resolving cross-boundary conflicts swiftly and creatively; and promoting a 'How can we help you?' orientation of team members towards those in other teams (or organisations). Psychological safety in teams is a consequence of both intra-team and inter-team processes.

Conclusion

To meet the challenges of delivering health and social care, compassionate leadership must increasingly meet people's need for belonging and develop and sustain trust. The purpose of compassionate leadership must be to create effective teams and team and organisational cultures of psychological safety. Such leadership must support health and social care staff to be more collaborative, compassionate and caring in order to effectively shape our future as health and social care organisations and the future well-being of all those in the communities we serve. In so doing, compassionate leadership will enable staff to experience joy at work and a sense of fulfilling engagement every day, rather than exhaustion and burnout, to ensure their health and the health of the services they provide.

Resources

Exercises/Discussion questions (to reflect on or discuss with a colleague)

1. How psychologically safe is it for those in your team/organisation?

2. To what extent do you have a shared vision, values and goals within the team/organisation, and what do you need to do to develop them better?

3. To what extent within your team/organisation do you make time for reflection/reflexivity; do you promote and value continuous learning; do you support people's ideas for new and improved ways of doing things?

4. Do you make enough time for building trust and relationships within the team, across teams, within the organisation, and across organisations by having regular, positive, supportive contact? What can you do better?

5. Do you truly and openly value diversity and difference in all its forms within the team/organisation? To what extent do you value diversity in professional background, ethnicity, gender, disability, difference of opinion, sexuality, etc? How can you improve the climate of positive diversity within the team/organisation?

6. How well do you deal with conflict in the team/organisation? Do you approach conflict openly, courageously, ethically, and creatively with a commitment to work through it and achieve a better understanding and more trust? How can you ensure conflict is managed effectively within the team/organisation in a positive and courageous way?

7. To what extent do you support each other and behave generously and altruistically within the team/organisation, particularly when you work across boundaries (between teams, departments, organisations and sectors)? How can you improve that in a significant and sustained way?

8. What else can you do to better ensure a climate of psychological safety in the team/organisation in the future?

Questionnaires

The first three copyrighted instruments described below are based on the work of Michael West and colleagues over the last 35 years on teamworking in health and social care (for further information, see *https://www.affinaod.com*).

The Affina Team Performance Inventory (ATPI) - a comprehensive online assessment tool for measuring a team's potential to deliver effective performance. The ATPI's design is based on research into what we know about high performing teams. It assesses:

- Team inputs - including task design, team effort and skills, organisational support and resources

- Team processes - including team objectives, reflexivity, participation, task focus, team conflict and creativity and innovation

- Leadership processes - including leading, managing and coaching

- Team outputs - including team member satisfaction, attachment, team effectiveness, inter-team relationships and team innovation.

The Affina Real Team Profile Plus (ARTP+) - an online assessment tool for measuring team effectiveness. The ARTP+ measures the seven structural features that are essential for 'real teams':

- Team identity

- Team contribution

- Team autonomy

- Team objectives

- Team member interdependence

- Team member role clarity

- Team leader clarity.

It also measures the six process dimensions that predict team success:

- Team communication

- Team focus on quality

- Team innovation

- Team reflexivity

- Lack of team conflict

- Inter-teamworking.

The Affina Team Journey - an online team assessment and development tool for team leaders and HR/OD leads to use with their teams. It improves performance by giving teams a structured, evidence-based experience. The journey:

- Leads teams through a 10-stage structured programme based around team discussion

- Invites team members to provide feedback and use reports to support team discussion

- Provides team leaders with structured tools and techniques to develop effective teamworking

- Supports teams in-house

- Improves performance system-wide through effective teamworking and inter-teamworking

- Aligns team objectives and team climate to organisational aims and values

- Tracks progress and monitors return on investment.

The Fearless Organization Scan, based on Amy Edmondson's work, maps how team members perceive the level of psychological safety. *https://fearlessorganization.com/*

Guidance on using these questionnaires is provided in Appendix 1.

Websites

1. Affina Organisation Development
   AffinaOD aims to create sustainable change through the implementation of team-based working by providing team tools and techniques; training staff in health and social care organisations to use the team tools and support teams in-house; and collaborating with research partners to increase the knowledge base around team effectiveness. *https://www.affinaod.com/*

2. The Fearless Organization
   This website has been developed in partnership with Amy Edmondson of Harvard Business School. It argues that psychological safety is required for team high-performance. Psychological safety is defined as 'a belief that one will not be punished or humiliated for speaking up with ideas, questions, concerns, or mistakes.'
   The website describes the tool for measuring psychological safety. *https://fearlessorganization.com/*

See also Amy Edmondson's web page at Harvard Business School.
https://www.hbs.edu/faculty/Pages/profile.aspx?facId=6451

3. The Point of Care Foundation
   An independent charity since 2013, the foundation delivers training and
   support for health and care organisations in the NHS to offer Schwartz
   rounds for their staff.
   https://www.pointofcarefoundation.org.uk/our-work/schwartz-rounds/

Videos

Taken from a series of short videos, produced by AffinaOD, with Michael
West on teamworking: Team-based working in modern organisations and
how it relates to human evolutionary history. (49 seconds)
https://www.youtube.com/watch?v=x2vp-Qnc4Is

How teams improve staff engagement and why it matters.
(1 minute 48 secs)
https://www.youtube.com/watch?v=Gmw7EsfUfNg

The difference between a 'real team' and a 'pseudo team'.
(2 minutes 16 secs)
https://www.youtube.com/watch?v=bqipJlb1oMM

How to prevent teams from becoming dysfunctional. (2 minutes 45 secs)
https://www.youtube.com/watch?v=RgdVnMmZUN0

Four outcomes of psychological safety in teams – learning, risk
management, innovation and job satisfaction, with Amy Edmondson,
Harvard Business School. (3 minutes 17 secs)
*http://www.ihi.org/education/IHIOpenSchool/resources/Pages/
AudioandVideo/Amy-Edmondson-Why-Is-Psychological-Safety-So-
Important-in-Health-Care.aspx*

Building psychological safety in the workplace with Amy Edmondson,
Harvard Business School. (11 minutes 26 secs)
https://www.youtube.com/watch?v=LhoLuui9gX8

.

Chapter 6.

Compassionate leadership is effective leadership

Summary

Compassionate leadership must be effective leadership. The purpose of compassionate leadership in health and social care is to work with others to create the conditions where all in our communities are supported to live the best and most fulfilling lives they can. This chapter describes a powerful model of the outcomes of effective leadership as direction, alignment and commitment - the Center for Creative Leadership's DAC model[1]. In the context of compassionate leadership, these three elements are described along with the consequences of both succeeding and failing to achieve direction, alignment and commitment. Commitment – people's trust and motivation – is critical to the effectiveness of health and social care organisations. Understanding how to increase commitment and ensure effective leadership requires leaders to understand the core motivations of people at work. Meeting people's core needs at work ensures they have high levels of trust, motivation and well-being. This chapter explains how this is achieved using another powerful model - the ABC framework of core work needs (A - autonomy/control, B - belonging, C - contribution/competence).

Introduction

Compassionate leadership involves ensuring that the health and social care team or organisation is delivering high-quality and compassionate care for the people and communities it serves. Such leadership must therefore be effective, inclusive, collective and systemic (working across boundaries), as shown in the figure below. In this and the next three chapters, the means to develop such leadership are outlined.

Figure 1: Compassionate leadership is effective, inclusive, collective and systemic

This chapter focuses on effective leadership. Compassionate leadership includes being effective as a leader in health and social care, in service of an inspiring vision by ensuring direction, alignment and commitment[1]. Good leadership is evident when direction, alignment and commitment are clear and powerful, whether this is in a team, department, organisation, or wider system:

a.   *Ensuring Direction*
    i. A clear, shared, inspiring purpose or vision

b.   *Supporting Alignment*
    i.   Clear goals for people and teams aligned with and springing from the vision
    ii. Creating an effective feedback environment
    iii. Ensuring good coordination between people, teams and departments

c.   *Nurturing Commitment*
    i.   Developing trust and motivation
    ii. Providing positive emotional leadership
    iii. ABC – meeting core human needs at work

Drawing from extensive health and social care services research, there are five key elements which are necessary for sustaining cultures that ensure high-quality, compassionate care for patients: inspiring visions operationalised at every level; clear aligned objectives for all teams, departments and individual staff; supportive and enabling people management; learning and quality improvement embedded in the practice of all staff, and effective teamworking[2]. The first three neatly mirror the core leadership elements of the Center for Creative Leadership's (CCL) guiding model – DAC or Direction, Alignment and Commitment[1].

For leadership to be effective, the interactions and exchanges among people at work must produce:

• *Direction:* agreement on what they are collectively trying to achieve together

• *Alignment:* effective coordination and integration of their efforts at work so that they align together in service of the shared direction

• *Commitment:* people make the success of their work together (not just their individual success) a personal priority.

These three outcomes – direction, alignment and commitment – make it much more likely that individuals will work together willingly and effectively to ensure success in their work. CCL suggests that the only way to know if leadership is happening is to look for the presence of these three outcomes. The more present they are, the better the leadership. Compassionate leadership must therefore deliver direction, alignment and commitment out of compassion for those people health and social care systems serve.

Collective hospital leadership

The senior management team of a US hospital was concerned about the hospital's recent results on a set of 'quality of care' metrics. Its performance was above average, but the team agreed it should set its goals higher.

Achieving change required the concerted efforts of all the staff. The management team consulted all in the organisation about their vision and the associated goals. It was clear that the staff wanted to be part of an organisation that delivered high-quality care for patients and they were eager to participate in generating strategies for achieving the goals. The result was a detailed two-year plan for improving care quality, involving every department in the hospital. All managers scheduled time each week to talk with staff about the initiative and reinforced its importance. Two years later, the hospital's quality of patient care was rated tenth best in the US. Staff satisfaction was also very high.

Clearly, leadership happened in this case. There was a shared direction. Staff were coordinating their efforts in service of that direction and commitment to the initiative was high. How was all this DAC created?

Direction was created by:

- Creating and strengthening a movement to enhance the quality of patient care in the hospital

- Adapting organisational goals to local contexts (eg, team, department)

- Crafting organisational goals through discussion and shared agreement at senior level and then testing for acceptance with staff throughout the organisation

- Encouraging 'converts' to encourage others in supporting the movement.

Alignment was created by:

- Involving as many staff as possible throughout the hospital in producing an implementation plan that specified department and team goals

- Managers monitoring implementation and providing support

- Having an influential coordinating committee that monitored progress and made adjustments.

Commitment was created by:

- Making explicit that the initiative was tightly aligned with the motivation of staff to deliver high-quality patient care

- Celebrating success and achievements

- Sustaining the wave of enthusiasm and commitment.

Adapted from McCauley, C. (2011). Making leadership happen. A White Paper. Greensboro, NC: Center for Creative Leadership[3].

Direction

Compassionate leadership prioritises a vision and develops a strategic narrative focussed on delivering high-quality, compassionate care. In the best performing healthcare organisations, all leaders (from the top to the frontline) make it clear that high-quality, compassionate care is the core purpose and priority of the organisation[4].

Targets, productivity, cost-cutting, efficiency and meeting the requirements of service regulators are important, but high-quality, safe care is the top priority in the best performing health and social care organisations. While cost-effectiveness is vital given the demands on health and social care services, the research evidence shows that leaders must be vigilant in ensuring that their concern with cost-effectiveness does not appear to staff to eclipse a concern with delivering high-quality, safe and compassionate care.

Visions must also be translated into leadership actions because the messages that leaders send about their priorities are communicated more powerfully through their actions than their words. Leadership authenticity is revealed by what leaders monitor, attend to, measure, reward and model, and this, in turn, regulates and shapes the efforts of staff[5]. If leaders focus more on targets, cost efficiencies, productivity and costs (vital though these are) than patient experience, quality of care and patient safety, it undermines trust in the organisational vision and shapes the culture accordingly. And given that the values of most health and social care staff revolve around high-quality care giving and compassion, it is important that leaders are seen to endorse the priority of this value in practice[6].

Research in the NHS has shown that in poorer performing organisations, senior leaders are more likely to ignore staff concerns, dismiss staff stress, avoid discussing workload pressures and fail to deal with systems problems, such as problems in patient pathways, unnecessary bureaucracy and inter-departmental conflicts[4].

Cultures reflect what leaders value, what they do and what all in the organisation take for granted as the right way to behave[7]. Therefore, it is crucial that compassionate leadership demonstrates an unwavering commitment to high-quality and compassionate care.

Where direction is not clear:

- There is disagreement on priorities

- People feel pulled in different directions

- People feel they are not making sufficient progress – just going in circles[1].

Where direction is clear:

- There is a clear vision and set of overarching organisational goals that everyone is committed to

- People say why those goals are worthwhile and with conviction

- There is strong agreement on what success will look like[1].

Alignment

The second key cultural component for high-quality care cultures is clear goals/objectives at every level. Staff in health and social care are often overwhelmed by excessive workload and unclear about their priorities resulting in stress, inefficiency and poor-quality care[4].

Compassionate leadership involves nurturing cultures that are focussed on high-quality care by ensuring there are agreed, clear, aligned and challenging objectives at all levels (in all departments, directorates and teams) that ensure such care is the priority[8]. This is not the same as the institution of target-driven cultures that are used by some to drive change in the system – but with limited success[9]. The number of goals should be limited to a maximum of five or six[10].

Researchers have shown how having clear objectives ensures efforts are not diverted to irrelevant activities; that they activate relevant knowledge and skills; and motivate the effort and persistence of staff[11]. Good objective/goal setting will ensure staff are not subjected to chronic excessive workloads. When people, teams and departments have agreed clear, challenging objectives at work, they are generally motivated to work harder and to innovate[11]. Such clear objectives begin with the top management team having clear purpose and five or six clear objectives[12]. This clarity of objectives must then be replicated at every level so that each directorate, department, team and individual (the latter via their appraisal process) has clear objectives aligned with the purposes, vision, mission and values of the organisation.

Where staff report such clear goals, patients report better care – patient satisfaction is higher in NHS organisations where staff indicate there are clear goals at every level[13]. In such organisations, patients describe experiencing good communication and high levels of involvement in their care decisions. By aligning objectives across the organisation, efforts are collectively aligned to achieve the same outcomes.

It is equally important that compassionate leaders use measures to assess progress towards the achievement of such goals in order that this information can be fed back to staff, enabling them to adjust and improve their performance.

Where alignment is not clear:

- There is disarray, deadlines are missed and there is duplication

- People are unclear, overworked and frustrated

- People feel isolated from one another

- Teams compete rather than collaborate[1].

Where alignment is clear:

- People are clear about each other's roles and responsibilities (and their own)

- People and teams integrate their work effectively to achieve success

- There is strong coordination and synchronising of efforts[1].

Commitment

Commitment is achieved when leadership enhances rather than undermines staff trust and motivation. Compassionate leadership fundamentally embodies a supportive people management approach. Research has repeatedly demonstrated the relationships between staff management, customer service satisfaction and financial performance in the commercial service sector[14-17].

Research in health services in the UK also shows very strong links between staff experience and patient outcomes such as care quality, and that staff views of their leaders predict patients' perceptions of their care quality. In fact, staff experience in health and social care is the best predictor of organisational performance. Where health service staff report being well led and have high levels of satisfaction with their immediate supervisors, patients report that they, in turn, are treated with respect, care and compassion[13]. There are also strong relationships between staff satisfaction and commitment and patient satisfaction[13]. The more positive staff were about their working conditions, the more positive patients were about their care. These relationships also apply to care quality, financial performance and, in the acute sector, to patient mortality rates[18].

Similar findings emerge from other studies examining the relationship between nurse leadership and patient outcomes[19]. Directive, brusque managers dilute the ability of staff to make good decisions, deplete their emotional resources and hinder their ability to relate effectively to patients, especially those who are most distressed or difficult[8,20,21]. Analysis of data from health services also shows that good people management practices implemented across healthcare organisations are associated with low and decreasing levels of patient mortality[22,23]. Staff engagement appears to be a key factor[24].

Healthcare staff who are engaged are likely to deliver high-quality care, to be focussed on improving services and to have more capacity for compassion[25-27]. Engagement describes an experience of work as being involving, meaningful, energising, stretching and connecting. In the engagement literature, engagement is typically described as having three components: vigour, dedication and absorption[28].

The average level of staff engagement in health service organisations in the NHS predicts (positively) care quality and financial performance (based on independent audit body ratings), staff health and well-being, patient satisfaction and (negatively) patient mortality, staff absenteeism and stress[24]. The results are consistent across the different healthcare sectors:

primary care, ambulance services, mental health and acute hospital services. Furthermore, analysis of the data reveals that the relationship is more strongly directed from engagement to outcomes than vice versa. It is also noteworthy that the 'involvement in decision-making' component of the engagement measure was the strongest predictor of outcomes, suggesting a need to move away from command and control to more compassionate cultures.

This is confirmed in a review of the literature on culture and climate in high-performing healthcare organisations internationally[29]. Engagement appears to be higher in healthcare organisations where compassionate leaders create a positive climate for staff so that they feel involved and have the emotional capacity to care for others.

The implication is that the fear, pain, anxiety, loss and uncertainty that patients inevitably and often experience and that therefore characterise the culture of healthcare organisations must be balanced by positivity. In primary care, positivity and positive reflections reduce staff stress and improve health[30]. The results from the four UK NHS Staff Surveys also showed how staff reports of positive climates predict positive outcomes for both staff and patients[31,32].

Key to creating cultures of engagement are high levels of staff trust in their leaders[33]. Leaders who exhibit more positivity have been shown to generate higher levels of perceived trust from their teams and have higher evaluations of leader effectiveness[34]. Treating staff with respect, care, compassion, dignity, supportiveness and honesty is likely to build good quality leader-member exchange relationships[35] along with consistent striving towards fair and just treatment of staff.

Where commitment is not strong:

- Important tasks are not done and easy work is prioritised

- People are not mutually supportive

- People do not express faith in their immediate or senior leaders

- There is cynicism and passivity[1].

Where commitment is strong:

- People are more likely to put their hearts into delivering high-quality care

- There is a strong sense of trust and shared responsibility for the work

- People are positive, passionate and motivated about their work

- People support each other to cope effectively[1].

Meeting people's core work needs

Understanding how to increase commitment and ensure effective leadership requires that compassionate leaders constantly seek to understand and meet the core needs of people at work[36]. Meeting people's core needs at work ensures they have high levels of intrinsic motivation and high levels of well-being. They are likely to be highly motivated and to find their work joyful rather than depleting and damaging. To illustrate this, it is helpful to use a clear model – the ABC framework of core work needs:

- Autonomy and control – the need to have control over our work lives, and to act consistently with our work and life values

- Belonging – the need to be connected to, cared for, and caring of others around us in the workplace and to feel valued, respected and supported

- Contribution and competence – the need to experience effectiveness and deliver valued outcomes, such as high-quality care.

Leaders must be constantly vigilant about sustaining the well-being of health and social care staff, by ensuring they are continually improving the fulfillment of their needs for autonomy and control, belonging, and contribution and competence (the ABC of core work needs)[36,37].

> When these needs are met, people are more intrinsically motivated and have better health and well-being, and if any one of them is not met, well-being and motivation suffer.

Autonomy refers to the need for volition, choice and freedom to organise our experiences for ourselves and for self-integrity – being able to integrate our behaviour and experiences with our sense of self and our values, for example, as a provider of high-quality and compassionate care.

The need for belonging reflects our desire to feel and to be connected to others - to feel valued, respected and supported in teams and organisations and to care and be cared for in those contexts. The fact that we are at least as likely to die from loneliness as from the effects of obesity or smoking is a powerful indication of the strength and importance of this human need[38]. It also captures the importance of working in nurturing cultures and climates that reinforce a sense of relatedness: having a clear, enacted and shared vision focused on, for example, the delivery of high-quality and compassionate care; aligning all efforts around that vision; creating commitment through leadership and management that ensures trust, motivation and positivity; and building effective team and inter-team working. This means ensuring inclusive and compassionate leadership at every level.

The need for contribution reflects a need to make a positive difference through our work as well as to achieve valued outcomes, such as to deliver high-quality care that improves patients' lives. This reflects a deep human motivation to be able to influence our environments for the better. The need for contribution is met, first and foremost, when workloads do not exceed the capacity of staff to deliver valued outcomes. It is also met by ensuring that staff have enabling supervisory support, focused on removing obstacles in the workplace, which creates cultures of learning and accountability rather than directive, controlling cultures focused on blame. And it requires ensuring that all staff are continuously learning, developing their skills and growing their professional knowledge.

An integrated, coherent strategic approach to meeting these needs will powerfully transform the work lives of health and social care staff, their productivity and effectiveness and, thereby, the safety and quality of the care that they lead and deliver.

Inquiries into the mental health and well-being of doctors, nurses and midwives across the UK[31,32] suggest there are eight key workplace factors that impact the well-being, flourishing and work engagement of health and social care staff, aligned across these three core work needs (see figure 2). Implementing these recommendations helps ensure staff thrive, work effectively and experience joy rather than depleting stress at work[31,32].

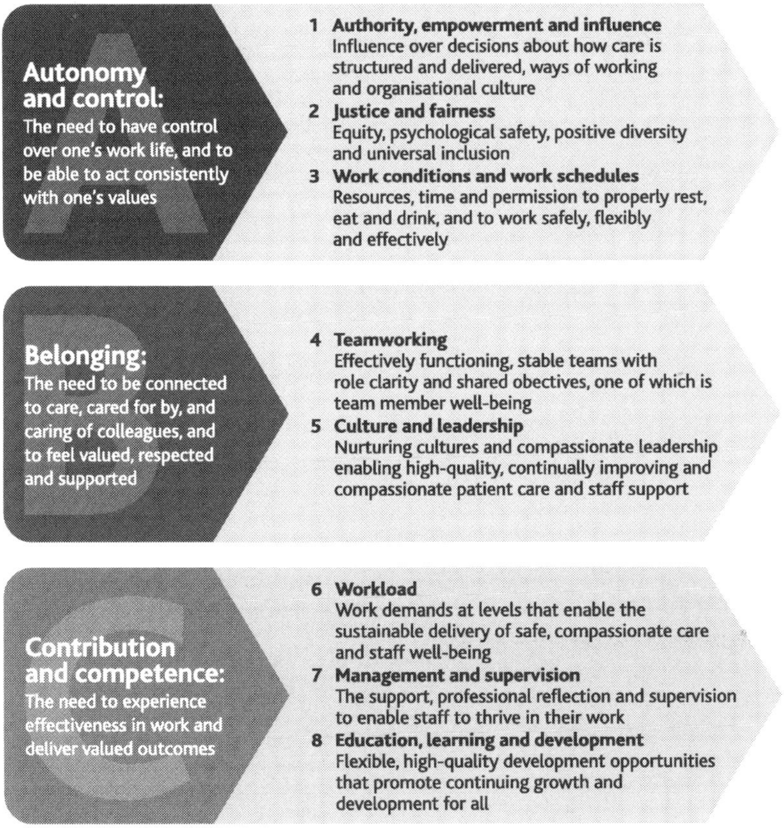

Autonomy and control:
The need to have control over one's work life, and to be able to act consistently with one's values

1 **Authority, empowerment and influence**
Influence over decisions about how care is structured and delivered, ways of working and organisational culture
2 **Justice and fairness**
Equity, psychological safety, positive diversity and universal inclusion
3 **Work conditions and work schedules**
Resources, time and permission to properly rest, eat and drink, and to work safely, flexibly and effectively

Belonging:
The need to be connected to care, cared for by, and caring of colleagues, and to feel valued, respected and supported

4 **Teamworking**
Effectively functioning, stable teams with role clarity and shared obectives, one of which is team member well-being
5 **Culture and leadership**
Nurturing cultures and compassionate leadership enabling high-quality, continually improving and compassionate patient care and staff support

Contribution and competence:
The need to experience effectiveness in work and deliver valued outcomes

6 **Workload**
Work demands at levels that enable the sustainable delivery of safe, compassionate care and staff well-being
7 **Management and supervision**
The support, professional reflection and supervision to enable staff to thrive in their work
8 **Education, learning and development**
Flexible, high-quality development opportunities that promote continuing growth and development for all

Figure 2: ABC of core work needs[39]

Autonomy and Control

1. *Authority, empowerment and influence*
Introduce mechanisms for staff to shape the cultures and processes of their organisations and influence decisions about how care is structured and delivered.

2. *Justice and fairness*
Nurture and sustain just, fair and psychologically safe cultures and ensure equity, proactive and positive approaches to diversity and universal inclusion.

3. *Work conditions and working schedules*
Introduce minimum standards for facilities and working conditions for staff in all health and social care organisations.

Belonging

4. *Teamworking*
   Develop and support effective multidisciplinary teamworking for all staff across health and social care services.

5. *Culture and leadership*
   Ensure health and social care environments have compassionate leadership and nurturing cultures that enable both care and staff support to be high-quality, continually improving and compassionate.

Contribution/Competence

6. *Workload*
   Tackle chronic excessive work demands on staff, which exceed their capacity to sustainably lead and deliver safe, high-quality care and which damage their health and well-being.

7. *Management and supervision*
   Ensure all staff have the effective support, professional reflection, mentorship and supervision needed to thrive in their roles.

8. *Learning, education and development*
   Ensure the right systems, frameworks and processes are in place for learning, education and development throughout people's careers. These should promote fair and equitable outcomes.

Conclusion

All health and social care leaders should lead with compassion by implementing the recommendations both for staff well-being and to achieve the purposes of our health and social care organisations.

> Organisations with cultures of compassion promote fairness and foster individual, team and organisational well-being.

They meet the needs of staff for autonomy, belonging and to be able to make an effective contribution in their work which, in turn, improves care quality and efficiency, and better promotes the well-being of the patients, people and communities they serve. By ensuring commitment of staff, the leadership outcomes of direction and alignment are far easier to achieve. Leadership should therefore prioritise sustaining the commitment of those who work in our health and social care teams by fulfilling their core work needs. This is how we achieve the alignment and integration that sustains progress towards the vision of high-quality and compassionate care for all.

Resources

Exercises/Discussion questions (to reflect on or discuss with a colleague)

1. In your organisation or team to what extent would you say:
   - There is disagreement on priorities?
   - People feel pulled in different directions?
   - People feel they are not making sufficient progress – just going in circles?
   - There is a clear vision and set of overarching organisational goals that everyone is committed to?
   - People say why those goals are worthwhile and with conviction?
   - There is strong agreement on what success will look like?

   What needs to change and how can this be done?

2. In your organisation or team to what extent would you say:
   - There is disarray, deadlines are missed and there is duplication?
   - People are unclear, overworked and frustrated?
   - People feel isolated from one another?
   - Teams compete rather than collaborate?
   - People are clear about each other's roles and responsibilities (and their own)?
   - People and teams integrate their work effectively to achieve success?
   - There is strong coordination and synchronising of efforts?

   What needs to change and how can this be done?

3. In your organisation or team to what extent would you say:
   - Important tasks are not done and easy work is prioritised?
   - People are not mutually supportive?
   - People do not express faith in their immediate or senior leaders?
   - There is cynicism and passivity?
   - People give the extra effort for the team or organisation to deliver high-quality care?
   - There is a strong sense of trust and shared responsibility for the work?
   - People are positive, passionate and motivated about their work?
   - People support each other to cope effectively?

   What needs to change and how can this be done?

4. To what extent are your core work needs met at work? What would need to change for each to be fully met? To what extent are each of the eight recommendations in figure 2 and the means of enabling them implemented in your work? How could you change your work and workplace to enable better fulfilment of your core work needs?

5. What about each of those you lead? To what extent are each of the eight recommendations implemented for each of them? How could you change their work and workplace to enable better fulfilment of their core work needs?

Questionnaires

Access the questionnaire to assess *Direction, Alignment and Commitment* via this link: *https://www.ccl.org/landing/direction-alignment-and-commitment-assessment/*

- Assess the extent to which your team/organisation has direction, alignment and commitment. How can you, as a leader, improve each of these outcomes? How can you influence leadership across the organisation to improve direction, alignment and commitment for the people you serve?

- What are the main obstacles to improving direction and alignment, and to increasing commitment in your organisation? How can these be weakened or removed?

The *ABC of core work needs* can be assessed with the Basic Psychological Need Satisfaction and Frustration Scales (specifically for the Work Domain) produced by the developers of self-determination theory.
The measures are available at *https://selfdeterminationtheory.org/basic-psychological-needs-scale/*

Guidance on using these questionnaires is provided in Appendix 1.

Websites

1. The Center for Creative Leadership website (CCL)
   CCL has been pioneering in leadership development for nearly 50 years. Its Leadership Development Program (LDP)®, offered globally over 100 times per year, is the longest-running program of its kind in the world. As a top-ranked, global, non-profit provider of leadership development, CCL has worked with organisations of all sizes from around the world, including many of the Fortune 1000.
   https://www.ccl.org/

2. Making DAC leadership happen
   A paper from CCL on DAC leadership. What brings about DAC in one situation may not bring it about in another situation. It also makes the point that sometimes we can put too much emphasis on leadership, forgetting that it is only one ingredient in the recipe for organisational success.
   https://cclinnovation.org/wp-content/uploads/2020/02/making-leadership-happen.pdf

3. Self-determination theory

   The website for self-determination theory argues that people are centrally concerned with motivation. 'Everywhere, parents, teachers, coaches, and managers struggle with how to motivate those that they mentor, and individuals struggle to find energy, mobilise effort and persist at the tasks of life and work. People are often moved by external factors such as reward systems, grades, evaluations, or the opinions they fear others might have of them. Yet, just as frequently, people are motivated from within, by interests, curiosity, care or abiding values. These intrinsic motivations are not necessarily externally rewarded or supported, but nonetheless they can sustain passions, creativity, and sustained efforts. The interplay between the extrinsic forces acting on persons and the intrinsic motives and needs inherent in human nature is the territory of self-determination theory.'
   https://selfdeterminationtheory.org/the-theory/

   Research on self-determination theory can also be found on the following website. *https://selfdeterminationtheory.org/research/*

4. Self-determination theory of motivation and why intrinsic motivation matters.
   https://positivepsychology.com/self-determination-theory/

Videos

Identifying DAC in teams - a practical video from the Center for Creative Leadership with Cindy McCauley. (6 minutes 10 secs)
https://vimeo.com/138977172

How to get more DAC in your team? A practical video from the Center for Creative Leadership with Cindy McCauley. (3 minutes 57 secs)
https://vimeo.com/138977173

An interactive session from the Shift Forward virtual conference on June 25, 2020 where Katherine Pappa and Princess Cullum share how leadership is more about what groups of individuals can accomplish working together than it is about what one person achieves alone. (1 hour 29 minutes)
https://www.youtube.com/watch?v=84hXQkzSynA

A brief video on self-determination theory by Richard Ryan. (1 minute 45 secs)
https://www.youtube.com/watch?v=3sRBBNkSXpY

A video on what self-determination theory proposes by Edward Deci. (8 minutes)
https://www.youtube.com/watch?v=m6fm1gt5YAM

Chapter 7.

If it's not inclusive, it's not compassionate leadership

Summary

Inclusion was a founding value of the welfare state in the United Kingdom, but organisational cultures in health and social care continue to reflect discrimination within the wider society. The pandemic has shone a spotlight on the effects of discrimination on health in society, with far higher proportions of those with disabilities or those from minority ethnic groups dying from covid-19. This chapter proposes that without inclusiveness, leadership cannot be characterised as compassionate. It describes how inclusive leadership promotes equity, cultures that value diversity in all its forms, and ensures inclusion in practice. Compassionate leadership offers a means by which inclusive leadership can be achieved, including the compassionate management of conflict and developing strategies to ensure all individuals, teams and leaders take responsibility for sustaining inclusive cultures. This must be augmented by comprehensive organisational strategies. Resources to support such strategies are also described.

Introduction

Why should we be inclusive? Positively inclusive teams and organisations are more productive and innovative than those which are less inclusive. Why? Because they utilise much more fully than non-inclusive teams and organisations the knowledge, skills, motivation and experience of all who work within them[1-3]. Moreover, the outcomes are greater than simply the sum of the parts because the synergies that emerge from capitalising on and combining everyone's contributions generate creativity, innovation, commitment and smart decision-making that enable us to deal effectively with the challenges we face.

This is particularly true for the complex settings of health and social care where multi-professional teamworking and the integration of diverse perspectives are key to promoting the health and well-being of people and communities[4,5]. Diverse health and social care teams with clear purpose and goals and a positively diverse and psychologically safe climate are far more productive, effective and innovative than less diverse teams, and team members have better health and well-being[1,4,6].

The welfare state (including the NHS) was launched in 1948 during a post-war era of huge challenge, austerity and community rebuilding. It was founded on the principle of providing free, high-quality care to all who needed it regardless of, for example, wealth, status, skin colour, ethnicity, prestige or socioeconomic background. The core founding values of the NHS were (and remain) therefore compassion and inclusion[7].

Leadership in health and social care must always make the best use of our scarce resources and ensure inclusion through positively valuing diversity. From both performance and core values perspectives, ensuring we are developing a positively diverse environment is therefore fundamental. Compassionate leaders in health and social care must embody inclusiveness in their leadership and work constantly to sustain positively diverse, inclusive workplaces that promote the growth, development and contribution of every individual. That also means creating workplaces where the needs for autonomy and control, belonging and competence of every individual are well met[8,9].

If leadership is not inclusive of all in the organisation, it is not compassionate. Compassion involves attending to every individual, understanding each person's challenges, empathising with every individual, and having the motivation to act to help each and every person to whom we offer leadership. Compassion means being present for all and helping all those we lead. Inclusive leadership means all leaders are focused on ensuring equity, promoting the valuing of diversity and ensuring all they lead are included. It is important to understand the implications of these three leadership concepts, beginning with leading to ensure equity.

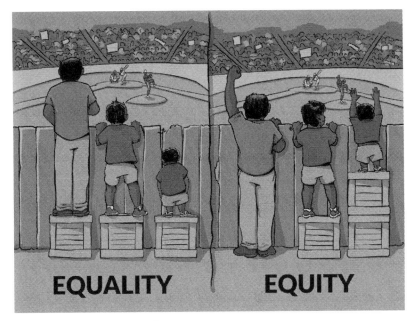

Figure 1: Equality vs. Equity[10]
(Image from Interaction Institute for Social Change, Artist: Angus Maguire)
(www.interactioninstitute.org and www.madewithangus.com)

Promoting equity and equality

The figure above illustrates why equality does not mean the same as equity. Although both promote fairness, equality achieves this through treating everyone the same regardless of need, while equity achieves this through treating people differently according to need.

Compassionate leadership requires us to attend to each person by being present with them and 'listening with fascination'. It also requires that we seek to understand the challenges they face which may spring from their gender, nationality, ethnicity, (dis)ability, socioeconomic background, professional grouping, sexuality, health condition or neurodiversity.

Seeking to understand these challenges is not a virtue signalling process – wanting to appear understanding to communicate how virtuous we are. Rather it must reflect a genuine curiosity about the challenges that are faced by those we lead. Being inquisitive about differences and challenges is helpful because it enables us to be more empathic or caring.

By understanding the challenges, we can more easily imagine how it would be to face them and experience the emotions that go with those challenges ourselves if we were in the other's position (such as hurt, fear, rejection, frustration, fury, or bewildered incomprehension). That then gives us the motivation to help by taking the steps that will help create equity – ensuring fairness by treating people differently according to their needs. The four elements of compassionate leadership provide the means by which we can effectively deal with the issues of equity and fairness.

Valuing diversity

Compassionate leadership is underpinned by a core value, modelled in leadership, of seeing diversity as a positive in all its forms – including professional background, age, religion, gender, nationality, (dis)ability, socioeconomic background, ethnicity, sexuality, health condition and neurodiversity. The research evidence shows clearly that diversity in boards, teams, organisations and society is enriching and generative[1-3]. Diverse teams that have positive climates, clear objectives, good communication and in which diversity is valued are more productive and innovative than less diverse teams (whether on the frontline or at board level)[1].

> Team diversity is associated with better quality team decision-making[1].

Quality improvement in health and social care requires diversity of knowledge bases, professional orientations and disciplinary backgrounds. The integration of diverse perspectives creates the potential for combinations of ideas from different domains and better decision-making in the interests of patients and service users. This is likely to produce new and creative ideas.

People with different professional training, skills, life experiences and demographic backgrounds have divergent perspectives. Such divergence often causes conflict, which is why diversity can often lead to conflict in the workplace and society generally. But research evidence clearly shows that if a team's diverse knowledge and experience can be harvested, the team will have a greater wealth of knowledge and experience to draw upon.

Compassionate leadership behaviours include paying attention to diversity in the team – being aware of the multiple dimensions of diversity and valuing those differences between team members. It requires 'listening with fascination' to the diverse contributions and experiences of team members which, in turn, communicates a valuing of that diversity. It also models for all team members the value of attending to, and appreciating, the diverse knowledge, skills, experiences and orientations of others. Teams that attend to, understand and value diverse perspectives, find it relatively easy to implement new ideas and improve quality, for several reasons.

First, such teams are better able to anticipate potential problems that may emerge as ideas move from initial conception to implementation, through a more comprehensive processing of the information all members have.

Second, teams whose members have the skills to work with people from diverse backgrounds will be better able to adapt and improve the care they provide for those they serve, because they better understand and represent their communities. Indeed, there is strong evidence that such representativeness is associated with greater civility and compassion towards patients and service users. In turn, that has an impact on care quality and on the financial performance of healthcare organisations[11].

Third, such teams are likely to be more adept at networking and dealing with the political agendas that surround innovation implementation because they can adopt more flexible and fully informed perspectives on issues. They have a diversity of perspectives within the team and have explored these through attending, understanding and empathising, so they are much better equipped to understand the reactions of others and to navigate potential conflicts.

Fourth, where leaders model understanding and appreciation of diverse perspectives, team members are likely to take the time to fully understand, rather than resist, each other's contributions. The greater wealth of information available to diverse teams, which comes from the motivation to understand and appreciate everyone's input, helps them to make better decisions. The richness of the information they have available and make use of enables them to undertake a more comprehensive and detailed analysis of problems they face. They are more likely to be creative and develop effective innovation and quality improvement[1,12,13].

It is teams that implement change. The extent to which team members offer support for innovation determines their ability to adapt to change, demands and uncertainty. This has been evident throughout the covid-19 pandemic. Teamwork in health and social care requires continually improving processes and procedures – as Don Berwick (President Barack Obama's former healthcare advisor) has said, "If quality is not improving, it is going backwards." But there is an important difference between simply developing ideas for quality improvement (or new and improved ways of doing things) and implementing them. Creativity refers to developing new ideas, while innovation and quality improvement are about putting ideas into practice. Support for innovation in teams requires not just verbal, but practical support.

Compassionate leadership is key to enabling quality improvement and innovation in diverse teams because of the focus on helping team members. Compassionate leadership involves supporting teams in their quality improvement efforts by removing the obstacles which get in their way. Such leadership also involves supporting the team's quality improvement efforts by providing the resources they need – for example, the right number of staff with the right skills, the necessary technology, the training needed and financial resources[14].

Modelling inclusive leadership

Compassionate leadership is the means by which we ensure inclusive leadership. In practice, this means everyone in the team feeling included by the leadership, rather than excluded. Compassionate leaders will be rated as inclusive by all those in their teams.

Having an above average inclusive leadership rating from one's team members counts for nothing if seven team members who are white rate their leader as high on inclusion, but two from minority ethnic group backgrounds rate the leader as much less inclusive.

Where leadership is inclusive, everyone has an opportunity to progress based on their needs; has an opportunity to take on challenging tasks; is provided with the support they need; and is listened to and respected.

Most leaders understand that they must be inclusive, but struggle to know what to do in practice. Or they comfort themselves with the thought that they are already sufficiently inclusive. Changing culture requires all leaders to be more inclusive. Compassionate leadership is the means by which we can achieve that.

Compassionate leadership involves attending to every person we lead, understanding their challenges, empathising with them, and helping them. It is quintessentially inclusive. It implies our ability to be equally present with all team members; to have frequent positive contact and develop our understanding and empathy; to respond differentially in a supportive way with team members based on differences between them; and to support, help and mentor all team members, including managing the inevitable team conflicts in a way that is respectful and inclusive.

Presence, attending and listening – Compassionate leadership means being self-aware in order to 'catch' ourselves when we are physically, but not psychologically or emotionally present with those we lead. This is central to our ability to be inclusive in our interactions. Interacting with someone in an apparently attentive way, but in fact thinking anxiously about the next meeting and the need to read relevant information beforehand, is an example of not being present. Leadership, and particularly compassionate leadership, is embodied in our presence. A leader who has presence is present with others in their interactions.

Self-awareness of those moments should not be a stimulus for guilt, but a celebration of our developing capacity to be aware and to make a conscious choice to be present. This might involve arranging a meeting later in order to be truly present rather than simply making a hasty getaway for the next meeting. What is important in the context of inclusivity is to ensure we practise being aware and present in the moment, particularly in interactions with those who differ from us – people we lead who we are more likely to see as 'other'. This may be because they differ from us in ethnicity, nationality, gender, (dis)ability, socioeconomic background, age, sexuality, professional background, political views, or any other dimension of diversity[15]. For example, inclusive leadership implies we make eye contact appropriately with everyone in the team in meetings, not disproportionately with those who are most like us (in professional backgrounds, opinions, skin colour, sexuality, religion, etc), while taking account of neurodiverse preferences.

Contact, understanding and empathising – Research has shown that leaders spend more time with those they see as like them[16]. They also see those they feel more like, or more similar to and comfortable with, as more competent than those they see as dissimilar[14]. There are several reasons for this, including the fact that leaders may think less effort is required, or experience greater ease in interacting, with those they see as competent or as like them. This may well be an unconscious process. In effect, all leaders have 'in groups' and 'out groups' of followers and tend to spend more time with the former. They also attribute their success to ability rather than to luck. The opposite is the case for those they see as dissimilar.
Of course, those in their teams generally know which group they are in.
One clear implication of this is that we must consciously seek to have more contact and to be present with those we see as 'other' or more difficult in our leadership roles.

Compassionate leadership requires courage,
and that includes the courage to practise
self-awareness in the moment and to identify
how our relationships differ among those we lead.

Who among those we lead do we find it easier or more difficult to interact with? Who do we like more and less? To what extent do we practise being present with those we find more 'difficult'? Compassionate leadership involves working harder to understand, empathise and help all of those we lead rather than just those we are most comfortable with.

There are real consequences in terms of team effectiveness and team member well-being. The less such variation there is in leaders' behaviour towards different team members, the more positive is the team climate and the more effective the team is in its functioning[13]. The four behaviours of compassionate leadership provide a practical means by which leaders can reduce damaging variation in their behaviour and attributions towards those they lead.

Helping, supporting and mentoring – The key element that distinguishes compassion from other empathic and caring behaviours is helping. Helping is fundamental to being inclusive as a leader. Being inclusive therefore requires we help, not merely listen, understand and empathise.

For example, those from minority ethnic groups and other groups that experience discrimination are likely to have been hampered in their growth and development by lack of opportunity and frustrated ambition. Research evidence shows that women and those from minority ethnic groups are less likely to be given challenging assignments when they arise, depriving them of growth opportunities, skill development and valuable experience[17].

Compassionate leadership is embodied, for example, by ensuring that those who are likely to be victims of discrimination are especially offered challenging opportunities, with the important proviso that they are given the necessary support to ensure successful completion of these challenges.

More broadly, helping means removing the obstacles and providing the resources (staff, equipment, training and funding) that enable those we lead to do their jobs effectively and ensuring they are also receiving the high-quality, continually improving and compassionate support they need to enable them to thrive in their roles.

Another way in which compassionate leadership embodies inclusion is when leaders offer coaching or reverse mentoring opportunities to those who may be subject to discrimination. Reverse mentoring ideally involves wise, experienced leaders working with those with different backgrounds and experiences and listening to and learning from them.

It helps to build confidence, trust and the likelihood of success, and the more experienced leader can offer advice for their mentor's career development. The current head of NHS England, Sir Simon Steven, has had a reverse mentoring relationship for several years with Dr Habib Naqvi, now Director of the NHS Race and Health Observatory.

Consistent leadership – Leading different people in a compassionate way will rightly lead to variations in leadership behaviour. That is appropriate because for a less experienced member of staff, a more directive style may be appropriate when the task is clear. When the task is complex and uncertain, a more participative style is appropriate when the staff member is skilled. However, it is important that in other respects leadership is consistent when dealing with people, especially those from minorities who are discriminated against. And it is important for us as leaders to ask the questions, 'In my interactions with these different team members, am I consistently:

- Authentic

- Honest and open

- Optimistic

- Appreciative

- Compassionate?'

Compassionately managing conflict

Compassionate leadership involves moving towards rather than away from conflict. Diversity demands extra efforts at integration since diversity creates the potential for conflict as much as for creativity[13,18]. Where diversity reduces group members' clarity about and commitment to shared objectives, their levels of participation (interaction, information-sharing, and shared influence over decision-making), the team's commitment to high-quality performance, and support for new ideas, then it is likely that innovation attempts will be resisted.

Amy Gallo distinguishes between four types of conflict at work: task, process, status and interpersonal conflict[19]. Task conflict refers to conflict over what the task is, or what the objectives or goals are. Process conflict arises when there is a disagreement about how to undertake the task or how we achieve the goal. Status conflict is a consequence of disagreement about who has authority or who is in charge (particularly likely across teams or departments). Interpersonal or relationship conflict is where personal feelings result in resentments, desire to hurt or punish and feelings of anger. Any of the first three conflicts can easily develop into relationship conflict if they are not addressed and resolved.

Chronic interpersonal conflicts are profoundly damaging to team performance, so compassionate leadership involves engaging with those involved in such conflicts by 'listening with fascination', achieving a shared understanding, empathising and helping[19]. It also involves requiring that those people in conflict 'listen to each other with fascination', arriving at a shared understanding, empathising with each other, and committing to helping each other. The courage of compassionate leadership is also to make clear that team members cannot be permitted to allow interpersonal conflicts or dislikes to become chronic, thereby undermining team effectiveness and team member well-being[19]. Conflicts happen in families and, of course, teams; we learn, forgive and move on and as a result, have stronger relationships. It is when interpersonal conflicts become long term that they profoundly undermine team well-being and performance.

Conflicts over task-related issues — such as how best to meet work demands, improve quality or support team members — are an inevitable consequence of team decision-making in a context of seeking to continually improve performance. Compassionate leadership provides a safer context for the management of conflict, partly by modelling a climate for teamworking based on listening to each other, arriving at a shared understanding, empathising and mutually supporting and helping each other[19].

> The focus of compassionate leadership in diverse teams must be to transform conflict into constructive controversy and innovation.

Dean Tjosvold has worked for over half a century to advance the understanding of how we can compassionately and effectively manage conflict in diverse teams. He suggests there are three key elements:

- *Drawing out positions* – which is enabled by being present, attending and 'listening with fascination' as positions are argued.

- *Searching for understanding* – enabled not by imposing or assuming understanding, but by checking the accuracy of our understanding of the other's position.

- *Integrating perspectives* – enabled by leaders encouraging team members to find solutions based on shared, rational understanding rather than because of interpersonal dominance. Compassionate approaches to integrating perspectives (helping) involve encouraging people to combine or integrate positions to find creative, innovative ways forward[20].

His and other's research suggests compassionate and inclusive leadership will encourage:

- Exploration of opposing opinions

- Open-minded consideration and understanding

- Concern for integration of ideas

- Concern with high-quality solutions

- Valuing diversity.

To enable this, compassionate leaders must encourage co-operative team climates, commitment to shared team goals, and team members to confirm each other's personal competence, show appreciation and team members to be supportive in the way they seek to mutually influence each other.

Time may be a factor too. Studies of culturally homogenous and culturally diverse student teams engaged in a task involving analysing case studies showed that the diverse teams performed less well early on. After 17 months of working together, the diverse teams had group processes as effective as the homogenous teams and outperformed them in relation to range of perspectives on the task and number of alternative solutions developed. Thus, when diverse perspectives are integrated in a climate of constructive controversy, over time the cross-fertilisation of different approaches results in more innovative solutions[21].

Being a Compassionate Inclusion Ally as a Leader*

Being an inclusion ally means supporting people from marginalised or under-represented groups even though you may not be from that group.

- Active allies use their power and privilege to create an inclusive environment and challenge situations where this is not happening

- It's okay to make mistakes if you can then learn from them

- Anyone can be an ally – just listen, learn and act.

Key tips for listening, learning and acting:

1. *'Listen with fascination' to perspectives different from yours*
- Seek out information from those with differing views to you about a topic
- Explore resources and conversations that describe different life experiences to yours, eg, different ages, religions, races, abilities, sexual orientation
- Initiate 'curious conversations' with colleagues.

2. *Be open to learning about the barriers people face*
- Attend meetings and events (eg, equality network meetings) to learn
- Talk to colleagues who you have a good relationship with about their experiences and explore how they might differ from yours
- Be prepared to believe other people's experiences. Don't assume something couldn't happen just because you haven't personally experienced it.

3. *Own your privilege and use it to make the change you want to see*
- Reflect on the advantages you have if you are in a majority group, whether this is in context of gender, disability, nationality, socioeconomic background, race or sexual orientation, and how you can use these to uplift others
- Be prepared to understand that acknowledging you have privilege may not be comfortable
- Recognise that how you are perceived may make life easier for you than for others, and use that to make changes towards a fairer world.

4. *Amplify the voice of under-represented groups at every opportunity with their permission*

- Assist under-represented groups to be heard and support them in being taken seriously, but be careful not to take away their power or control
- Challenge when you see or hear unacceptable comments or behaviours
- Share the knowledge you have gained to educate others.

5. *Create safe spaces for people to share their lived experiences*

- Create safe spaces for people to be themselves and be able to share parts of their identity that they want to, but always by invitation, not invasion
- Invite diverse people to team meetings and events to share their stories and remember to observe confidentiality, if requested
- Be mindful that often people don't want solutions or need 'fixing', but just want to be heard.

Adapted from Nadeem, S. (2020)
Being an Inclusion Ally. London: Care Quality Commission[22].

Compassionate leadership for cultures of inclusion

What does research tell us about the team and organisational characteristics that enable us to develop and sustain inclusive team climates and organisational cultures? The key elements of climates and cultures of inclusion are described below under four headings (individuals, teams, leaders and organisations), drawing on the research literature[1-3,23-26].

The responsibility of all individuals

Changing cultures so that everyday discrimination does not go unchallenged requires the involvement of all of those working in health and social care, as well as through leadership development and teamworking interventions. These must focus on ensuring that positively diverse and universally inclusive behaviours are modelled and practised at every level of the health and social care system:

- This requires that all staff treat those from different backgrounds to their own with greater civility, respect and compassion.

- All staff should be familiar with the research evidence on the impact of sexism, racism and other forms of discrimination on health, life chances and mortality[27,28]. These include systemic pathogenic processes such as inflammation leading to many chronic diseases and problems, for example, hypertension; more rapid declines in cognitive function in old age; lower birth weight of babies among pregnant women experiencing discrimination; elevated risks of visceral fat in women associated with hypertension; and premature mortality.

- Messages communicated through diversity training interventions must be carefully shaped. They can have inadvertent negative consequences. For example, asserting that most people exhibit unconscious race bias can legitimise that bias, making people feeling less motivated to discover their own prejudice and change their attitudes and behaviours. A particularly successful intervention asks people to take the perspective of those in target groups, eg, 'If I spent a day in this organisation as someone from a minority ethnic group, I would probably experience...'. Training *should* encourage political correctness[29,30].

- Training programmes, in which participants (and this applies especially to leaders) agree several specific goals for their behaviour and attitudes and review their progress, are more successful than interventions that focus on simply educating participants or encouraging discussion[29].

- All should have training in how to intervene when they observe discrimination, incivility, sexism or racism towards colleagues and to be inclusion allies and champions of equity, equality, positive diversity and inclusion. Evidence suggests that allies (and particularly leaders) from non-disadvantaged or less discriminated against groups can confront and have an impact on others' discriminatory behaviour more effectively than members of targeted groups alone.

- All should be educated about the subtler aspects of discrimination. Although in society more generally there has been some move away from overt forms of discrimination (racist or sexist comments; consciously rejecting candidates because they have a mental health problem), more covert, subtle forms of discrimination continue – eg, negative humour, harassment and ridicule without overt discriminatory content – and these are harder to identify, assess and eradicate[23].

- All leaders must have, as part of their training and role description, positively and overtly valuing equity, equality, diversity and inclusion, both for its own sake and for its impact on care quality and staff well-being.

- All leaders must practise compassionate leadership – attending to all of those they lead, understanding their challenges, empathising and helping.

The responsibility of teams

It is within teams that most discrimination occurs and where the opportunities to bring about change are most likely to be effective. The approaches likely to have the greatest benefit are those that encourage inclusion, value diverse perspectives and create a climate of psychological safety (see chapter 5). Evidence[4,5,31] suggests that teams are more inclusive when they are well-structured and have:

- A clear direction - a positive and motivating vision of the team's work and five or six clear, agreed, challenging team objectives and regular, useful feedback on performance in relation to the objectives.

- A compassionate team leader who reinforces the value of a diversity of voices, views, skills, experiences and backgrounds as vital for creativity, innovation, good decision-making and team effectiveness.

- All team members sustaining a climate of valuing diversity and listening to and valuing all voices within the team.

- Clear roles and good mutual understanding of these.

- Shared team leadership where the hierarchical leader does not dominate but supports and facilitates.

- A strong commitment to quality improvement and innovation.

- An optimistic, compassionate, cohesive climate and co-operative and supportive ways of working with other teams in the organisation.

- Regular 'time out' and 'after-action' reviews to reflect on and improve team performance.

The responsibility of leaders

Fundamentally inclusive cultures are developed and sustained by compassionate and collective leadership. Compassionate leadership styles are supportive, respectful, warm and enabling. Collective leadership is characterised by all members of the organisation being able to play leadership roles at various points in their daily work and in their careers.

- All leaders must practise compassionate leadership – attending to all of those they lead, understanding their challenges, empathising and helping.

- All leaders must have, as part of their training and role description, positively and overtly valuing equity, equality, diversity and inclusion both for its own sake and for its impact on care quality and staff well-being.

- All leaders must provide stretching project and career opportunities for staff from disadvantaged groups, while providing good support.

- All leaders must be familiar with the research evidence on how well-led diversity is associated with team and organisational effectiveness[4,5,31] and innovation in health and social care, and with the research evidence on the impact of racism and discrimination on health, life chances and mortality[27,28].

- All leaders must work to create fair and just cultures in their teams and organisations.

- All leaders must seek to mentor and coach staff from disadvantaged groups and create opportunities for reverse mentoring.

- All leaders must assess their performance as inclusive leaders, ensuring that all of those they lead feel included by their leadership.

The responsibility of organisations

Health and social care leaders must quickly reform the structures, policies and processes that affect inclusion, for example, appointment and promotion processes, disciplinary procedures and complaints handling. Each organisation must have a clearly articulated and ambitious equity and diversity vision and an associated strategy with clear goals. This must include hardwiring equity, diversity and inclusion (EDI) policies into corporate objectives and activities. These can include, among other things:

- Demonstrable leadership of the strategy from the top and at every level continually and leaders fully understanding the diversity profiles of the organisation and the communities served. It is particularly important to have visible and sustained top management support for positive diversity and inclusion policies and practices.

- A culture of justice and fairness with an emphasis on restorative, learning cultures.

- Reinforcing zero tolerance of inequities and establishing that equity, equality, diversity and inclusion are everyone's business; and involving middle managers continually.

- Thoroughly planning, implementing and monitoring interventions; tracking progress continuously (bi-monthly or quarterly).

- Embedding equity, equality and celebration of diversity in the organisation.

- Recruitment and selection focused on achieving equity; promotion policies focused on achieving equity; mobility policies and the use of quotas to influence promotion decisions; and coaching and mentoring of under-represented groups.

- Fair and transparent appraisal processes, disciplinary procedures and rewards systems; anti-discrimination training for interviewers; supporting managers when dealing with grievances and disciplinary cases; and processes for actively seeking minority groups' talents and enabling their development.

- Pervasive methods for encouraging staff participation in decision-making, information sharing, dialogue and interaction throughout the organisation.

The key elements necessary for cultures of inclusion are also associated with high-quality healthcare[32]. These elements include the following:

- *Vision and values* - A clear, compelling vision is important for encouraging staff to identify with their organisation and is likely to increase a sense of shared identity and to work against the development of 'in' and 'out' groups, which contribute to discrimination and exclusion. The vision must include reference to inclusion and positively valuing diversity. Moreover, managers need to enact this shared vision and set of common values rather than merely espouse them.

- *Clarity of objectives and performance feedback* - A limited number of clear, agreed objectives with regular, frequent feedback on performance for individuals and teams at every level creates clarity and accountability, minimising the ambiguity and confusion that feed stereotyping and discrimination. This must also include objectives in relation to EDI for the organisation, all teams, departments, directorates, leaders and individuals.

- *People management, engagement and positivity* - All relationships – between staff and patients/service users, among staff members themselves, and between managers/leaders and staff – must be characterised by support, respect, care and compassion. Positivity reduces stereotyping and the psychological distance that people perceive between themselves and others who are dissimilar.

- *Quality improvement, learning and innovation* - Where there is strong emphasis on quality improvement, learning and innovation in NHS organisations, there should also be strong emphasis on the value of a diverse workforce for creativity, innovation and representativeness, on the importance of hearing everyone's voice and on the need to encourage constructive debate or controversy. Quality improvement and innovation processes must also be applied to dramatically improve EDI cultures at every level.

- *Team and team-based working* - The extent of team-based working in organisations will also affect diversity and inclusion. When most staff work in effective teams, where diversity is valued in practice rather than only in rhetoric, there will be a culture of co-operation, support and inclusion that patients/service users and staff benefit from. Teams must demonstrate how they are continually improving their climates to ensure equity, positively valuing diversity and inclusion.

Equity, inclusion and positive diversity – North East London NHS Foundation Trust (NELFT)

NELFT, a mental health and community services provider employing 6,000 staff working over 200 sites, has achieved sustained improvements across all Workforce Race Equality Standard (WRES) indicators from 2016 - 2018.

Equality and inclusion-related issues were discussed by the board, the ethnic minority network (EMN), and at all meetings and levels in the trust, including inductions for new starters. There was a clear message that race inequality was an issue that required the concerted effort of everyone in the trust. The board reviewed and endorsed a strategy to address racial inequality at the trust, and each executive board member worked with an EMN strategic ambassador to deliver specific actions for which they were accountable.

The delivery of the strategy was monitored through regular reviews against measurable ambitions at all levels, including for minority ethnic group representation at band 8c and above to reflect the proportion of minority ethnic group staff in the workforce as a whole; an increase in the number of minority ethnic group executive and non-executive directors, and a reduction in the number of minority ethnic group staff involved in any HR procedures and litigation cases.

Recruitment

Changes were introduced to make recruitment practices fairer and more transparent. The trust trained 80 minority ethnic group staff to be part of diverse interview panels, and minority ethnic group panel members were enabled to overturn interview panel results and escalate them for review. As a result of these changes, the relative likelihood of minority ethnic group applicants being appointed from short-listing, compared to white applicants, improved. In 2016, minority ethnic group applicants were 3.12 times less likely than white applicants to be appointed. By 2018, this was 1.46 times less likely. Still a long way to go, but a considerable improvement.

Career progression

NELFT invested in training, coaching and better recruitment processes to help minority ethnic group staff develop to their full potential. As part of this, the recruitment policy was updated so that interviews for all band 8a and above posts needed an EMN panel member. The minority ethnic group staff who went through the training and sat on interview panels reported growth in their confidence and ambition, along with demystification of the interview process – particularly for senior posts. Between 2013 and 2017, the percentage of minority ethnic group staff at band 8a and above increased from 18.4% to 29.3%, and the number of people at band 8c increased from two to thirty-two.

Formal disciplinary

The trust sought to address the disproportionate representation of minority ethnic group staff in formal disciplinary cases. Alongside a review of policies and practices across the trust, white managers attended mandatory training to help them understand the differences in opportunities and experiences between minority ethnic group and white staff in the NHS. Investigation panel members were also given cultural awareness competency training. The relative likelihood of minority ethnic group staff entering the formal disciplinary process compared to white staff improved from 2.02 in 2016 to 1.18 in 2018.

Reverse mentoring

A key component of the trust's cultural transformation has been built on understanding the lived experiences and stories from minority ethnic group staff. All board members have a reverse mentor from a minority ethnic group background.

NELFT has the highest proportion in London of minority ethnic group staff reporting that the organisation provides equal opportunities for career progression. It also has the second lowest proportion of minority ethnic group staff (and the fourth lowest proportion of white staff) in London reporting discrimination, harassment and bullying from colleagues.

For more, see: https://www.england.nhs.uk/wp-content/ uploads/2019/11/nelft-case-study.pdf

Conclusion

Health and social care organisations employ around one in nine of the working populations of the four UK countries. Developing and sustaining compassionate and inclusive cultures within those organisations can have a profound effect in changing the cultures of those societies. The effects of developing such cultures ripple out to the community via staff experience and patient/service user experience. The pandemic has shone a harsh spotlight on the effects of discrimination on health and well-being throughout society, with groups such as those with disabilities and those from minority ethnic group backgrounds dying in far higher numbers proportionately than others.

> This is a moment in history where we must rise to the challenge of changing organisational and societal cultures to value every human equally and to ensure there is equity and care for all.

This is an opportunity to achieve such a change that we cannot let slip, and health and social care organisations can lead the way. That is the challenge and opportunity for all those who aspire to be compassionate leaders within our health and social care systems.

Resources

Exercises/Discussion questions (to reflect on or discuss with a colleague)

1. How inclusive are you of all those you lead?

2. How and why should you show greater civility to those you lead who are different from you?

3. To what extent do you understand the lived experience of those who are different from you?

4. What do you need to do to develop your inclusiveness as a leader?

5. How can you ensure you have genuine feedback about your inclusiveness as a leader from all those you lead?

6. What can you do to strengthen your ability to act as an inclusion ally?

7. How can you design a strategy for developing a culture of positive diversity, equity and universal inclusion in your organisation?

8. What can you and your team do to ensure a positive team climate of valuing diversity and promoting universal inclusion?

Questionnaires

A measure of valuing diversity[33]:
a. Managing diversity helps my organisation to be more effective
b. My organisation has classes, workshops and seminars on diversity
c. My organisation puts a lot of effort into diversity management
d. My organisation values diversity.

A measure of procedural justice[34,35]:
a. Consistent rules and procedures are used when making decisions in this organisation
b. Procedures used in this organisation are free from bias
c. Procedures in this organisation use just and fair standards
d. Accurate information is used for making decisions
e. We can get feedback about decisions made in this organisation.

The second measure, of procedural justice, is based on an amalgam of two other measures. Guidance on using these questionnaires is provided in Appendix 1.

Websites

1. David Williams: videos, podcasts and featured papers on the social
   influences on health
   A social scientist at Harvard University, Williams has focussed his
   research into the social influences on health and the interventions
   that could make a difference. His work shows how our life experiences,
   particularly discrimination and racism, dramatically affect health.
   He also explains how the effects of racism play out in wider social
   inequalities, including housing, education and employment.
   The weathering effects of frequent experiences of discrimination
   profoundly affect health outcomes. Some of the solutions for society
   become clearer from his cogent analysis.
   https://scholar.harvard.edu/davidrwilliams/pages/videos-0
   https://www.kingsfund.org.uk/audio-video/podcast/david-williams-
   racism-discrimination-health
   https://www.apa.org/members/content/williams-health-disparities

2. Discrimination – effects on health generally
   - Chronological age captures the duration of exposure to risks for
     groups in adverse living conditions. Those from minority ethnic
     groups experience greater physiological wear and tear, and age
     biologically more rapidly than their white counterparts.
   - It is driven by the cumulative impact of repeated exposure to
     psychological, social, physical and chemical stressors in their
     residential, occupational and other environments, and by coping
     with these stressors.
   - Compared to the white majority, those from minority ethnic groups
     experience higher levels, greater clustering, and greater duration
     and intensity, of stressors.

   See resources from David Williams above and also:
   https://www.research.manchester.ac.uk/portal/james.nazroo.html

Videos

How do our life experiences shape our health? What can we do to tackle
social inequalities? Helen McKenna spoke with David Williams from
Harvard University about his research into the social influences on health
and the interventions that could make a difference. (30 minutes)
https://www.kingsfund.org.uk/audio-video/podcast/david-williams-racism-
discrimination-health

A TEDMED presentation from David Williams on how racism affects health. (17 minutes 43 secs)
https://www.youtube.com/watch?v=aUO0fclc6tw

Pearn Kandola and Skill Boosters - Inclusive leadership video series with an introduction by Binna Kandola and Nic Hammerling. (2 minutes 21 secs)
https://www.youtube.com/watch?v=TwJR5EMqh-g

Further reading

a. Gender inequity in the English NHS

NHS Employers analysis of gender inequity: summary of the findings

Around one million women work for the NHS in England, making it one of the largest employers of women in the world. However, despite making up the majority of the NHS workforce, women are more likely than men to face structural constraints within the workplace (managing work-life balance, for example), are paid less, are less likely to get promoted and less likely to be represented in senior roles within the NHS.

To help NHS organisations address gender inequity, NHS Employers has brought together key information on good practice.
https://www.nhsemployers.org/retention-and-staff-experience/diversity-and-inclusion/policy-and-guidance/gender-equality-in-the-nhs

b. Inequity in relation to ethnicity in the English NHS

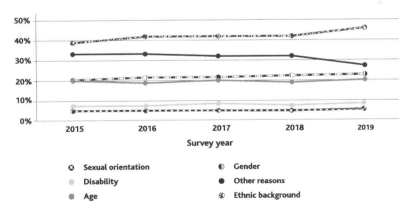

% of staff saying they experienced discrimination on each basis, from those who reported personally experiencing discrimination at work in the last 12 months (q15c)

In the 2019 NHS Staff Survey, 12.6% of staff reported experiencing discrimination at work, including based on their gender, age, disability, religion and sexual orientation; however, ethnicity continued to be the most common reason for discrimination[36]. Other key findings included:

- 1.4 million people worked in the NHS in England, with 20% of staff being from minority ethnic group backgrounds.

- 21% of nurses and midwives (qualified and unqualified) were from a minority ethnic group background, rising to more than 50% in London. Out of a total of 227, only 10 trusts (4.4%) had directors of nursing from minority ethnic group backgrounds.

- 46% of hospital doctors were from minority ethnic group backgrounds, but only 16% of medical directors were from minority ethnic groups.

- Across 223 trusts, there were only eight minority ethnic group CEOs, 10 chairs and 10 executive directors of nursing.

- Only 6% of very senior managers were from minority ethnic group backgrounds.

Just 7% of members of boards were from minority ethnic group backgrounds (though this is steadily improving). A survey of 487 doctors who became consultants in the NHS across the UK in 2017 revealed that white doctors applied for fewer posts (1.29 vs. 1.66); were more likely to be shortlisted (80% vs. 66%); and were more likely than minority ethnic group colleagues to be offered a job (77% vs. 57%). Female minority ethnic group doctors fared even worse.

A study of 750,000 staff salaries in the NHS in England revealed that minority ethnic group staff, from porters to doctors, are paid less than white staff; on average, minority ethnic group doctors in the NHS in England earn £10,000 less a year; minority ethnic group nurses earn £2,700 less annually than white colleagues; and white consultants earn £4,664 more per year than their minority ethnic group counterparts[37].

Why does this matter? Research evidence on whether the extent to which senior staff in the NHS are representative of other staff matters. The study in the English NHS examined the representativeness of leaders compared with non-leaders and linked this with aggressive behaviour from colleagues. Where representativeness was low, aggression (bullying, harassment, and discrimination) was higher – especially against minority ethnic group staff[38]. For further information, see: *https://www.nhsrho.org/*

A review of the evidence on discrimination in the NHS in England based on staff survey data: *https://www.kingsfund.org.uk/sites/default/files/field/field_publication_file/Making-the-difference-summary-Kings-Fund-Dec-2015.pdf*

A review of race equality in health and social care in Northern Ireland: *https://www.equalityni.org*

The NHS has one of the most ethnically diverse workforces in the public sector. However, ever year, ethnic minority staff report worse experiences in terms of their lives and careers when compared with white staff, and people from an ethnic minority background are under-represented in senior positions in the NHS. The impact of this on people can be profound. For powerful first-person accounts collected in connection with this research, see: *https://features.kingsfund.org.uk/2020/07/ethnic-minority-nhs-staff-racism-discrimination*
More detail of the research is at: *https://www.kingsfund.org.uk/publications/workforce-race-inequalities-inclusion-nhs*

c. **Workplace equity, diversity and inclusion**

Three sources for a broader look at inclusion in the workplace:

i.   The Universities of Lancaster, Aston, Liverpool, Rice University Texas and Sheffield, WRES and multiple international collaborators have created an open-source set of resources hosted at the NHS Race and Health Observatory *https://www.nhsrho.org/*. It reviews many relevant research papers such as these two on staff representativeness, civility and NHS trust performance; and on the relationship between equality and inclusion and patient satisfaction.

   •   Staff representativeness and patient civility: Does the extent to which health and social care staff are representative of their communities matter?

      Studies looking at diversity in organisations yield inconsistent results, and suggest that the question of 'If diversity affects outcomes' is better replaced with 'When and how does diversity lead to positive outcomes?'

      One large-scale study showed that ethnic diversity in hospital staff was related to a higher probability of incivility towards patients. However, when comparing the level of hospital diversity of frontline staff to community diversity, it was found that the closer they were, the more likely patients were to be treated with civility. Greater civility reported by patients led to better organisational performance of that hospital. Representativeness predicted patient experiences of civility, CQC ratings of care quality and of hospital financial performance. Representativeness of staff in relation to their community is important and civility is a key factor[11].

- Equality, inclusion and patient satisfaction: Are equality, diversity and inclusion relevant to patient satisfaction?

  Research on the determinants of NHS patient satisfaction in England shows that among the top three predictors are equal opportunities for staff (second) and discrimination experienced by staff (third and a negative predictor). The most important predictor is staff perceptions of workload, which also predict patient dissatisfaction. *https://www.england.nhs.uk/wp-content/uploads/2018/02/links-between-nhs-staff-experience-and-patient-satisfaction-1.pdf*

ii. Juliet Bourke and Andrea Titus give their take, in two articles in Harvard Business Review, on the key to inclusive leadership. What makes people feel included in organisations? Factors include feeling that they are treated fairly and respectfully, valued, and belong, and that will be influenced by an organisation's mission, policies, and practices, as well as co-worker behaviours.
https://hbr.org/2020/03/the-key-to-inclusive-leadership
https://hbr.org/2019/03/why-inclusive-leaders-are-good-for-organizations-and-how-to-become-one

iii. Deloitte describes six signature traits of inclusive leadership, including curiosity, cultural intelligence, courage, commitment, collaboration and cognizance (avoiding bias).
https://www2.deloitte.com/us/en/insights/topics/talent/six-signature-traits-of-inclusive-leadership.html

Chapter 8. # Collective leadership

Summary

Traditional approaches to leadership have important limitations, with an emphasis on developing individual capability while neglecting collective leadership capability. They are also limited in that they can hamper the dialogue, debate and discussion that enable a shared understanding about care quality problems and solutions. Compassionate leadership, in contrast, enables all to feel they have leadership responsibility, rights, and accountability, effectively ensuring the skills of all are harnessed in the delivery of high-quality care. This chapter describes how compassionate leadership enables collective leadership: all contributing to leadership; shared leadership in teams; leaders working collaboratively across boundaries; and consistent approaches to leadership across the leadership community of health and social care organisations.

Introduction

Collective leadership focuses on ensuring dialogue and encouraging and enabling all staff to adopt leadership roles in their work[1,2]. They are then more likely to take individual and collective responsibility for delivering safe, effective, high-quality and compassionate care for patients and service users. In health and social care delivery or corporate services, monitoring safety and quality is far more effective when these responsibilities are owned, managed and promoted by the staff who deliver those services. This has long been the practice in other industries that recognise that local ownership and management of quality and safety issues is far more effective than top-down control.

In compassionate and collective leadership cultures, responsibility and accountability function simultaneously at both individual and collective levels. They breed regular reflective practice focused on failure, exploratory learning and making continuous improvement an organisational habit[3]. By contrast, command-and-control leadership cultures invite the displacement of responsibility and accountability onto single individuals, which can lead to scapegoating and climates of fear of failure, rather than an appetite for innovation.

Leadership comes from both the leaders themselves and the relationships among them. Organisational performance does not rest simply on the number or quality of individual leaders. What counts is the extent to which formal and informal leaders work collectively in support of the organisation's goals and in embodying the values that underpin the desired culture. Leadership also incorporates the concept of followership – everyone supporting each other, including leaders, to deliver high-quality care, and everyone taking responsibility for the success of the organisation or system[1,2,4,5].

Why collective leadership?

Leaders can use their privileged positions to acquire more power and limit others' access to it, and we see many examples of this in political leadership and in work organisations. It is referred to by researchers as 'personalised power'. This approach includes acquiring information that is of value to others and not making it available; building cabals that accumulate power, information and resources; undermining others' power and success; using aggression and intimidation overtly or subtly; and manipulating uncertainty in difficult situations to accrete power and influence. Such leadership may also focus on sustaining, extending or strengthening hierarchies so that leadership power is protected or enhanced[6].

> Compassionate leadership is the opposite of personalised power. Compassionate leadership involves seeking to share power and resources so that leadership is deployed most effectively in delivering health and social care services - what is called 'socialised power'.

The focus of compassionate leadership in health and social care is on ensuring the provision of high-quality, continually improving and compassionate health and social care services for those in our communities. It is also focused on providing high-quality, continually improving and compassionate support for the staff who provide that care.

Collective leadership is focused on engaging all in leadership and decision-making in health and social care – effectively promoting staff engagement[5]. Engagement at work is characterised by strong identification with the organisation and a drive to be involved in decision-making and innovation – in the case of health and social care, to improve the quality of care[7,8]. Data from the NHS England National Staff Survey reveals that staff engagement trumps all other measures as the best overall predictor of NHS Trusts' outcomes. It predicts care quality and financial performance (based on Care Quality Commission ratings), patient satisfaction, and patient mortality (in the acute sector)[8,9].

Leaders help create the conditions for high levels off staff engagement through compassionate leadership and by:

- Promoting a positive climate

- Recognising staff contributions

- Providing information relevant to people's jobs

- Giving helpful feedback

- Supporting staff innovation

- Promoting fairness and transparency

- Developing trusting relationships[8-10].

Sustaining cultures of high-quality care involves all staff focusing on continual learning and improvement of patient care, 'top to bottom and end to end', and thereby taking leadership responsibility for improving quality[11]. The same applies to staff 'continually and forever reducing harm' - ensuring reflective practice is endemic and taking responsibility for giving both positive and negative feedback on safety behaviours to colleagues (regardless of seniority).

> Compassionate leadership seeks to ensure that everyone has and feels responsibility for leading in service of the communities cared for by health and social care organisations.

It is manifested in an ethos of shared leadership in teams (which is explored in more depth below). There is also a focus on collective leadership, whereby leaders work together across boundaries (teams, departments, organisations and sectors) to collectively deliver for the communities they jointly serve. This involves prioritising the delivery of high-quality care overall, rather than focusing exclusively on the success of one's own specific area of delivery, potentially at the expense of others. It also involves consistent approaches to leadership characterised by authenticity, openness, optimism, humility, appreciativeness and of course, compassion.

When we consider traditional leadership in the context of healthcare, there is an obvious paradox. The NHS in the UK has the largest, most skilled and motivated workforce in any area of industry — 1.4 million people, the vast majority of whom are highly educated and skilled. They are also a group of people who have dedicated a large proportion of their precious, unique lives to caring for those around them by becoming healthcare professionals. Highly motivated and skilled people do not need command and control environments to do their jobs well – on the contrary, it will undermine their motivation and well-being[1,12]. Yes, they need an overall direction for their work, but they are well able to determine goals, gather feedback and develop new and improved ways of delivering services. Yet, the NHS is probably more hierarchical than any other sector. Take nursing for example. In a typical hospital setting, there may be as many as five levels of nursing hierarchy on a ward alone.

During the covid-19 pandemic, there have been many examples of hierarchies being blurred or erased altogether. Frontline healthcare and corporate teams have developed new and improved ways of working at scale and pace, freed from some of the constraints of hierarchy and bureaucracy. Consequently, hospitals, primary healthcare teams, mental health services and community healthcare organisations have adapted quickly and effectively to respond to the crisis.

It is important that this learning shapes the future of services. Reverting to the past should not be an option – we need to transform rigid hierarchies and excessive bureaucracies to ensure more collective, enabling and empowering leadership across our health and social care organisations. This is intrinsic to compassionate leadership. Compassionate leadership involves helping and valuing others as much as we would help and value ourselves.

> The arguments above imply a collective approach to leadership: leadership of all, by all, and for all.

Such collective leadership is characterised by constant changes in leadership and followership, dependent on the task at hand or the unfolding situational challenges. There is still a formal hierarchy, but the ebb and flow of power is dependent on expertise at each moment.

Collective leadership in practice involves:

- Enabling all to lead

- Shared team leadership

- Leaders working together across boundaries

- Leaders working with the community

- Consistent leadership styles and values.

Enabling all to lead

Collective leadership means the distribution and allocation of leadership power to wherever expertise, capability and motivation sit within (or outside) organisations[1]. Collective leadership ensures that leadership and expertise are correlated at every level in relation to every task. This means that, regardless of rank, status, pay band or title, those with expertise, skills or experience relevant to the task in hand are naturally accorded leadership rights and responsibilities. The domestic worker who raises an issue to do with hygiene in the ward should have as much power in initiating action as the chief executive in their shared commitment to safe patient care. Collective leadership means valuing everyone's voice in healthcare, not just that of those with senior hierarchical ranks[13].

> The purposeful, visible distribution of leadership responsibility onto the shoulders of every person in the organisation is vital for creating the type of collective leadership that will nurture the right culture for healthcare[14]. In such a culture, roles of leadership and 'followership' shift depending on the situation.

Compassionate leadership is the means for achieving this - where everyone is given attention and listened to; staff seek to understand each other's perspectives and opinions; people put themselves in each other's position by empathising and caring; and everyone seeks to help their colleagues regardless of seniority.

Shared team leadership

There is considerable evidence that shared leadership in teams consistently predicts team effectiveness, particularly but not exclusively within healthcare[15-17]. There may be a formal hierarchical leader, such as the senior partner in a primary healthcare team or the ward manager in a hospital setting, but they enact their roles through ensuring all team members contribute their knowledge, skills, experience and abilities to the work of the team. Leadership shifts seamlessly in work processes depending upon who has the relevant expertise for the task in hand. Sometimes this might be the practice nurse; at other times, the practice manager. Such collective or shared team leadership is associated with better performance and is markedly different to team interactions where one or two people dominate discussion and decision-making while other team members sit silently or passively. Compassionate leadership in teams is enacted by modelling and encouraging all to listen to each other's contributions, understanding the roles of other team members, nurturing a supportive caring environment, and developing an ethos in which team members support each other or back each other up, particularly when the work is demanding or unusually difficult.

Leaders working together across boundaries

Collective leadership also refers to leaders working together across boundaries, focused on how to support each other and how to sustain a collective leadership culture across the organisation (or system). This involves seeing leadership as not simply an individual capability or characteristic, but as collective. Leadership across an organisation exists collectively to ensure direction (what we are trying to achieve), alignment of efforts in service of that purpose, and commitment of all founded on high levels of trust and motivation[18]. Collective leadership as a concept, therefore, emphasises the function of that collective in nurturing and sustaining direction, alignment, and commitment.

In practice, what that also requires is that leaders work together to prioritise overall health and social care services, rather than focusing only on their own areas of responsibility. It requires leadership to encourage attentiveness to the outcomes for the people the system serves, not the narrow outcomes of their own service, potentially at the expense of the effectiveness of other parts of the system.

For example, it is important that primary and secondary care services work together to ensure high-quality care for patients. If primary care services become more concerned with reducing workload and referring people to secondary care as a way of achieving that, it simply leads to secondary care being swamped by inappropriate referrals. And if secondary care consultants do not work with primary care staff to help develop both appropriate referral decision-making and post-treatment primary care management, patients' needs are not well met. Collective leadership should be implemented beyond the boundaries of specific teams or organisations and beyond the personnel of specific organisations.

Collective leadership is enabled by the behaviours that constitute compassion, of course – listening carefully to each other; understanding the other's challenges; empathising with the other leader(s) or service providers; and always asking the question 'How can we help?'. A collective leadership strategy emerges from a conscious and intelligent effort to plan for an integrated, collective network of leaders, distributed throughout the organisation or system and embodying shared values and practices[19-21].

The aim of the strategy must be to create a leadership community in which all staff take responsibility for nurturing cultures of high-quality and compassionate care. The strategy requires all staff to prioritise the effectiveness of the organisation and sector in creating this culture, rather than focusing only on individual or team success. Every member of staff has the potential to lead at many points in time, particularly when their expertise is relevant to the task in hand. Conscious, deliberate attention must be paid to enabling people at every level within the organisation to adopt leadership practices that nurture the collective leadership cultures that the health and social care system requires.

Leadership with the community

Collective leadership describes how the whole health and social care system and the community can forge an interdependent network of organisations that work together to deliver high-quality care. Because health and social care organisations can no longer work in isolation to achieve the best possible care, their cultures must support interdependent working within and across the system. We saw this during the covid-19 pandemic with the health and social care sectors working more closely together; homeless people being housed in private hotels; over a million volunteers supporting the health service; and the development and distribution of vaccinations in a dramatically foreshortened time, as a result of collective leadership across boundaries.

| **Refugee health in Lebanon: GOAL partnership** | There are over one million Syrian refugees living in Lebanon (making up 30% of the country's population), with the majority living in Lebanon for over five years. Consequently, the country has high unmet mental health needs among refugees and the host population. Its government has offered only fragmented health policy responses. |

Designing effective mental health services requires collective and compassionate leadership, including the close involvement of Syrian refugees and Lebanese living with mental disorders. GOAL is a partnership set up by the National Mental Health Program of Lebanon, the London School of Hygiene and Tropical Medicine, ABAAD, St Joseph's University of Beirut, War Child Holland, and Positive Negatives. GOAL applies a co-production approach, with key stakeholders centrally involved in the project design and implementation. The overall aim of GOAL is to support government and partners in strengthening the ability of health systems to meet the mental health needs of refugee and host communities affected by protracted displacement, focusing on Lebanon.

https://www.lshtm.ac.uk/research/centres-projects-groups/goal

Bromley by Bow Centre

In London, the combined Bromley by Bow Centre and Health Partnership have developed various community engagement interventions, based on collective and compassionate leadership, intended to respond to locally identified health needs and aspirations. They have developed new relationships between patients and professionals and new ways to do consultations, manage the workload, and support patients in managing their own health. Their innovative approaches represent a shift from a service provider model to a model based on identifying, supporting, and growing community assets and capabilities.

They have created 'East Exchange', an initiative which builds community resourcefulness and resilience through bringing together hundreds of local people to collaborate, matching individual and community needs and capabilities. Through this and other projects, they support community innovation and nurture the capabilities of local people, especially of those who are socially isolated, have low skill levels, and/or are unemployed.

https://bjgp.org/content/68/672/333

Well Communities

This is another innovative framework that enables collective leadership by supporting disadvantaged communities and local organisations to work together in improving health and well-being, building community resilience and reducing inequalities. The framework has been implemented in 33 London neighborhoods across 20 London boroughs.

The vision is of empowered local communities, who have the skills and confidence to take control of and improve their individual and collective health and well-being. They are achieving this by developing a robust framework for community action for health and well-being that influences policy and practice, to enhance well-being and reduce health inequalities. Key to the approach are whole systems, holistic and assets-based working, community participation and action, community development and capacity building.

Well Communities builds and strengthens the foundations of good health and well-being by:

- Increasing community participation and volunteering in activities that enhance health and well-being through a range of community engagement and development processes

- Building individual and community knowledge, confidence, cohesion, sense of control and self-esteem, which underpin health and well-being

- Stimulating the development of formal and informal community and social support networks, which are key to mental well-being and resilience

- Providing a coherent framework for, integrating with and adding value to existing activities, ensuring value for money

- Building individual, community and organisational resources to develop and deliver activities.

http://wellcommunities.org.uk/

Consistent leadership styles and values

Collective leadership also refers to developing consistency in leadership cultures. Such cultures are developed when all or most leaders portray the same fundamental values or styles of leadership. Based on research evidence, this would most appropriately include authenticity, openness and honesty, humility, optimism, appreciativeness and, of course, compassion[10].

Collective leadership at Wrightington, Wigan and Leigh NHS Foundation Trust: empowering dialogue

The journey to staff engagement at Wrightington, Wigan and Leigh NHS Foundation Trust began 18 years ago as a joint initiative between senior managers and staff to increase mutual understanding and bridge hierarchical divides.

Directors' 'walkabouts' give them the opportunity to listen to staff at the frontline and give staff regular opportunities to talk directly to the senior team. This engagement is greatly strengthened by large-scale staff listening events led by the chief executive and other directors. Staff are asked three questions: what works well, what needs to improve, and what are the barriers to improvement?

A team-focused practice of collective leadership is the 'Pioneer Teams' programme, with staff running their own listening events and implementing local changes to improve services. Teams are encouraged to come together for 15 minutes on a daily basis to determine priorities, provide updates, address problems and recognise and appreciate successes. They record their progress visually at a central point to keep the whole team updated.

The trust has seen major sustained improvements in staff survey scores, sickness absence levels and expenditure on temporary staffing, as well as many benefits for patients, including improvements in patient care.

More information in an online video:
http://bit.ly/1dB2fwO

Conclusion

In summary, collective leadership founded on the four compassionate leadership behaviours helps create cultures in which high-quality, compassionate care can be delivered by encouraging all staff to play a role in leading.

This is fundamentally important in healthcare because mastery of quality and patient safety sciences and practices is everyone's responsibility. It occurs where there are high levels of dialogue, debate and discussion about quality and safety across the organisation (top to bottom and end to end) to achieve a shared understanding about quality problems and solutions[22-24]. This is precisely what collective leadership implies. Similarly, all staff will feel safer and encourage, welcome, and explore feedback and treat complaints and errors as opportunities for system learning rather than as a prompt for blame. This collective openness supports learning from errors, near misses and incidents.

> Shared leadership in teams is a strong predictor of team performance[16].

Where multi-professional teams work together with an ethos of shared leadership, patient satisfaction is higher, healthcare delivery is more effective, there are higher levels of innovation in the provision of new and improved ways of caring for patients, lower levels of staff stress, absenteeism and turnover, and more consistent communication with patients[25-28].

Leadership that ensures effective team and inter-team working (both within and across organisational boundaries) is essential if health and social care organisations are to meet the challenges ahead. Creating such cultures requires a conscious, collective approach to ensuring that the right leadership is in place to nurture the right values with the right behaviours. This can be achieved by implementing a compassionate and collective leadership strategy sustained now and for the long-term future.

Resources

1. What is collective leadership? To what extent are all enabled to lead in your organisation, department or team? How could this be improved?

2. To what extent is there shared team leadership in your team? What would have to change for team leadership to be better shared in your team? What can you do (alone or with others) to influence this?

3. Where in your organisation do leaders work well together across boundaries, and where is it not happening? What would most help to transform the least effective into the most effective cross-boundary working? What can you do (alone or with others) to influence this?

4. To what extent does the leadership in your organisation involve communities in the genuine co-design and co-ownership of health and social care services? How could this be improved and what can you do (alone or with others) to make a significant difference?

5. How consistent are leadership styles and values across your organisation, in relation to authenticity, openness and honesty, humility, optimism, appreciativeness and compassion?

Questionnaires

Collective leadership – the health and social care systems of all four UK nations have a commitment to developing collective as well as compassionate and inclusive leadership. Here you can find a questionnaire already used successfully (in terms of reliability and validity) in NHS organisations. Either the complete measure or a shortened four item version (with just those items marked with an asterisk) can be used.

1. Leaders here prioritise overall patient/service user care, not just their own work area.*

2. Leaders across different departments work together to ensure high-quality overall patient/service user care.

3. Leaders here go out of their way to help each other across different departments to provide high-quality care.

4. Everyone in this organisation is expected to act as a leader in ensuring high-quality care.*

5. Team leaders encourage everyone to lead changes in order to improve the work we do.

6. We all play a leadership role in our teams in this organisation.*

7. We all listen to each other's views so we can best lead this organisation.*

8. Leadership in teams is shared rather than the responsibility of only one person.

Guidance on using this questionnaire is provided in Appendix 1.

Websites

1. The Collective Leadership and Safety Cultures (Co-Lead) programme
    This is a five-year University College Dublin research project that aims to develop and test the impact of collective leadership in healthcare on team performance and patient safety. Co-Lead's approach develops the team as a dynamic leadership entity and is based on the premise that healthcare is delivered through teamwork, and teams should share responsibility and accountability for quality and patient safety. Co-Lead takes a systems approach, recognising healthcare as a complex system and identifying key points and levels of intervention as essential to enabling a collective leadership approach to create a change in culture. It is working with seven hospital groups, emphasising the importance of networks in delivering integrated, safe care.
    https://www.ucd.ie/collectiveleadership/

2   Health and Social Care Collective Leadership Strategy, Northern Ireland
    Northern Ireland introduced a collective leadership strategy for all of health and social care in 2017 with an emphasis on compassionate leadership, leadership being everyone's responsibility, interdependent leadership (collaborative leadership across boundaries) and shared leadership in and across teams. Evaluations of progress have been undertaken using the Culture Assessment Tool. This inspirational initiative, led by Myra Weir, is helping to develop work contexts in health and social care that enable the core work needs of staff to be better met and promote staff voice, influence and innovation.
    https://www.health-ni.gov.uk/publications/hsc-collective-leadership-strategy

3. The Collective Leadership Institute (CLI)
   CLI empowers people at the individual level by building the competence for collective leadership and stakeholder collaboration, as well as dialogue expertise. Additionally, CLI builds competence at the systemic level by strengthening the collective capacity of collaborating actors to implement dialogic change and shift towards more co-creation.
   CLI offers capacity building through open courses, tailor-made courses, online learning, the Young Leaders for Sustainability programme and the training of facilitators.
   https://www.collectiveleadership.de/

4. NHS England/Improvement: Culture and Leadership resources
   NHSE/I offers a comprehensive set of evidence-based and open-source tools to support health and social care organisations to develop a culture and leadership strategy. The tools focus on developing individual and collective leadership, emphasising the value of compassion. The process involves three stages for organisations to work through: discovery, design and implementation. This is being implemented by over 100 NHS organisations across the UK as well as by health and social care organisations in other countries. The materials can be found at this website:
   https://webarchive.nationalarchives.gov.uk/20210107182025/https:// improvement.nhs.uk/resources/culture-leadership/

5. The Compassionate Leadership Interview
   Chris Whitehead interviews public, private and third sector leaders who have adopted compassionate and collective leadership approaches. This builds on Chris Whitehead's book Compassionate Leadership that combines life experience, psychology and neuroscience for leaders seeking to learn how to create supportive workplaces. It is based on the observation that people thrive when they are involved and listened to, when they are growing and developing and when they are motivated by the vision of the organisation.
   https://www.compassionate-leadership.co.uk/

6. New Local
   New Local is an independent think tank and network with a mission to transform public services and unlock community power. Its recent report 'Community Power: The Evidence' is the first research to take a comprehensive view of what community power looks like – featuring examples from across the UK and internationally. It is also the first to collect and analyse existing evidence of the impact of community power.
   https://www.newlocal.org.uk/publications/community-power-the-evidence/

Videos

Collective leadership culture change in the NHS. Michael West explains that to continually improve health and social care, we must design collective leadership into NHS strategy – encouraging the participation and involvement of all NHS staff. (5 minutes 43 secs)
https://www.kingsfund.org.uk/audio-video/michael-west-collective-leadership-culture-change

Graeme Currie, Warwick Business School, describes the notion of leadership as 'distributed' or 'collective'. (5 minutes 33 secs)
https://www.futurelearn.com/info/courses/healthcare/0/steps/27531

Collective and compassionate leadership in public services - 'Nurturing work cultures for people and performance'. Michael West speaks to leaders from the Northern Ireland Civil Service. (15 minutes)
https://www.youtube.com/watch?v=PLmt8NwF9Uk)

A CCL perspective on collective leadership. Rachael Hanley-Browne, CCL's Regional Director UK and Ireland, speaking at the Corporate Research Forum Spring Symposium in 2013 and arguing that leadership comes from the bottom, the middle and the top, but begins with leadership of self. (2 minutes 24 secs)
https://www.youtube.com/watch?v=WO9SHl5MB34

Chapter 9.

Compassionate leadership across boundaries

Summary

This chapter describes how and why we find it difficult to work (and lead) across boundaries, based on the competing pulls of belonging that create both a sense of interconnectedness and separation that gives us a distinct and valued identity. Drawing on research into two fundamental aspects of human experience – the need to belong and intergroup relations – the chapter describes five ways of working that constitute an effective strategy for promoting compassionate leadership across boundaries.

Introduction

What helps us can also ail us. Meeting our need to belong is fundamental to our health and well-being. Loneliness and social isolation are profoundly damaging to our health and well-being, whereas connection, love and inclusion enable us to thrive[1]. Evolution has equipped us with the means to get this core need met, such as the hard wiring of babies to make eye contact with their mother (or father and other caregivers) and thereby nurture connection. Others are our impulse to help, the ubiquity of compassion and the value of altruism. Being kind to others, helping them and showing we care enables bonding, connection and builds trust in relationships – effectively reinforcing a sense of mutual belonging.

Belonging is rewarded at a biochemical level through the release of oxytocin and in life experience by feelings of happiness and safety. Empathy, forgiveness and caring have deeply beneficial effects upon well-being and resilience[2-4]. Neglect, incivility, exclusion, bullying and harassment have quite opposite and profound effects[5]. Throughout our evolutionary history, by bonding and creating supportive social groups, we could survive far more effectively. We could share food, mate, safely raise our young and be protected from the predations of other animals (including some humans). Bonding and thereby building social groups are powerful and fundamental currents in the flow of our lived experience.

Yet, contained within the impulse to connect and bond is also a key challenge for modern humanity. We come to identify with the groups of which we are part – where we feel that our needs to belong are met – such as male, young, white, British, football club supporter, jazz lover, vegetarian, etc. 'We come to identify' means we use the bricks of these categories to construct an identity which we project out into the social world as a story of 'who I am.' This story is also how we enable our private selves to feel a sense of reassuring solidity in the uncertainty of our existence. I am, and what I am is made up of all those categories plus my memories, attitudes, beliefs, experiences, thoughts, body, bodily sensations, etc.

Preserving a positive sense of our constructed identity is important because it enables us to feel more secure and happier about ourselves. By extension, I can come to evaluate those who belong to other categories in slightly (or considerably) less positive terms because they are not part of the groups by which I define myself. This can apply to even the most arbitrary or superficial of category differences such as accent, skin colour or eye colour. Thus, I may come to dislike or denigrate those with different political views, coming from other countries, who eat meat, who are from a different religious tradition to my own, or even whose shade of skin colour is darker or somehow different from mine. This social categorisation leads to both subtle and overt forms of in-group and out-group differentiation and favouritism. The groups I am part of and accepted in constitute my in-groups, and I will tend to show favouritism to them. In contrast, I am likely to devalue the groups I am not a part of in relation to my own. Such social identity processes are underlying causes of discrimination, prejudice and cruelty in human society[6].

The need to belong and the associated identity formation processes create a tension between forces that have been both evolutionary boons and disasters. Wars, racism, sexism, genocide, violence between rival sports fans, violence against women, ageism, populism and religious persecution are expressions of this underlying human tendency to create identities based on group and intergroup processes.

This is particularly salient at this time in our history because we face threats to our existence that can only be prevented by working together across all of humanity with a sense of shared identity. These threats are real. Pandemics are the most obvious, given our recent shared experience, but even greater are climate change and the destruction of other species threatening the biodiversity which is at the heart of the health of the ecosystem. Other threats we have created ourselves, including weapons of mass destruction, which could eliminate human life and other species because of accident or intent.

Our growing awareness of our interdependence and interconnectedness with each other, other species and our fragile ecosystems, as well as the planet, demands we learn how to create a wider sense of identity. This will be based on our experienced sense of shared humanity and intergroup similarity. Such a shared sense of belonging may help us to work more collaboratively, but more is needed as outlined below. Financial crises spread across the world; labour laws in one country affect workers in others; and industrial pollution affects the lives of all of us.

> There is a powerful existential imperative that we act with compassion towards all we are connected with if we are to ensure healthy evolution of the ecosystems and communities we are part of. Compassionate leadership across boundaries is essential for us to succeed in facing these challenges and overcoming them.

Collaboration across boundaries

As we increasingly engage with the reality of our interconnectedness, the practice of compassion offers us a way of building effective collaboration and teamwork for the future. Leading researchers exploring compassion in organisations describe an ethic of care which is more likely to occur in institutions "that foster integration, nurture trust and respect the emotional lives of members, and where members have the opportunity to become competent carers"[7]. Training leaders to develop compassionate ways of working will equip them to deal effectively with the challenges they face: to work effectively as teams; to work collaboratively across team boundaries; and to work across organisational boundaries in supportive and co-operative ways. When our focus is on understanding and helping others in service of a shared vision or cause, our collaboration and teamwork are more effective than when our focus is on meeting our own goals, regardless of the needs of others.

Why is this important in health and social care? Because the same forces are at work in tensions between different professional groups (nurses, midwives, doctors, social workers, managers), different hierarchical levels, different teams and departments (radiology and A&E, reception staff and practice nurses, for example), members of different organisations (GPs and secondary care consultants, community nurses and social workers, local authority and hospitals) and even different sectors (health service and social care, private sector and public sector, community groups and statutory services, voluntary groups and public sector staff).

The need for compassionate leadership modelling co-operation across boundaries is not only intra-organisational. Governments, practitioners, and policy makers agree that health and social care services must be integrated to meet the needs of patients, service users and communities both efficiently and effectively. Health and social care must be delivered by an interdependent network of organisations, including community groups. This requires that leaders work together, spanning organisational boundaries both within and between organisations, and prioritising overall patient care rather than the success of their component of it. That means leaders working collectively and building a co-operative, integrative leadership culture – in effect, compassionate and collective leadership.

We can draw on our deep understanding of both how we meet our needs to belong and how to reduce intergroup prejudice to help articulate a five-point strategy for leading compassionately across boundaries[1,6]. All five must be implemented for the strategy to be successful – it is not a pick and mix option. The five points are:

1. Articulating and continually emphasising a shared vision focused on the health and well-being of patients, people, and communities.

2. Agreeing clear, challenging, shared and inspiring long-term goals aligned around the vision.

3. Ensuring frequent, positive and supportive contact across boundaries (ideally face-to-face).

4. Preventing chronic or unresolved conflict within and across boundaries.

5. Establishing a norm of mutual support within and across boundaries – 'How can we help you?'

These five factors are described below in more depth and draw on research literatures and case examples[8,9].

Shared purpose and vision

Leaders must work together across boundaries to develop a compelling shared vision of transforming the health and well-being of communities. A key step in the development of system leadership is, therefore, shifting from reactive problem-solving to building positive visions for the future.

This vision must be embodied, affirmed, reaffirmed and rediscovered continually within and between all the organisations involved. It must act like a beacon that guides decision-making and actions day by day, hour by hour and moment by moment.

Leaders must ensure that the vision keeps guiding the partnership and partners back to that strong, still point of focus in their challenging world.

This typically happens as leaders help staff and communities to articulate their deeper aspirations. This is likely to involve confronting difficult truths about the present reality such as inadequate services, growing health inequalities, poor collaboration across boundaries, fear of failure, understaffing, and chronic excessive workload. They must then use that tension between the vision and the reality to inspire truly new approaches[10].

A long-term commitment to collaboration

We have a greater sense of belonging and have stronger motivation to maintain and nurture relationships when we anticipate long-term continuity and stability in those relationships (rather than feeling that they will not last or will be superseded by other relationships). That is why we can build stronger long-term relationships across boundaries through agreeing clear, valued and shared long-term goals aligned to the vision alongside the other team, department, group or organisation we must work with to realise that vision.

Leaders must build a shared commitment to working together for the medium and long term (avoiding a focus only on short-term objectives) to engender a sense of long-term continuity and stability in the relationship. Collaboration is more likely when leaders truly sense a commitment to working together for the longer term. This matters because of the investment of time and energy needed to build effective relationships. Leaders are likely to think it is worth investing in if it seems clear that those they are collaborating with will be ongoing, rather than merely transient, partners in transforming health and social care services for the benefit of patients, service users and others.

Building an understanding of long-term possibilities and aspirations and engaging people in shaping those plans that will impact the future health and social care of populations takes time, and this investment helps to deepen commitment and trust.

The need for frequent personal contact

Frequent personal face-to-face contact between leaders builds trust across boundaries. Collaboration is a team activity that is more difficult to achieve via virtual technologies or at a distance. During the pandemic, we were unable in many cases to be with loved ones, to have physical contact, to hug and to read the love in each other's eyes. That has an impact on our well-being. In some cases, those we loved were forced to die alone – it has been heart-breaking. It felt as though the roots of our very being were withering.

Similarly, sometimes we had to work with colleagues via virtual technologies, unable to read the subtle nuances in people's facial movements or body postures that enrich the information we receive. That rich information is necessary for us to distinguish between statements of fact, complaints, underlying messages of frustration, and expressions of pain or anxiety. It enables us to differentiate between an innocent joke and a spiteful dig. The richer our contact, the more able we are to establish shared understanding and belonging through each of us attending, seeking to understand, having the emotional intelligence and motivation to empathise, and then finding ways of helping.

Care Home Assessment and Response Team	A decision was taken to co-ordinate the support for care homes in Forth Valley during the pandemic through a dedicated multi-professional and multi-agency team called CHART (Care Home Assessment and Response Team). CHART was comprised of different professionals that included GPs, social care workers, palliative care specialist nurses and advanced nurse/paramedic practitioners. Coming together from so many different disciplines as a new team was a challenge. However, the depth and breadth of the health and social care experience within this new team was immediately evident. There was a clear common purpose which immediately focused their minds.
NHS Forth Valley: Dental Services Teamwork	Where previously General Dental Practices and Public Dental Services worked in silos, the teams came together to work side by side during the pandemic, triaging and treating patients seven days a week across three Urgent Dental Care centres. Several benefits resulted:

- Strengthened relationships and a compassionate approach to the provision of urgent dental services in a time of crisis.

- Lightbulbs 'switching on' – where there was once was a lack of knowledge around services, there was a new visible respect for the other teams and what each of them could bring to patient care.

- A desire from staff to further build on this in the future.

Attending, understanding, empathising and helping together enables leaders to hear different points of view and to appreciate each other's reality, emotionally as well as cognitively.

Compassionate conflict management

The journey of compassionate and collective leadership involves both agreements and disagreements, which can fester and undermine relationships and trust. Leaders should therefore commit together to surface and resolve conflicts quickly, fairly, transparently and collaboratively. It is helpful to identify conflicts or potential conflicts early and decide on where the conflict derives from:

- Disagreement about the task (what to do, its goals)

- The process (such as who is responsible for what)

- Status (who has authority over which situations)

- Relationships (interpersonal dislikes).

Status conflicts are particularly likely when leaders work across teams, departments, organisations, or even sectors (healthcare and local authority; hospitals and community care, for example). Of course, many conflicts will have elements of more than one of these, but it is helpful to know what the main source of the conflict is and to deal with it accordingly. It is also helpful to note that task, process and status conflicts can quickly escalate into interpersonal conflicts. Amy Gallo offers helpful, practical advice about how to deal with each of these types of conflict compassionately and effectively[11].

The absence of conflicts might be more of a worry than their presence. This is because conflicts occur when difficult truths are confronted rather than suppressed. Conflicts and challenges should therefore be welcomed as a step towards leadership across boundaries, while recognising that persistent or high levels of conflict can also be damaging.

> When we lead across boundaries, a good barometer of success is the extent to which the collaboration is leading to innovation – new and improved ways of doing things.

If there is no innovation, then the value of cross-boundary working could be questioned. Equally, innovation generates conflict. When we seek to implement new and improved ways of working, conflict is inevitable; as Machiavelli observed back in the 15th and 16th centuries. Those who seek to innovate will encounter potential opposition from those who are unsure of the value of the change and those who are satisfied or wedded to how things currently are.

"There is no more delicate matter to take in hand, nor more dangerous to conduct, nor more doubtful in its success, than to set up as a leader in the introduction of changes. For he who innovates will have for his enemies all those who are well off under the existing order of things and only lukewarm supporters in those who might be better off under the new. This lukewarm temper arises partly from the fear of adversaries who have the laws on their side and partly from the incredulity of mankind, who will never admit the merit of anything new, until they have seen it proved by the event."

Niccolò Machiavelli, Il Principe (The Prince)

It helps if leaders who are attempting to improve their collaborative leadership have agreed on a common approach to conflict management, such as the Thomas Killman model of conflict management style or, as mentioned above, the more extensive and helpful guide on managing conflict from Amy Gallo[11]. The Thomas Killman approach describes five styles of conflict management that people may typically adopt: accommodating, compromising, competing, avoiding and collaborating[12]. These styles can also be understood as responses to the situation, dependant on the strength of interest we have in meeting our own needs or goals, and on our interest in helping the other party meet theirs.

Collaborating is the ideal choice to work together to seek to meet or exceed both parties' needs by finding creative solutions. Implicit in this is that it is necessary to first understand what the needs of both parties are, rather than focusing on expressed positions that may camouflage what their real concerns are. A team member may resist change arguing that it will be less efficient to change role responsibilities within the team, when their real need may be to avoid losing a close working relationship with a colleague, or a fear of losing status in their role. The more we take a collaborative approach to conflict via modelling compassion and a commitment to shared problem-solving, the stronger the working relationships will become.

Altruism across boundaries

Compassionate leadership across boundaries essentially manifests itself in a sustained commitment to helping leaders from other teams, departments, organisations, or sectors. This is not simply undifferentiated altruism or kindness. The aim of this cross-boundary help is to ensure that collectively, all can be more effective in meeting the health and social care needs of the communities they serve. Compassionate leadership across boundaries in our health and social care sectors requires an overt commitment from all leaders at every level to behave altruistically towards each other's teams, departments, or organisations, mutually supporting success to transform the health and well-being of the communities they serve.

The human need to belong implies that leaders who behave altruistically towards others in this way will be highly effective in developing trust, stability and continuity in relationships – nurturing a sense of connection by assuaging the need to belong[1]. It requires that leaders approach relationships with other leaders, teams, departments or organisations by asking 'How can I help?' and not 'How can I use our relationship to further my own position and that of my organisation?'. It means approaching collaboration by asking not 'How can I win in this relationship?', but rather 'How can we succeed together?'.

Collaboration in practice

Leadership across boundaries is needed to address the 'tragedy of the commons' (see below) that leads to apparently intractable global challenges such as climate change, youth unemployment, inequality and loss of biodiversity[10]. However, leaders often fail in addressing such issues because they do not embrace the truth that transforming systems requires transforming relationships among the people who shape those systems.

The Tragedy of the Commons	The 'tragedy of the commons' is a concept used particularly in economics to describe a situation in which every individual has an incentive to consume a resource, but at the expense of every other individual and with no way for anyone to exclude anyone else from consuming. It derives from the situation widespread in the United Kingdom in the Middle Ages when villages had an area of common land which could be used by all to graze their animals (sheep, cattle or horses). The problem arises from the fact that continual overgrazing depletes and destroys the resource to the point where there is no grazing left. It requires a system of shared responsibility to ration use so that all may continue to benefit, and that the incentive for individuals to maximise their own benefit does not lead to the tragedy of the destruction of the shared resource. Issues of sustainability, climate change and the destruction of habitats resulting in wide scale loss of biodiversity exemplify the tragedy of the commons.
	In Salford, the CCG and the council created an integrated commissioning committee to oversee the commissioning decisions for all adult health and social care services across the resident population. The hope is that by discussing how to meet the needs of the population being served, they will make progress in developing altruism and mutuality and avoid 'the tragedy of the commons' which occurs when self-interested behaviour works against the common good[13].

Compassionate system leadership means being open to hearing and acting on different points of view (*attending* and *understanding*). This, in turn, depends on creating time and space for stakeholders to come together to have the creative conversations on which understanding and change rest. It means prioritising consultation, engagement, persuasion and influence, rather than hierarchical power[14]. Other key skills include being able to *empathise* or 'walk in other people's shoes', identifying those who will form a coalition of the willing. Finally, such compassionate system leadership involves *helping* people, for example, to develop ideas for progress by involving them in decision-making. The prize, especially in the context of tough or 'wicked' problems, is that especially innovative ideas for progress naturally and dynamically emerge from such collaborative and compassionate leadership across boundaries.

Canterbury District Health Board, New Zealand

The experience of the Canterbury District Health Board in South Island, New Zealand, is an example of what can be achieved through a long-term commitment to compassionate and collaborative leadership. Faced with a growing and ageing population and with the prospect of having to build a second acute hospital to cope with rising demand, leaders in Canterbury committed to working together as 'one system, one budget', even though it was neither a single system nor did it have one budget. The district health board acted as a catalyst in this process, bringing together clinicians, managers and other stakeholders to plan services for the future.

Through an extensive process of attending, understanding, empathising and helping via engagement across the community, agreement was reached on a shared vision of a single integrated health and social care system in which patients were at the centre. The key strategic goals were that services should enable people to take more responsibility for their own health and well-being; as far as possible, people should stay in their own homes and communities; and when people needed complex care, this should be timely and appropriate[15].

The work done in Canterbury not only helped to avoid a new hospital being built by 'bending the demand curve', but also enabled the system to manage the impact of a succession of earthquakes that destroyed the centre of Christchurch and damaged healthcare facilities. Independent analyses have demonstrated the achievements of the district health board in relation to other health boards in New Zealand[14] and the way in which integrated care helped moderate the growth in demand for acute care[15]. A fuller account of how this was done can be viewed at *https://www.kingsfund.org.uk/ audio-video/david-meates-making-integrated-care-work-canterbury-new-zealand* and at *https://www.kingsfund. org.uk/publications/reforming-nhs-within/case-study-5-canterbury-district-health-board-new-zealand.*

There are many other examples of compassionate leadership across boundaries cited by The King's Fund, including on the development of new care models[16,17], sustainability and transformation plans[18], and accountable care organisations (ACOs)[19]. The King's Fund also reviews the experience of people who have occupied system leadership roles[16,18].

Why is compassionate leadership across boundaries so important? Because the future of health and social care is planned to be a future in which the various services and institutions that provide or influence health and social care will work together to influence the delivery of integrated services.

The Nuka System of Care, Alaska

Southcentral Foundation's Nuka System of Care is a shining example of compassionate and collaborative leadership across boundaries. It is a relationship-based, Alaska Native-owned, non-profit healthcare organisation serving nearly 65,000 Alaska Native and American Indian people living in Anchorage and 55 rural villages. 'Nuka' is an Alaska Native word meaning strong, giant structures and living things. The organisation has developed comprehensive health and social care services to meet the needs of the Native community, to enhance rather than weaken the culture, and to empower individuals and families to take charge of their lives. Leaders work together with the Native community to promote wellness through health and social care services. Alaska Native people oversee the design and delivery of healthcare[20].

The Nuka System of Care incorporates a patient-centred model of care, with multidisciplinary teams providing integrated health and social care services in primary care centres and the community, co-ordinating with a range of other services. This is combined with a broader approach to improving family and community well-being that includes initiatives such as Nuka's Family Wellness Warriors programme, which aims to tackle domestic violence, abuse and neglect through education, training, and community engagement. Traditional Alaska Native healing is offered alongside other health and social care services, and all of Nuka's services aim to build on the culture of the Alaska Native community. There is community participation in locality-based advisory groups, active involvement of Alaska Native 'customer owners' in Southcentral Foundation's management and governance structure, and use of surveys, focus groups and telephone hotlines to ensure that people can give feedback that is heard and acted upon.

The Nuka System depends on collaboration between Southcentral Foundation and a range of local, regional and national partners. The Nuka System has significantly improved access to primary care services; hugely improved performance on 75% of health outcome measures; and increased levels of customer satisfaction, with respect for cultures and traditions positively rated at 94%. There have also been reductions in hospital activity, including a 36% reduction in hospital days; a 42% reduction in urgent and emergency care services; and a 58% reduction in visits to specialist clinics[20].

https://www.southcentralfoundation.com/nuka-system-of-care/

https://www.kingsfund.org.uk/publications/population-health-systems/nuka-system-care-alaska

The Gwent Frailty Project, Wales

This project in Wales uses multiple mechanisms to integrate health and social care, working to meet frail older people's severe to complex needs within the community. Services include rapid nurse-led response, reablement, emergency social care, falls co-ordination, mental health and community resource teams. Community response teams try to have a combination of social workers, physiotherapists, occupational therapists, service coordinators, rapid response nurses, discharge liaison nurses and support and well-being workers, wherever possible.

The project involves multiple organisations including Aneurin Bevan Health Board, Blaenau Gwent County Borough Council, Caerphilly County Borough Council, Monmouthshire County Council, Newport City Council, and Torfaen County Borough Council.

The Gwent Frailty Project uses a whole system model to deliver care across five localities, one local health board and the voluntary sector. There is joint directorship and financial arrangements between services, as well as joint administration and some sharing of resources. It was one of the first large-scale models of integrated care to be established in Wales.

http://www.wales.nhs.uk/ (Search for 'Gwent Frailty')

Local Care Partnerships (LCPs), Leeds	LCP is the term used in Leeds to describe the model of joined-up working to deliver local care for local people, working in and with local communities. The LCPs build on a history of Leeds City Council, the NHS and third sector (community organisations) staff working together. There are 19 LCPs covering all of Leeds, and they are tailored to local need and to the features of that community.
	All LCPs have a range of people working together, regardless of the employing organisation, to deliver joined-up collaborative care that meets the needs of the population. Each LCP includes statutory organisations, third sector and elected members, alongside local people, to develop services that support people to access the right support when they need it and thrive using their individual and community assets.
	The LCPs are aligned with the Leeds Health and Well-Being Strategy 2016-21, which has an aspirational vision for Leeds to be a healthy and caring city for all ages, where people who are the poorest improve their health the fastest. LCPs are widely committed to ensuring that decisions made locally about people involve the local community.
	http://inspiringchangeleeds.org/whats-changing/local-care-partnerships-2/

Conclusion

Interconnectedness is our reality. To meet the challenges we face, we will have to increasingly understand how to develop belonging and trust and create team climates and organisational cultures of compassion. Humans make up teams and organisations and leaders must come to see those they lead and work with across boundaries as more collaborative, compassionate and caring than is typically portrayed. We need to repeat the stories that emphasise the success of compassion and collaboration, such as those heard throughout the pandemic. As individuals, we can learn the skills of compassion[21,22] in the way we work with others to create the collaborative and supportive institutions of the future. Where teamwork and collaboration are underpinned by cultures of compassion, they foster individual, team, inter-organisational and community interconnection characterised by justice, trust, thriving and well-being. That is the challenge and the imperative – to achieve compassionate integrated health and social care and empowerment for the communities we serve.

Resources

Exercises/Discussion questions (to reflect on or discuss with a colleague)

1. What do you understand by the notion of compassionate leadership across boundaries, and why is it important in health and social care? What good examples can you describe of compassionate leadership across boundaries in health and social care?

2. To what extent is there shared compassionate leadership across boundaries in your organisation, both internally and across the health, social care and third sectors?

3. Bearing in mind the five ways to compassionate leadership across boundaries, what would have to change for compassionate leadership across boundaries to be better modelled in your organisation – both within the organisation and in relationships with other organisations and sectors? What can you do (alone or with others) to influence this by focusing on the five ways to compassionate leadership across boundaries?

4. Where in your organisation do leaders work well together across boundaries, and where is it not happening? What practical examples can you describe of how the five ways of enabling such compassionate leadership across boundaries are being implemented? And where they are not? With reference to the five ways of leading compassionately across boundaries, what would most help to transform the least effective into the most effective compassionate leadership across boundaries in your work context? What can you do (alone or with others) to influence this?

5. With reference to the five ways of leading compassionately across boundaries, how might the leadership in your organisation better involve communities in the genuine co-design and co-ownership of health and social care services? How could this be improved, and what can you do (alone or with others) to make a significant difference?

Questionnaires

Michael West and AffinaOD have developed a multi-dimensional survey to assess *compassionate partnership working across boundaries*. This examines nine dimensions listed below (along with examples of items from the questionnaire):

Shared vision and values

1. There is a clear, shared vision for our work in the partnership.
2. We have taken the time to carefully agree a set of partnership values to guide our work together.

Roles and teamworking

1. Partnership members are committed to achieving the partnership's goals.
2. There is good leadership in this partnership.

Frequent positive contact

1. We meet regularly to review our objectives and our progress.
2. There is a lot of face-to-face interaction between key people in the partnership.

Long-term commitment

1. There is a strong sense that we are in this partnership for the long term.
2. We plan a long way ahead together, not just for the short term.

Conflict management

1. We identify potential conflicts between us quickly and openly.
2. Conflict does not tend to linger in the partnership.

Mutual support

1. We are strongly focused on how we can help each other in this partnership.
2. Members of the partnership do not just focus on what they can get out of it for their organisations.

Trust

1. Those in the partnership act with integrity in their dealings with each other.
2. We can rely on members of this partnership to do what they commit to.

Innovation

1. The way the organisations in the partnership work together is readily changed in order to achieve the vision.
2. The methods we use to achieve the vision are often discussed.

Compassion

1. People in the partnership are very compassionate towards each other when they face problems.
2. People in the partnership are quick to help each other when they are under pressure.

This tool is copyrighted (Michael West and AffinaOD).
For more information, see: *https://www.affinaod.com/*

Guidance on using this questionnaire is provided in Appendix 1.

Websites

1. Scottish Social Services Council for leading and managing across boundaries
   They recognise that collaborative gain is possible when people work together to achieve better outcomes for people using services and for unpaid/informal carers. They know that effective partnership working needs trust, respect and interdependence. Valuing different perspectives and working constructively with competing priorities requires skill, commitment and perseverance.
   https://www.stepintoleadership.info/middle_leadingboundaries.html

2. Working across organisational boundaries with service communities
   This website offers powerful and practical advice for working with service communities - networks of people formed around user journeys. Service communities can help people from across the public sector, including policy, digital and operations, to work together. Collaborating in this way has helped community members address the more common collaboration challenges, as well as do things like:

   - Better understand their users - for example, some communities have developed personas (Mrs Green, Ms Chowla) to help them gain a better understanding of what their users are trying to achieve
   - Collaborate across organisational boundaries - for example, by gaining access to the people they need to talk to at regular meetings and workshops
   - Shape the design of the wider user journey.
   https://www.gov.uk/service-manual/design/working-across-organisational-boundaries

3. A description of The King's Fund programme on Building Collaborative Leadership across health and social care organisations.
   https://www.kingsfund.org.uk/courses/building-collaborative-leadership

4. The Scottish government's review of progress on integrated health and social care with action plans for change.
   https://www.gov.scot/publications/ministerial-strategic-group-health-community-care-review-progress-integration-health-social-care-final-report

Videos

Amy Gallo explaining how to manage conflict with kindness and compassion. (14 minutes 47 secs)
https://www.youtube.com/watch?v=MnaLS7OE2pk

Nicholas Timmins talks about the Canterbury District Health Board's quest for integrated care in New Zealand. He considers the impact of the devastating earthquake in 2011 and how Canterbury District Health Board implemented a successful system that created one vision for care, empowered staff and changed the funding model. (11 minutes 15 secs)
https://www.kingsfund.org.uk/audio-video/nicholas-timmins-canterbury-new-zealands-quest-integrated-care

A King's Fund interview with Katherine Gottlieb, President and CEO of Southcentral Foundation, about the Nuka System which delivers care to an Alaskan Native American population. Katherine relays the successes of this system and the reasons for this success, including developing a shared vision, working in partnership with their patients and measuring the outcomes effectively. She also explains what has changed for the population as a result and what inspiration community health providers could take from this system. (7 minutes 11 secs)
https://www.kingsfund.org.uk/audio-video/southcentral-foundations-nuka-system-care

Chapter 10.

Compassionate leadership for quality improvement and innovation

Summary

This chapter[1] explains what is meant by innovation and shows the importance of collective, compassionate leadership for enabling innovation in health and social care. Drawing on research evidence, it describes four fundamental elements of a culture for innovative and high-quality care: an inspiring vision and strategy; positive inclusion and participation; enthusiastic team and cross-boundary working; and support and autonomy for staff to innovate. The chapter describes how compassionate leaders play a key role in nurturing each of these elements of culture.

Introduction

Only innovation can enable modern health and social care organisations and systems to meet the radically changing needs and expectations of the communities they serve. While adequate financial support is a necessary precondition, more money on its own, without transformative change, will not be enough. During the pandemic, people implemented astonishing and transformational change across both health and social care. These were mostly local initiatives springing from the seedbeds of staff determination to do all they could to successfully care for patients and service users during the crisis. Innovation and improvement efforts were also supported where there were pre-existing collaborative relationships with organisations that support quality improvement, such as The Social Care Innovation Network, The Health Foundation, the US Institute for Healthcare Improvement, NHS Quest and NHS Improvement.

Supportive, compassionate leadership and cultures stimulate innovation and quality improvement to become established as a cultural norm and to then spread within health and social care teams and organisations. By ensuring that organisational and systems environments support innovation and quality improvement, we can better meet the health and social care needs of our communities after the worst of the pandemic has receded and for the long-term future. Compassionate leadership is fundamental to creating cultures of improvement and radical innovation across health and social care. Such continuous improvement is essential because without improvement, quality will tend to decrease.

Compassionate leadership enhances the intrinsic motivation of health and social care staff and reinforces their fundamental altruism.

It helps to promote a culture of learning, where risk-taking, within safe boundaries, is encouraged, and where there is an acceptance that not all innovation will be successful. This directly contrasts with cultures of blame, fear and bullying. Compassion also creates the psychological safety, described in chapter 5, that helps staff feel confident in speaking out about errors, problems and uncertainties. That, in turn, prompts them to feel empowered and supported to develop and implement ideas for better ways of delivering services. They also work more co-operatively, creatively and collaboratively in a compassionate culture, with the affirmation of cohesion, optimism and effectiveness.

Creativity refers to coming up with novel and useful ideas; innovation is both the generation of creative ideas and their implementation[2-5]. How does compassionate leadership help innovation? Compassionate leadership creates the necessary conditions for innovation among individuals, in teams, in the process of inter-teamworking, in organisations and in cross-boundary or systems working.

Compassionate leadership, problem-solving and innovation

Innovation is often spurred by a challenge or problem that confronts us – much as the pandemic led to astonishing innovation and change across society, such as the vaccination programme, the NHS volunteers programme and new models of remote monitoring of patients. We can understand the innovation process better by examining the key stages of problem-solving: problem identification and exploration, ideation (the generation of ideas), evaluation, and implementation. Compassionate leadership is a powerful facilitator at each stage of the problem-solving process and, by extension, innovation.

How, then, does compassionate leadership influence problem-solving and innovation?

- *Attending:* Attention is vital for ensuring that the key challenges that staff face are clearly identified (a prerequisite for innovation) and that there is an awareness of where innovation and improvement are needed. When leaders pay attention to difficulties, challenges and problems (such as chronic excessive workload, staff stress and high levels of staff turnover), they can be explored in depth. This is the most critical phase of innovation because a good understanding of the issues ensures that innovation attempts are appropriately directed. Attention is focused on the real problem, not on first impressions. Leaders must actively listen, pay attention, withhold judgement, clarify, summarise, reflect and communicate in their interactions with those they lead. All this helps generate deeper insights that provide a clearer picture of the real problem. Active listening requires leaning towards learning and gaining insight, as well as an empathic connection with the other person[6]. It establishes the caring and compassionate connection necessary for strong bonds between leaders, team members and colleagues.

- *Understanding:* Compassionate leaders work with staff to make sense of the challenges they face. A collective, compassionate approach to leadership is not hierarchical and directive, but engaging and supportive. It is based on dialogue that enables an emergent shared verbalisation and thereby a shared understanding of the real problem. The more staff are enabled, supported and empowered to develop a comprehensive understanding of the challenges they face, the more likely they are to develop effective innovations in response. Compassionate leaders who coach those they lead, help them discover solutions for problems themselves, enhancing their self-awareness and feelings of self-efficacy[7,8]. This is particularly important for staff who have previously been disempowered, disenfranchised, or discriminated against[9]. And it is not the primary role of leaders to find solutions – their role is to help those they lead develop solutions by drawing on their collective knowledge, skills and experience.

- *Empathising:* Empathic leadership increases team members' motivation, commitment and engagement, which are vital for innovation. Empathy creates connection, trust and warmth - a positive emotional environment, which stimulates creativity and innovation[10]. People are more likely to identify problems, notice opportunities, explore new ideas and have confidence to overcome challenges by innovating when they feel positive and emotionally supported. They are more likely to make suggestions knowing their voices are listened to and their perspective is appreciated. When staff feel positive, they have greater resilience and learn from mistakes and failure[11]. And when leaders empathise with those they lead, team members are more motivated to find solutions to the challenges they face[12-14]. Feeling valued, respected, understood and supported by leaders fosters staff engagement and innovation[15]. Compassion, which involves present attention, a desire to understand, the feeling of care and the impulse to help, evokes in the other a sense of being valued[16].

- *Helping*: The fourth element of compassionate leadership is taking thoughtful and intelligent action to help – leaders working to support team members. Helping means helping to remove obstacles, find solutions and acquire the necessary resources such as staffing, equipment and training. Of course, most leaders believe that what they do is to help, but thoughtful and intelligent action that engages and involves staff is different from merely telling others what to do or imposing hierarchical 'solutions'. Compassionate leadership means helping staff develop and implement their ideas for new and improved ways of doing things, be it providing care, completing administrative tasks, supporting people and their families, or overseeing financial probity within the organisation. Such leadership also helps staff evaluate options in a non-threatening environment where leaders do not hierarchically impose or reject solutions.

Research into cultures of high-quality care internationally suggests that dominant, hierarchical and top-down approaches to leadership are the least effective ways of managing healthcare organisations[17]. Compassionate and collective leadership creates a culture in which high-quality, compassionate care can be delivered because all staff accept the distribution and allocation of leadership power to wherever expertise, capability and motivation sit within the organisation (as detailed in chapter 8). That, in turn, stimulates individual, team and cross-boundary innovation.

The key elements of a culture for innovative and high-quality care

Health and social care staff are subject to sustained and high levels of work demand. This can significantly influence innovation because people innovate partly in response to such demands, but only when those demands are not excessive. Very low and very high levels of work demands inhibit innovation, whereas moderate to high levels of work demands stimulate innovation. Among health and social care staff, moderately high work demands have led to individual innovation[18-20] and team innovation[21], but only under supportive conditions. Where teams function well, there are higher levels of team innovation, particularly in demanding contexts. Research involving top management teams in NHS hospitals[22,23] also suggests that external demands can create organisational innovation when those teams work in effective and supportive ways.

However, sustained excessive work demands increase stress levels, absenteeism and staff turnover[24,25] and are likely to produce 'learned helplessness' rather than innovation. Compassionate leadership must therefore support staff in both dealing with their highly demanding work environments and reducing chronic excessive workloads[26]. Research evidence built over several decades suggests there are four key elements of culture that must be in place within teams, organisations and across systems to create strong cultures for innovation. These and the role of compassionate leadership are described below (Figure 1).

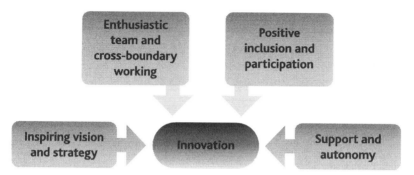

Figure 1: Compassionate leadership and innovation

Inspiring vision and strategy

Teams and organisations that have an inspiring vision and strategy focused on high-quality, continually improving and compassionate care are likely to innovate in pursuit of that vision and strategy. All leaders must demonstrate an unwavering daily focus on the vision and strategy, and nurture optimism and a sense of efficacy about progress towards achieving it[15,27,28]. It must be a beacon that explicitly guides decision-making day by day, meeting by meeting, and hour by hour.

Staff in the English NHS report often feeling overwhelmed by work pressures as well as unclear about their priorities, which leads to stress, inefficiency and poor-quality care[28,29] (see chapter 2). Similar reports emerge from the beleaguered context of social care. Compassionate (and skilled) leadership involves helping translate the vision and strategy into a limited number of challenging but manageable priorities, with clear, aligned and challenging goals for all teams[30]. Such conditions also facilitate innovation by enabling efforts to be focused on the key areas of activity that align with the vision.

> Compassionate leaders seek agreed rather than imposed goals, based on a shared understanding of the work context faced by the team.

This is quite different from target-driven cultures - an approach that we know has limited success[31]. Compassionate leadership also addresses the problem of chronic work overload, which both damages staff health and inhibits effective innovation. When leaders recognise that staff are unacceptably overloaded, compassion ensures clarity and focus through dialogue, negotiation, exploration, and a shared commitment to high-quality outcomes. Workload itself can be continuously and explicitly discussed to encourage innovation that enables better balanced demands on people and teams. Teams that have agreed a limited number (five or six) of challenging, clear and motivating objectives or goals are both more effective and innovative than other teams without such clarity of direction[32].

Aravind Eye Care Systems	Dr Govindappa Venkataswamy set up Aravind after his retirement in the late 1970s, as a small clinic from his home, aiming to provide high-quality eye care for all. With a spiritual commitment to 'seeing all as one and giving sight to all'[33], he focused on using surgeons' time in the most efficient way. Aravind organises clinics rather like factories, with semi-skilled crews preparing patients for surgery and rolling them into theatre, while two assembly lines operate in parallel, so that surgeons move immediately from one patient to the next[34].
	In keeping with its ethos of affordability and inclusion, it maintains a ratio of 1:2 between paying and non-paying patients, to allow the cross-subsidy to cover those who cannot pay. In the 1990s, Aravind invented a low-cost intraocular lens which costs just US$2 and is now exported throughout the world[35], making up 9% of the global intraocular lens market[36]. In 2011, each day the group saw 7,500 patients, performed between 850 and 1,000 procedures and provided workshops for 400 visitors/professionals to learn how it operated. A sense of deep compassion and commitment, and strong leadership, are the key elements of the Aravind model[34].
	https://aravind.org/

Positive inclusion and participation

Compassionate leadership is inclusive in ensuring that the voices of all are heard in the process of delivering and improving care. It is also marked by humility, a key trait of the most effective leaders[37,38]. Compassionate leadership creates psychological safety and encourages team members to pay attention ('listen with fascination') to each other, develop mutual understanding, empathise and support each other[39]. In such psychologically 'safe' team environments, there are higher levels of learning and innovation[39].

Making it safe to speak up - NHS Ayrshire & Arran	"Building psychological safety in our teams is a core leadership responsibility and we have developed a range of interventions and resources to provide an understanding of what this is, together with some materials to help our leaders develop local action plans, to promote and encourage an effective culture for all of our staff." The acute paediatric services team focused on understanding why staff did not always speak up in multidisciplinary discussions around the ward. A survey found that some staff lacked confidence or were worried they had knowledge gaps. The resulting campaign was designed to encourage staff, give them confidence to speak out, and ensure they felt that their opinion was valued.

Empathic responding by leaders that mirrors emotions creates the sense of psychological safety that is vital for developing innovation in health and social care teams – what Amy Edmondson from Harvard Business School calls 'learning when it's safe'[39] (see chapter 5). Psychological safety also ensures that the benefits of diversity are realised more fully.

Engaging all staff within a team or across an organisation, especially those with different perspectives, helps create opportunities for radical innovation[40].

Diversity contributes positively to the pool of task-related skills, information and perspectives within a team. The size of the pool represents the potential for comprehensive and creative decision-making. It also leads to 'informational conflict'. This is generated when different team members have varying information that bears on the decision. They must then collectively and carefully process that information to enable high-quality decision-making[41,42]. Compassionate and inclusive leadership values all voices in a team. This leads to informational conflict being managed in a way that ensures effective decision-making and high-quality patient care. Contrast this with conflict that is managed in order to win or prevail, or conflicts that arise because of personal interest (such as wanting more power or trying to maximise one's own resources). The result of well-managed informational conflict is improved performance and innovation[43-48]. Groups and teams that work in a positive emotional environment, coupled with diverse but overlapping knowledge and skills, are particularly creative[49-51].

Diversity of people, inputs and voices must be complemented by consistently positive attitudes to difference (of opinion, professional background, experience and demographic features such as ethnicity, gender or sexuality). Positive inclusion ensures that difference and all voices are valued, thus stimulating psychological safety, trust and engagement (as described in chapter 7). Compassionate, collective and inclusive leadership across an organisation promotes positive attitudes to diversity, inclusion and creativity which, in turn, stimulates innovation in every team and department at every level of the organisation.

Such positive inclusion and compassionate leadership must also apply to the involvement of community groups, patients, service users, the voluntary sector and families in the development, design and delivery of health and social care services (as detailed in chapter 7). The voices of service users and communities are powerful aids for innovation – we know that extensive patient and carer involvement in organisations stimulates innovation and improvement[15]. And citizens' and patients' groups that model compassionate leadership in their organisations and in the process of co-designing services with health and social care organisations create the basis for productive and innovative partnerships.

All leaders must be encouraged to develop their natural skills of leading compassionately.

This is because compassionate leadership offers a fundamental and powerful way of enabling organisations to develop cultures within which there are powerful norms for valuing the voices and contributions of all, be they minority ethnic group staff, people with disabilities, religious or faith groups, service users, patients, carers and the wider public. Inclusion and diversity are powerful forces for innovation when successfully integrated into a wider innovation strategy.

Sankara Eye

Sankara Eye had humble beginnings, starting out as a tiny clinic near the home of its founders, Dr R.V. Ramani and Dr Radha Ramani, in 1977. They started this free clinic for their local community because they were driven by the tangible difference the 'Gift of Vision' could make and because they wanted 'to do good and to do more'.

Sankara Eye has since grown into one of the largest community eye care networks in the world, whilst maintaining its not-for-profit status by using a cross-subsidy model similar to Aravind, which ensures that 80% of their patients are treated for free. It has performed over 1.9 million free eye operations for adults and children. Sankara Eye has also expanded to other states in India through, for example, their Rainbow preventative eye care programme, which trains school teachers to perform preliminary screening for eye problems. Since 1996, the Rainbow programme has screened over 6 million children for visual defects and provided free vision aids and eye surgery to those that needed further eye care.

Sankara Eye achieves a high-volume throughput at its hospitals via case-finding in their rural community outreach camps. In 2018-19, Sankara Eye ran 2,159 camps and screened almost 400,000 people. It introduced the use of tablet personal computers to field workers for the purposes of registration, surveillance and follow-up, and the rich data collected is used to develop targeted public health programmes, in diabetes and other diseases, for these usually underserved rural communities.

A 'Vision Care Technician' course is offered exclusively to girls aged 18 leaving school and provides a wage, subsidised board/lodging, and the opportunity to work at a Sankara Eye hospital upon graduation. It has become a women's empowerment programme. Many of their graduates are the sole breadwinners for their families and inspire other women to work at Sankara Eye.

https://www.sankaraeye.com/

Enthusiastic team and cross-boundary working

Good team leadership ensures connection and compassion across boundaries so that health and social care staff work together across professions to deliver high-quality care[32]. Compassionate team leadership encourages team members to listen carefully to each other, understand all perspectives, empathise and help and support each other. Such teams are considerably more innovative than teams that do not practise these simple teamworking skills[32].

Narayana Health

Narayana Health was founded in 2001 by Dr Devi Shetty, former cardiac surgeon to Mother Theresa. He believed he had a moral duty to make healthcare affordable and accessible to everyone, regardless of caste, creed, religion, or income[52]. Narayana Health was created to provide low-cost (or free) cardiac surgical care to the millions in India who could not afford care at all.

At the hospital in Bangalore, Narayana Health performs 4,000 cardiac surgeries per year, more than the top two hospitals in the US and with comparable if not better outcomes, at a cost of $2,000 each (versus $20,000-$100,000 in the US)[53-55].

Its model relies, as does Aravind's, on concentrating high volumes of patients in its centres, standardising processes and keeping costs low. The use of its theatres is maximised, and its high purchasing power gives it a strong negotiating hand with suppliers – it often leases rather than buys expensive equipment and has partnered with Texas Instruments to create low-cost X-ray plates.

Narayana Health has pioneered micro-insurance and flexible payment schemes so that those on low incomes can access its services, with 40% of its patients paying a discounted rate and 20% paying nothing at all. It has also worked with Stanford University to create the Care Companion programme, a two-hour training course that gives families the skills they need to become in-hospital caregivers for their relatives (eg, assisting with post-surgical care, personal care and rehabilitation), making them an integral part of the in-hospital patient recovery process and better preparing them to be caregivers at home[55,56].

https://www.narayanahealth.org/

Interaction between professional groups across traditional boundaries also generates innovation[57]. Supportive teams with compassionate team leadership have lower levels of stress than dysfunctional or pseudo teams (teams without clear goals, that rarely meet, or have chronic interpersonal conflicts).

> The more that staff work in supportive teams, the lower the levels of stress, errors, staff injuries, harassment, bullying and violence against staff, staff absenteeism and (in the acute sector) avoidable patient mortality[38,58-60].

Teams with these characteristics ensure greater role clarity for team members, provide higher levels of social support and buffer members from wider organisational pressures – all conditions for innovation[61].

A core objective of any team in modern health and social care must be to enthusiastically promote cross-boundary co-operation[62]. Their perspective of the organisation should expand to include the needs of other teams, their contributions to the organisation's goals and their interdependence and interconnection with each other. Compassionate leadership raises awareness within teams about how multiple parts of the organisation must work together and depend on one another to ensure they deliver high-quality care for the communities they serve. This, in turn, ensures lower inter-team conflict, more collaboration and compassionate communication, and more innovation[62].

The success of system working in health and social care depends on high levels of collaboration between organisations that historically may have little experience of working together – many achieved this astonishingly successfully during the worst of the pandemic. As the previous chapter describes, effective system working requires that leaders work together compassionately and collectively and build a collaborative leadership culture based on:

- A shared vision of high-quality, compassionate and continually improving care

- Frequent and supportive contact across boundaries between leaders

- A long-term commitment to co-operative working

- Active, transparent, ethical, creative and compassionate management of conflicts

- An orientation of altruism and collaboration.

Compassionate inter-organisational working (a form of leadership) requires frequent face-to-face contact to ensure attention, understanding, empathy and helpful support. The most important element of compassionate cross-boundary leadership is agreeing a norm of helping the other organisations make their contribution to the shared mission of high-quality care – in effect, always beginning with the question 'How can we help you?'

Lockdown innovations in social care

The pandemic lockdowns have meant that social care professionals, organisations and services have had to find new ways of providing support:

Kirklees Council in West Yorkshire focused on how it could implement its vision for co-production and developing more equal partnerships between people who use services, carers and professionals. Similarly to many other areas, the lockdown led to the upwelling of self-help and mutual aid, with the emergence of at least 140 self-help groups. Kirklees Council, wanting to ensure all who needed support had access to the richness and diversity of these compassionate groups, developed an online portal which links to these person-centred resources.

https://communityresponsekirklees.com/community-response/

In Thurrock, Essex, drop-in centres, which used to operate in community buildings, were moved online to become virtual 'Talking shops'. These were advertised on the council's website, via the local Community Voluntary Service and through community contacts. The social work teams arranged for practitioners from other teams and organisations to be available when the talking shops were in session. This meant that if someone had an issue requiring more than social care support, that person did not need to be referred, but could have immediate access to the right services and advice. If further conversations were needed, these could be arranged there and then.

https://www.thurrock.gov.uk/adult-care-and-support-drop-in-sessions/talking-shop-sessions

In Cambridgeshire, an arts therapy team from the Learning Disability Partnership knew that because of lockdown, many people with learning disabilities would be unable to go to their workplaces or day placements, or to meet with family and friends. They requested images, songs, performances and poetry to portray the experiences of the learning-disabled community during lockdown. 'The Arts of Lockdown' was built on these submissions and the virtual exhibition has attracted visitors from around the world. "Providing those with learning disabilities the platform to express how they have felt during this pandemic and the challenges they face is a great example of how our services are continuing to go above and beyond, to ensure that all communities receive the extra support they may need." Councillor Anna Bailey

https://www.cambridgeshire.gov.uk/news/virtual-exhibition-featuring-lockdown-inspired-pieces-launches-today

Gig Buddies, run by the charity Stay Up Late, enables people with learning disabilities and/or autism to buddy up with a volunteer so they can go to live music events together. However, when the pandemic started, they had to suddenly shift to doing things online, but there were no gigs to go to. In response, they created 'Coronavirus Fest', a self-curating festival, streamed live via Facebook, which featured performances every night by musicians with and without learning disabilities, and culminated in an epic 12-hour session!

https://www.facebook.com/coronavirusfest/

Support and autonomy for staff to innovate

Staff engagement is higher in health and social care organisations where compassionate leaders create a positive emotional climate for staff. Such leadership also provides compassion and support for staff that helps them cope with the inevitable negative experiences of health and social care such as the fear, suffering, anger or grief of service users or colleagues.

The positive emotions of leaders promote positive emotions among staff, enhanced team performance and higher levels of altruism[63-65]. Leader positivity leads to higher levels of team creativity and innovation[66,67].

However, how leaders behave affects not just the individuals they interact with. The affective states of individual group members can influence the general mood of the whole team, a phenomenon known as 'mood linkage' or 'emotional contagion'[68-70]. Compassion radiates out, directing caring and supportive behaviours towards others[71]. Such compassion can replenish the emotional resources that caregivers need and help cushion them against stress and burnout[71,72].

The positive ripples of compassion also affect witnesses and bystanders (beyond service users, patients and carers), who may experience a feeling of pride about the way staff in the organisation behave, encouraging people to act more for the common good[71,72]. All this, in turn, affects both the motivation and the capacity for developing new and improved ways of delivering health and social care.

At the same time, for innovation and quality improvement to flourish, command-and-control leadership must give way to collective leadership such that all staff embrace and aspire to leadership responsibility. Research into individual-, team- and organisational-level innovation consistently shows the importance of autonomy (rather than command and control hierarchy) as an enabling condition for innovation[73]. Creating the conditions for innovation requires giving frontline teams the autonomy to experiment, discover and apply new and improved ways of delivering care[74,75].

Where staff understand and are committed to the vision, aims and objectives of their teams and organisations, giving them the freedom to decide their work methods, scheduling, time management and goals ensures that they have the space to develop and implement new and improved ways of working. This, in turn, increases productivity and efficiency. Teams engaged in complex work with a high level of autonomy are more productive and innovative than other teams. Organisations that have fewer rules and regulations and less bureaucracy and hierarchy while offering high levels of autonomy and discretion are significantly more innovative in developing inspirational and effective ways of delivering health and social care[15].

> Caring for others, helping them grow and develop, and giving them the freedom to explore and experiment within safe boundaries is characteristic of compassionate leadership. Staff are more likely to challenge the status quo and be innovative within safe boundaries when they work in teams with compassionate and shared leadership.

The NHS Staff Survey, which has been conducted annually for 18 years, shows that if staff are to treat patients with compassion, respect and care, they themselves must be treated with compassion, respect and care. Where health service staff report that they are well led and are satisfied with their leadership, patients report being treated with respect, care, and compassion[76]. Directive, brusque managers dilute the ability of staff to innovate and to make good decisions; they deplete their emotional resources and hinder their ability to relate effectively to patients, especially those who are most distressed or difficult[60,77,78].

Conclusion

There are compassionate and inclusive leaders throughout health and social care, but there is a need to ensure that compassionate and inclusive values and behaviours are endemic, from national bodies through to local providers.

> Compassionate leadership must be written all through the DNA of health and social care organisations.

Most leadership development occurs through experience in the role and through observing good examples of leadership in our organisations. Therefore, we must go beyond simply developing compassionate leadership on standardised training courses and ensure that leaders at every level role model compassionate values and behaviours. We must also offer timely feedback to all staff to ensure that compassionate behaviours are being modelled consistently to nurture a culture of innovation that delivers high-quality, continually improving and compassionate care. Collective and interdependent leadership ensures that all are focused on working together across boundaries to ensure overall high-quality patient care. But such leadership must be consistent, with all leaders modelling authenticity, openness and transparency, curiosity about how to improve leadership, appreciativeness and, above all, compassion.

Resources

Exercises/Discussion questions (to reflect on or discuss with a colleague)

1. Think of an example of a team innovation you were involved in. What helped and hindered the team in implementing the innovation?

2. What highly innovative and less innovative teams have you worked in? What stood out about the innovative team that was different from the other? What are the implications for your team leadership?

3. To what extent does your team have an inspiring vision and strategy that is a strong daily guide for your work? What can be done to reinforce the team's direction and strategy?

4. To what extent does your team have a climate of positive inclusion (of all differences and diversity) and of high levels of participation? What can you do to reinforce a climate of positive inclusion and participation?

5. How supportive and positive is your team? How can you help make the team more supportive and positive?

6. How well does your team co-operate and support other teams within your organisation and in other organisations and sectors? How could this be improved and transformed?

7. How can you and your colleagues ensure your team is an exemplar in developing new and improved ways of working?

Questionnaires

Team innovation

Please indicate how strongly you agree or disagree with each of the following statements, as a description of your team, by circling the appropriate number.

Have each of your team members also complete the following questionnaire using the 1 to 5 response scale below:

Strongly disagree = 1, Disagree = 2, Somewhat agree = 3,
Agree = 4, Strongly agree = 5

1. This team is always moving toward the development of new answers

2. Assistance in developing new ideas is readily available

3. This team is open and responsive to change

4. People in this team are always searching for fresh, new ways of looking at problems

5. In this team we take the time needed to develop new ideas

6. People in the team co-operate to help develop and apply new ideas

7. Members of the team provide and share resources to help in the application of new ideas

8. Team members provide practical support for new ideas and their application

For more information, see Anderson, N. R., & West, M. A. (1998)[79].

Team positivity

Have each of your team members complete the following questionnaire using the 1 to 5 scale below:

Strongly disagree = 1, Disagree = 2, Somewhat agree = 3,
Agree = 4, Strongly agree = 5

1. Team members willingly provide support for each other

2. Team members complain about the contribution of other team members

3. Team members celebrate the team's achievements

4. Team members are cynical about the team's work

5. Team members celebrate each other's achievements

6. Team members express doubts about the team's ability to succeed

7. Team members are enthusiastic about the team's vision

8. Team members dwell on failures and difficulties

9. Team members encourage each other to succeed

10. Team members talk about the obstacles they see at work

11. Team members joke and laugh together

12. Team members talk about their wish to leave the team

How to increase your team positivity:

- Celebrate individual and team achievement and note what it was about the team's behaviour that enabled success.

- Talk more about what is going well.

- Use differences in opinion as opportunities to improve quality and build team resilience. Avoiding issues always leads to impaired team functioning in the longer term.

- Encourage the use of positive language – highly performing teams have six times more positive interactions and use more positive language than negative. Poorly performing teams use more critical and negative language than positive; team member interactions are also more likely to be negative.

- Take time out to reflect on performance and to adapt processes and behaviours to achieve required outcomes.

- Show interest in, and support for, team colleagues as individuals.

- Ensure that the team's structure and processes are appropriate and effective.

The Team Positivity tool was developed by Michael West. You may also wish to use other evidence-based diagnostic tools such as the AffinaOD Real Team Profile Plus (ARTP+, see chapter 5) or the AffinaOD Team Performance Inventory (*https://www.affinaod.com*).

Guidance on using these questionnaires is provided in Appendix 1.

Websites

1. The Social Care Institute for Excellence (SCIE)
   The SCIE has an innovation network that helps local areas take innovative approaches to social care and support. It provides answers to the challenge of scaling up primarily small, community-focused examples of innovation.
   https://www.scie.org.uk/transforming-care/innovation

   SCIE and other organisations like the Local Government Association and Skills for Care have helped develop new resources to help the social care sector. SCIE's covid-19 hub has supported over 640,000 visitors and provides good practice examples, updated guides and webinars.
   https://www.scie.org.uk/care-providers/coronavirus-covid-19

2. The Health Foundation (THF)
    THF has funded many programmes around innovation, from adoption
    to spread, in health and social care. Details of the programmes and the
    findings can be found on its website if you search for 'innovation'.
    https://www.health.org.uk

    The Health Foundation's GenerationQ is a funded leadership and
    quality improvement programme. It offers an opportunity for senior
    leaders working in clinical and non-clinical roles in and with the health
    service (including charity organisations and policymakers) to gain a
    postgraduate certificate in Leadership (Quality Improvement).
    https://www.health.org.uk/funding-and-partnerships/fellowships/
    generationq

3. The Welsh Accolades awards
    This award recognises, celebrates and shares the excellent work by
    organisations, groups or teams in social care, early years, and childcare
    in Wales. More details of inspiring innovations can be found at:
    https://socialcare.wales/service-improvement/the-accolades-2020

    The awards ceremony for 2020 can be found at:
    https://www.youtube.com/watch?v=TM__2YgCD7U&feature=youtu.be

4. The Institute for Healthcare Improvement (IHI)
    The IHI made a formal commitment to innovation a decade ago by
    establishing a Research and Development team and a process to
    consistently produce new thinking that would challenge the entrenched
    models that result in low-value, poor-quality care. It looked outside
    health and social care, studying the work of leading innovators from
    industry, manufacturing and energy. It borrowed, adapted and built a
    systematic approach "to creating new knowledge – sequential 90-day
    'waves' of projects to tackle vexing questions raised by our partners,
    our communities, and our patients."

    On its website (below), the IHI provides a wide range of resources and
    reflects on the Triple Aim, the concept of a healthcare campaign, the
    Breakthrough Series Collaborative model, and other frameworks and
    fresh thinking that have been replicated around the world.
    https://www.ihi.org/

Videos

Innovative models of practice in social care are at the forefront of developing personalised, asset-based care, delivering services based on the strengths and assets of an individual and their community. As these approaches have been replicated in other areas, they have highlighted valuable lessons in how best to deliver at scale in the health and social care system, without losing the core values and strengths of an innovative service. This King's Fund event explored the experiences of people who access care, provided support for providers and commissioners of social care to develop and scale innovation and highlighted examples of good practice. (58 minutes 44 secs)
https://www.kingsfund.org.uk/events/scaling-innovation

IHI's Dr Kedar Mate reflects on the innovations highlighted in the short video. (1 minute 54 secs)
https://www.ihi.org/resources/Pages/Publications/10-IHI-Innovations-to-Improve-Health-and-Health-Care.aspx

Leadership self-compassion

Chapter 11.

Summary

This chapter describes and explores the fundamental concept of self-compassion before applying it to leadership. It describes what self-compassion is and is not; explains the practice of self-compassion; and explores how it affects our relationships with others and with our experience of ourselves. The concept of leadership self-compassion is developed along with guidelines for how to develop self-compassion as a leader in practice.

Introduction

This final chapter offers guidance for how to deepen the wisdom, humanity and presence that sustain compassionate leadership and enable a life of authenticity and flourishing. Compassion is rooted in the relationships shared between people. Often overlooked in explorations of compassion, though, is the relationship we have with ourselves – how we think, internally talk to ourselves, judge ourselves, accept or reject our feelings and thoughts and how we experience varying emotions such as shame, joy, anger, love, anxiety and guilt. In particular, do we bring a nurturing orientation to our experience of negative emotions and savour the experience of positive emotions? This may seem an odd idea – splitting up subjective experience into two selves – a self that has a relationship with the self, that is our experience of self.

> Yet, our relationship with ourselves is the basis for our relationships with others. How we relate to ourselves determines how we relate to others.

If we are harsh and judgemental to ourselves, that is likely to have a profound effect on our ability to connect authentically with others. If, on the other hand, we are aware, open, accepting, nurturing and compassionate towards our experience, our sense of self is more integrated, authentic and connected. Our relationship or pattern of interactions with ourselves is at the core of our being and of our relationships with the world around us.

We spend our lives with ourselves, in an inner world made of thoughts that can sometimes feel like an 'inner voice', and feelings and emotions that can well up in response to our thoughts, or to what we perceive to be happening in our 'outer world'. We can deny our experience (anger, cruelty, fear), make excuses for ourselves, reinforce and sustain feelings of inadequacy or inferiority, be resentful of our life circumstances, and be harsh and unforgiving of ourselves.

Alternatively, if we are honest with ourselves, open to our experiences (thoughts, desires, fears, etc), not allowing them to become distorted by arrogance or pumped-up pride; if we are realistically positive in our view of ourselves, and quietly appreciative of our privileges, qualities and talents, we can also be compassionate towards ourselves.

What self-compassion is

Self-compassion means being warm, self-soothing and understanding towards ourselves in situations where we suffer, behave 'badly' or 'fail', rather than denying our pain or beating ourselves up[1,2]. Self-compassion involves a recognition that being imperfect, failing and experiencing life difficulties is inevitable[3]. Self-compassion also involves recognising that suffering and personal inadequacy are part of what it is to be human – it is part of the shared human experience. Such suffering and inadequacy do not just happen to me[4].

Self-compassion helps us take a balanced approach to negative emotions so that feelings are both accepted and regulated. This requires us to observe our feelings and thoughts, openly and clearly, and (ideally) in a non-judgmental way. We do not ignore pain, but neither do we over-identify with associated thoughts and feelings, so that we are not caught up and swept away in a negative spiral. Such over-identification can lead to self-pity where we exaggerate our own suffering and thereby feel even more separate from others by comparing ourselves with them and making judgements.

Self-compassion involves seeing our negative thoughts, feelings and behaviours and acknowledging them, including weakness or bad behaviour, rather than pretending they have not occurred in a misguided effort to minimise our pain.

The care intrinsic to self-compassion helps us understand, grow and change, in a context where we can see ourselves clearly without fear of constant self-condemnation. We don't suppress or exaggerate negative feelings.

What self-compassion is not

Self-compassion is not the same as self-esteem, which is based on self-evaluations. People feel compassion for themselves not because of their talents or traits (strong, generous, good looking, etc), but out of a recognition that the human condition is one of inevitable suffering at times – occasional for some, more enduring for others – and, of course, of positive experiences and emotions such as love and closeness[3].

Self-compassion does not involve thinking we are better or worse than others; rather it is based on a recognition that we are human just like others; and a recognition based on honesty, so that failings are acknowledged with gentle kindness rather than hidden or overblown[5]. Research suggests that in contrast to self-esteem, those who are self-compassionate have greater emotional resilience, more accurate self-concepts, more caring relationships, and are less prone to narcissism and angry outbursts[6].

Creating wellness in a pandemic: Rush University System for Health, Chicago, Illinois	A practical toolkit for health systems responding to covid-19 was developed by Dr Bryant Adibe, System Vice President and Chief Wellness Officer, Rush University System for Health.
	Every afternoon, a 'Wellness Response Team' met for a huddle to review what was happening in the various departments, wards, teams and units of the hospital. The 'Chief Wellness Officer' chaired the huddle. It began with an update on the leadership response to key issues like PPE, supplies and safety. Team members reported on concerns staff had raised, uncertainties and successes they had witnessed. They then visited all their assigned units for one or two hours, both reporting back and gathering more information. Senior staff from the institution were part of the huddle and the team that visited the units after the meeting, including leaders of clinical departments, the Community Health Equity and Engagement Officer and the CEO.
	Information was constantly fed to the hospital's leadership so that they could help, provide support and intervene as necessary. Because many staff were working at home during the pandemic, the organisation also hosted virtual wellness rounds and interactive online town hall meetings.
	https://www.rush.edu/sites/default/files/2020-07/creating-wellness-pandemic-toolkit.pdf

Self-compassion in practice

Self-compassion in practice means paying attention to ourselves, understanding the challenges we face, caring for ourselves and taking intelligent action to help ourselves[7]. Taking each of these in turn:

1. *Attending to myself*
   The idea of paying attention to ourselves or being present with ourselves may seem odd, but the experience of self is the most intimate and constantly present experience in our lives. We can become more aware of that sense of 'I-ness' when we are alone, perhaps in nature or when we are not working frenetically. Meditation and mindfulness practices also aim to help us connect with our sense of being, of self, of I-ness in a more deliberate way. Self-compassion first involves cultivating that sense of being present with the experience of self, in the moment. This enables us to see our situation and our experience more clearly, enabling understanding. It involves having the courage and commitment to relax into being present with ourselves in the moment – letting go of all the other activities, busy-ness and concerns.

2. *Understanding the challenges I face*
   The second element is understanding the challenges we face. Having an understanding, for example, of how we often feel overwhelmed by multiple responsibilities and tasks – the challenges of working in a health or social care system with too few staff and increasingly complex demands; the concurrent challenges of caring responsibilities for elderly parents; financial pressures; domestic tasks that pile up and can feel overwhelming; the difficulties of balancing the demands of work with the rest of life; and so on.

3. *Caring for myself*
   The third, caring element of self-compassion is the most difficult for many people, especially those who work in health and social care. Their commitment to care for others may involve an impulse to heroic self-denial – 'I can't waste time looking after myself because I must devote my energies and attentions to patients or service users'. The denial of one's own need for care jeopardises our ability to provide high-quality and compassionate care for others, not least if we become sick in the process because we have not taken care of (cared for) our own needs.

"Instead of mercilessly judging and criticising yourself for various inadequacies or shortcomings, self-compassion means you are kind and understanding when confronted with personal failings – after all, who ever said you were supposed to be perfect?"

Kristin Neff[2]

Caring involves a tenderness, concern, and love for the other. Self-compassion, then, implies a tenderness, concern, and love for the self[8]. And why not? This is not about indulging ourselves, feeling sorry for ourselves, or excusing our damaging behaviours. It is simply about having an orientation of love and acceptance for this unique being – my self. The Dalai Lama, echoing the Buddha, points out that there is no one more worthy of love and compassion than you. If we reflect on this, it is making the profound point that we are all equally worthy of love and compassion and so no one is more deserving than you. And this caring and empathy for ourselves gives us the motivation to act to help ourselves.

> Such a caring orientation is not about narcissistic or self-indulgent sweetness, but about valuing this 'me' as being precious, unique and capable of manifesting truth, beauty and love.

Therefore, we should do what we can to show ourselves love, warmth and care, recognising that this 'me' is worthy of such nurturing and of being enabled to be the best I can be as a person.

4. *Helping or supporting myself*

   Acting to help ourselves is the fourth element of self-compassion. This involves thinking through and arriving at conclusions about intelligent or wise action to help ourselves so that we can be our best selves. This is so that we can become who we know we are beneath the superficial difficulties and move closer to the core values that give our lives meaning – wisdom, courage, humanity, justice, prudence and forgiveness, and a sense of gratitude and wonder[9].

This is all very well in theory, but what happens when we experience times of grief, resentment, anger, hurt or shame? How do we deal with such feelings in a compassionate way rather than being carried along by a current of wild emotion and obsessive thoughts? One widely used practice is summarised in the acronym RAIN, most recently articulated by Tara Brach[10]. Brach is a psychologist, author and proponent of Buddhist meditation.

RAIN - Recognising, Allowing, Investigating, Nurturing

The acronym RAIN is a guide for practising mindfulness and self-compassion in four steps:

Recognising what is happening for me in this moment. This includes thoughts, feelings, sensations, strong emotions, memories, regrets, desires, irritations, etc. Recognition can be strengthened by our being self-aware in the moment. The regular practice of relaxed meditation can help us learn to be still enough in the moment to be aware of, present with and to recognise our feelings, thoughts, and subjective experience generally. It involves being present with our feelings just as compassionate leadership involves being present with those we lead.

Allowing or Accepting whatever is happening – all the thoughts, feelings, sensations and emotions – just as they are. This means allowing or accepting without judgement the tone and content of our inner voice, the feelings, thoughts, sensations, and whatever is happening. This non-judgemental acceptance in the moment is key to what follows. It means staying with what is experienced without rushing to reject the tiredness, irritation, anger, shame, etc. It means just accepting and allowing whatever is in my experience in this moment to be. This involves staying with the experience rather than controlling it or immediately turning away from it in some way.

The third element is **Investigating** or **Inquiring** into the emotions, thoughts or feelings. This is not so much about adopting an intellectual, analytical approach to investigating, for example, our feelings of irritation in our interactions with a family member, but being curious about what the feelings truly represent. It is particularly useful, as many teachers of self-compassion and meditation suggest, to be aware of the feelings in the body associated with the irritation and to stay with these. For example, I notice the tightness and prickliness in my chest as I sit here listening to this person express so many judgements about others. As I experience and explore that tightness, I detect that the feeling contains anxiety about my being judged and feelings of vulnerability associated with that. As I become aware of this through my investigation, I stop resisting the feelings and the other person and open more to them.

The final step is **Nurturing with self-compassion**, which means being caring and nurturing to myself in the context of these difficult feelings or thoughts. This might involve internally voicing a message of care to myself, a statement of love, understanding or warmth. Such self-soothing statements might be 'You are worthy of gentle loving at all times'; 'Be forgiving of yourself'; 'You are good and kind and generous'; or 'Trust in your goodness'. The nurturing element involves encouraging the best of ourselves by being present, rather than being sucked into the turmoil of separation from ourselves and what is beautiful, loving and truthful.

How self-compassion affects compassion for others

The relationship with self can be characterised by anxiety because we feel shame, blame ourselves, or feel inadequate or inconsistent, and that will make us anxious or defensive in our relationships with others. This can manifest as needing to please others and always seeking their approval (which undermines leadership effectiveness). We can also be self-condemnatory and hard on ourselves; punishing ourselves with angry self-blaming thoughts; damaging ourselves by abusing alcohol or other drugs; having an unhealthy diet; denying ourselves adequate sleep; and failing to nourish ourselves lovingly because of a misguided sense that we do not deserve to be cared for, or as a result of never considering that caring for ourselves was a possibility. This can lead us to avoid close, accepting, warm and trusting relationships with others.

When we create an attitude of acceptance, care and love towards our experience of self, we are less likely to bring our fear, anger, guilt, resentment, and shame into our interactions with others.

At another extreme, an authentic relationship with ourselves can be avoided and suppressed, and we simply create a superficial, artificial, or narcissistic self-concept. We fashion a well-defended sense of self as being always right, powerful, immune to criticism, or resistant to any challenge, and this enables us to avoid an authentic and loving relationship with ourselves or anyone else. It often manifests as bullying and overbearing leadership. Such leaders avoid genuine connection with and care for others. Narcissistic leadership is dark and damaging to individuals, teams and organisations and it is notable that these behaviours are around six times more likely amongst senior organisational leaders than in the general population, because they are often mistaken for signs of strong and effective leadership[11].

"Half the harm that is done in this world is due to people who want to feel important. They don't mean to do harm, but the harm does not interest them. Or they do not see it, or they justify it because they are absorbed in the endless struggle to think well of themselves."

T. S. Eliot, The Cocktail Party (1949)

How self-compassion affects our relationship with ourselves

Self-compassion based on recognition and acceptance of our feelings helps us create a deeper connection with our 'I-ness' or sense of being, in a secure, grateful, gentle, and wonder-full way. This, in turn, helps us connect with others authentically, honestly, with humility and with a sense of ease, optimistically, appreciatively, and compassionately. It also makes it more likely that we will care for ourselves in fundamentally important ways.

Caring for ourselves (amongst many other self-sustaining activities) will include spending good quality time with those we love and who love us, the most important determinant of our well-being. It is likely to include looking after our physical well-being by getting the exercise our bodies thrive on, getting enough sleep (for most of us, that is 7 to 8 hours per night) and ensuring we have a nourishing diet. Practising self-compassion will lead us to spend less time ruminating about the past or anxiously thinking about the future[12]. Self-compassion helps us be present, appreciating the natural world around us, seeing the faces of our loved ones, and being grateful for the privileges and relationships we have in our lives. We know that being present (whether through mindfulness, meditation or just learning to savour the here and now) is an important determinant of our well-being[12].

The power of self-compassion in enabling growth

Researchers have studied the consequences when people are asked to use self-compassion after bringing to mind a time when they did something they felt was wrong, such as infidelity in a love relationship, academic misconduct, dishonesty, betrayal of trust, or hurting someone they cared for[13]. They were then assigned to a self-compassion group, a boosting self-esteem group, or a control group. The self-compassion group wrote a short note to themselves expressing kindness and understanding in relation to their wrongdoing. The self-esteem group wrote notes about their strengths and positive qualities. The control group wrote about a hobby they liked. Questionnaire data subsequently showed that the self-compassion group was more motivated to make amends and not to repeat the transgression than either the self-esteem-boosting or control groups.

Other research showed that self-compassion increased people's resolve (among those who had been responsible for a relationship breakup) to be better partners in the future, compared with self-esteem or control group participants. Self-compassion appears to enable a 'growth mindset'. Carol Dweck has described how a 'growth' rather than 'fixed' approach to performance, such as learning to lead, parenting, or cooking, is associated with better performance. People with a fixed mindset are more likely to believe they cannot change, whereas those with a growth mindset believe they can change and see the potential for growth. They are thus more likely to try to improve and to be successful[14].

Self-compassion creates the conditions for self-improvement by increasing our wish to do better, reinforcing the belief that improvement is possible, and motivating us to make that happen.

https://hbr.org/2018/09/give-yourself-a-break-the-power-of-self-compassion

Leadership self-compassion

Leadership self-compassion means being warm, forgiving and understanding towards ourselves as leaders. As leaders, we are imperfect, we fail, we can never complete our leadership learning journey, and we do confront seemingly intractable work and life difficulties. It is unhelpful and damaging to think that as a leader I cannot be vulnerable, need feedback, be failing, or worthy of care and support.

Self-compassion helps us take a balanced approach as leaders to negative emotions by observing our feelings and thoughts openly and clearly and (ideally) in a non-judgmental way[15]. We should not ignore pain or anxieties, but neither should we over-identify with them. If we over-identify and ruminate about our pain, we are likely to become so caught up that we are unable to focus on the needs of those we lead. This can result in leaders indulging in self-pity, exaggerating their own suffering, and requiring - subtly or explicitly - that their followers take responsibility for their pain as leaders.

Self-compassion involves being aware of our challenges as leaders (both at work and outside of work), of our feelings and behaviours and acknowledging them, including weaknesses, mistakes or damaging behaviours (berating people publicly or exploiting others), rather than pretending they do not exist in a misguided effort to minimise our pain. It involves recognising, for example, situations where we experience chronic work overload, which prevent us from providing the compassionate leadership essential to the well-being and effectiveness of those we lead. Self-compassion helps us to understand, grow and change as leaders.

Leadership self-compassion is not the same as leadership arrogance, narcissism or inflated self-esteem, which can be fed by power. Self-compassion does not imply thinking of ourselves as better than those we lead or others we work with – more able, more powerful, or always right. It is based on honesty so that leadership failings are acknowledged with kindness, rather than hidden or overblown. Research suggests that in contrast to self-esteem, leaders who are self-compassionate will have greater emotional resilience, more accurate self-concepts, more caring relationships, and will be less prone to narcissism and angry outbursts[16].

Listening to staff during covid-19: Northumbria Healthcare NHS Foundation Trust

As the pandemic started, the trust adapted its staff engagement platform to develop Corona Voice – a short web-based survey that enabled staff to raise issues, voice concerns and share their experiences in real time. Each week, staff were asked to rate their motivation for work on a scale of 1–10, alongside a varying set of additional questions.

In the first three months, the survey received 10,400 responses. Each week, more than a third of responders left additional information through free-text comments. These comments were formally analysed, with key themes disseminated across the executive team and Silver and Gold Command. Measurement and evaluation were supported by dedicated data analysts within the patient and staff experience team, as well as researchers at Open Lab at Newcastle University.

The trust used this data to inform an evolving action plan focused on meeting the changing physical, social and emotional well-being needs of staff during the peak of the pandemic and beyond. Interventions carried out included weekly well-being calls for those shielding at home or not at work; daily staff briefing messages tailored around themes emerging from survey feedback; and the creation of chill-out zones and a 'going home checklist' for staff. The data enabled the trust to understand variation across the organisation, which meant it could tailor support across different locations and target the needs that staff said mattered most.

According to the trust, staff reported appreciating the sense of being listened to, the agility of the trust when responding to safety concerns, and the open and reliable communication from the organisation throughout the crisis.

Advice for others

Timely access to real-time measurement is crucial to enable a responsive and needs-led approach, alongside a willingness to be agile and flexible according to the changing needs of the workforce. Pay attention to stories and data – both need to improve. Create your virtuous circle – regular feedback to staff about actions taken in response to their feedback helps increase and maintain engagement.

Dr Judith Stonebridge, Consultant in Public Health

For more information, see: *https://www.northumbria.nhs.uk/blog/support-staff-through-covid19*

Leadership self-compassion in practice

In practice, leadership self-compassion includes the four elements of compassion:

1. Attending to myself or self-awareness

2. Understanding my challenges

3. Caring for myself as a leader

4. Acting to support myself as a leader

1. *Attending to myself*
   Self-compassion first involves cultivating our ability to be present with the experience of self as a leader in the moment. This enables us to see our situation and our experience more clearly, enabling understanding. It involves tuning in to our own moment-to-moment experience, so we become aware when we are feeling stressed, angry, hurt, threatened, as well as happy, joyful and connected in our roles as leaders.

2. *Understanding my challenges*
   The second element is understanding the challenges we face as leaders, not only at work but in our lives generally, because we cannot simply cordon off a major component in our lives in a mistaken attempt to separate out our emotional lives in one domain from our experience in another domain. Such splitting is psychologically damaging and unsustainable. It is important to have an understanding, for example, of how I often feel overwhelmed by multiple leadership responsibilities – the challenges of working in a health or social care system with too few staff and increasingly complex demands; the concurrent challenges of financial pressures; as well as domestic tasks that pile up and can feel overwhelming. By both identifying and understanding these difficulties, we have taken the first two steps toward managing them.

3. *Caring for myself*
   The third element of leadership self-compassion involves going against heroic leadership self-denial – 'I am not here to look after myself because, as a leader, I must devote my energies and attentions to those I lead'. The denial of our own need for care as leaders jeopardises our ability to provide high-quality and compassionate leadership for others.

> Leadership self-compassion means having an orientation of kindness, tenderness, and acceptance for this unique being – my self.

We may be in leadership roles, but we are equally worthy of love and compassion from ourselves (as well as others). Caring for ourselves as leaders gives us the motivation to act to help ourselves.

4. *Acting to support myself as a leader*
   This involves thinking through (taking the time to think) and arriving at conclusions about intelligent or wise action we can take to help ourselves, so that we can be the best leaders we can be. If we have chronic excessive workloads and we fail to deal with that issue, we will be less effective leaders because we will not have the time to lead effectively (to be compassionate in our leadership), nor the emotional, attentional and physical resources to sustain effective leadership.

> Self-compassion among leaders is fundamental. Such self-compassion enables us to become who we know we are beneath our superficial difficulties and move closer to the core values that help us be most effective as leaders – wisdom, courage, humanity, justice, prudence, forgiveness, and a sense of the privilege of leadership (manifested in gratitude)[9].

Conclusion

Self-compassion is at the heart of our leadership and working relationships with others and is key to our ability to model and embody compassionate leadership. Self-compassion is the starting point for developing compassionate leadership and developing compassionate teams, organisations and health and social care systems.

Leader self-compassion makes us more likely to be open to our core instinct of altruism – to help others.

> When we help ourselves and have a warm, accepting sense of ourselves, we are better able to have a warm and accepting appreciation of all those we lead, work with and encounter, thereby enabling us to show them compassion more easily. This is the most important message of this book to all of those who work in health and social care.

Dedicating ourselves to developing and practising self-compassion requires the courage of moment-to-moment self-awareness and to use the light of that awareness to guide our decision-making. That light gives us the opportunity to be aware of difficult experiences, thoughts, impulses, memories and feelings, and rather than being in a self-hypnotic trance and being carried along by them, we can choose to pause, be present and be self-compassionate. Recognising, accepting, investigating and nurturing enables us to make choices about our moment-to-moment experience. By attending, understanding, empathising and helping ourselves, we can be happier, healthier, and more present in the moments and relationships of our lives. This, in turn, helps us to lead in the delivery of health and social care in a way that is both affirming and enabling of ourselves and of others.

Our imperative for the future

Compassion is a sensitivity to suffering in self and others with a commitment to try to alleviate and prevent it. Most of us have a highly sensitive ability to notice and become aware of the distress of others and to pay attention to it, while having an empathic insight into their needs. These basic human orientations underpin our motivation to help. The 'commitment to alleviate/ prevent suffering' requires wisdom, humanity and presence that enables us to take wise and caring action. It requires a recognition of our interdependence and interconnection with each other and all around us. Compassionate leadership is leadership that embodies these fundamental human orientations in wise ways. Such leadership is not hidden behind a mask of organisational titles, hierarchical positions or formulaic phrases that inhibit authentic connection. It is courageous leadership that embodies presence – being present with ourselves and others. Present with their challenges and suffering; present with our own challenges and suffering; present with joy at work and present with the core values of compassion, inclusion, kindness and caring that must be woven into the genetic structure of our health and social care workplaces.

These workplaces constitute around 10% of all those who work outside the home in our societies, not including voluntary and community groups who provide health and social care. When these millions of people come to work and encounter compassionate leadership and compassionate cultures, these values spread back out into families and communities. And if all of those who use health and social care services (in the UK, over a million every day) receive compassionate support and care, they too take these values back out into their families and communities. The emotional ripples of presence, understanding, empathy, help and support spread out and are replicated across our communities and societies. Our communities and species desperately need such compassion at this point in our history and in our evolution if we are to successfully respond to the challenges we face.

These challenges of pandemics, climate change, weapons of mass destruction and loss of biodiversity can feel overwhelming, creating a sense of paralysed helplessness. Unrealistic optimism is also equally problematic when it insulates us from the uncomfortable urgency of the need for change. Hope is vital, and compassion in relationships, embodied in leadership and permeating our cultures and societies, is what gives us hope. Compassion and compassionate leadership are at the heart of hope for the future.

It is the responsibility of all of us to practice compassion, self-compassion and compassionate leadership in our health and social care services and more widely. Our imperative for our future and that of our children and our planet is to lead compassionately to sustain wisdom, humanity and presence for all our futures.

Meditations on self-compassion

Sit quietly with eyes closed (or open, if that feels more comfortable). Relax and be comfortable. Silently repeat each of the phrases under each heading below, slowly and with presence.

A self-compassion meditation

May I be safe, may I be happy
May I be healthy, may I live with ease

A leadership self-compassion meditation

Self-compassion:
May I be safe, may I be happy,
May I be healthy, may I live with ease

Compassion for a benefactor (a role model or supporter in your work-life):
May you be safe, may you be happy
May you be healthy, may you live with ease

Compassion for a neutral person at work (someone you feel no particular connection with and for whom you have no feelings one way or the other):
May you be safe, may you be happy
May you be healthy, may you live with ease

Compassion for a person you find difficult at work:
May you be safe, may you be happy
May you be healthy, may you live with ease

(Note: Go back to the easier meditations if and whenever wishing compassion for someone you find difficult is too hard. Persist with the practice and try to sustain the meditation on compassion for such difficult people a little more over subsequent days or weeks.)

Compassion for all those you work with:
May you be safe, may you be happy
May you be healthy, may you live with ease

Research in organisations shows these practices are powerful in shifting our attitudes and abilities as leaders and in positively nourishing our well-being and leadership effectiveness.

Resources

Exercises/Discussion questions (to reflect on or discuss with a colleague)

Compassion and compassionate leadership

1. Using the Kristin Neff questionnaire via the link below, what does it tell you about how you might develop your own self-compassion?

2. Why is self-compassion important for your health and well-being?

3. Why is leadership self-compassion important in developing effective and compassionate leadership?

4. Thinking of a recent difficult interaction, apply the RAIN approach to this situation. How does that help you in resolving the situation?

5. Practice each of the meditations on self-compassion for around 15 minutes. What insights does this give you to your leadership and your own self-compassion?

6. What resistance do you find in being self-compassionate? How might you overcome that?

7. Look at the resources and videos and plan for how you can better develop your self-compassion both in general and as a leader.

Questionnaires

Measuring your level of self-compassion
Kristin Neff offers a free questionnaire to assess self-compassion with scores on dimensions of self-kindness, self-judgment, common humanity, isolation, mindfulness, over-identification and an overall score.
https://self-compassion.org/test-how-self-compassionate-you-are/

Questionnaires for research
Kristin Neff also provides a range of questionnaires on self-compassion that researchers can use, including the self-compassion scale and scales for youth, short forms and a measure of state self-compassion (self-compassion in the moment).
https://self-compassion.org/self-compassion-scales-for-researchers/

Guidance on using these questionnaires is provided in Appendix 1.

Websites

1. Exercises to develop self-compassion can be found at:
   https://self-compassion.org/category/exercises/
   https://www.mindfulcompassion.com/
   https://soundcloud.com/dennis-tirch-phd/01-compassionate-mind-training
   https://soundcloud.com/dennis-tirch-phd
   https://centerformsc.org/
   https://www.compassionatemind.org.au/practitioner-tools

2. Guidance on developing leadership self-compassion:
   https://thriveglobal.com/stories/want-to-be-a-more-compassionate-leader-practice-self-compassion/

3. Tara Brach's website focuses on meditation, mindfulness, self-compassion, the RAIN approach, and the challenges of daily living. A guide to the practice of RAIN can also be found there.
   https://www.tarabrach.com/
   https://tarabrach.ac-page.com/rain-pdf-download

4. The Compassion Institute
   The Compassion Institute provides a well-developed care package for healthcare professionals and other frontline responders.
   https://www.compassioninstitute.com/
   https://www.compassioninstitute.com/healthcare/carepackage/

Videos

A meditation led by Kristin Neff for cultivating self-compassion. (20 minutes)
https://self-compassion.org/wp-content/uploads/2016/11/LKM.self-compassion_cleaned.mp3

A self-compassion break from Kristin Neff. (5 minutes)
https://self-compassion.org/wp-content/uploads/2015/12/self-compassion.break_.mp3

A self-compassion meditation for caregivers led by Kristin Neff. (9 minutes)
https://www.youtube.com/watch?v=jJ9wGfwE-YE&feature=youtu.be

Tara Brach's website contains many videos and talks on self-compassion, mindfulness, inclusion, racism, and dealing with negative emotions.
https://www.tarabrach.com/talks-audio-video/

Appendix 1: Using questionnaires and surveys

General principles

Gathering data using questionnaires to provide helpful information about the experience of staff, colleagues, patients, and members of the public is critical to understanding health and social care services. It is therefore critical to ensuring high-quality care and staff well-being.

Validity and reliability

Accurate measurement in health and social care is key to ensuring care quality and patient safety, in diagnosis, monitoring quality, and determining outcomes. Similar rigour is required in the use of measures to assess both staff and patient experience. A measure should accurately assess what it purports to be an indicator of and should be reliable. Measuring length by relying on rulers that are wildly inaccurate is self-evidently absurd. And if the ruler is rubbery and prone to shrinkage over time, it will not provide reliable measurements. Some measures of staff experience (and patient experience) are constructed without ensuring validity and reliability and so prove inaccurate and untrustworthy (even some widely used and popular measures in health and social care). It is important to rely on carefully constructed measures, surveys, questionnaires, etc, which have established validity and reliability data wherever possible to give confidence in the information they provide. Questionnaire design should be informed by those with expertise.

Ethics and confidentiality

The use of surveys must be guided by a commitment to high ethical standards. This means ensuring that those who complete questionnaires are guaranteed anonymity wherever possible and that, at least, the information they provide will be confidential, unless they have explicitly approved the release of their data after a process of informed consent.

Among the key ethical standards for survey researchers and the key ethical questions that should be addressed are the following:

- Those administering surveys must transparently explain what is being measured, why it is being measured, and what will happen to the data.

- Respondents must be told how their personal data or sensitive information will be used.

- Participation must be completely voluntary, and participants must understand that they can choose to withdraw from completion at any time.

- The questions that are asked should do no harm.

- Those administering the survey must ensure they have received informed consent from those participating.

- Survey administrators must have secure data storage systems in place so that information is not accessible to unauthorised users either by intention or inadvertently.

- The analysis of the data should be informed by appropriate data analytic techniques that ensure the findings presented are not mistaken, inaccurate or biased.

All surveys should be subject to ethical review to ensure adherence to these principles. For further guidance, see: *https://www.qualtrics.com/blog/ethical-issues-for-online-surveys/*

Practical support/External help

Expertise in measurement is readily available (for example) from psychologists and psychometricians. For help and support, the British Psychological Society (*https://www.bps.org.uk*) provides a list of Chartered Occupational and Clinical Psychologists. Dr Thomas West, Lecturer of Leadership in Healthcare and Occupational Psychology within Health Sciences at the University of Southampton, also offers such support (*T.H.R.West@southampton.ac.uk*) and is familiar with the tools in this volume.

Developmental orientation

Throughout the preceding chapters, the importance of helping people, teams and organisations to do their jobs effectively has been emphasised. Consistent with this is a developmental orientation to surveys. This suggests that the purpose of undertaking surveys is to provide information about how to support organisations, teams and individuals to do their work most effectively and to thrive. This contrasts with using surveys merely to evaluate and rate people or teams.

A developmental orientation implies having in place tools and support prior to administering surveys, in order to strengthen and spread already good practice and provide guidance, training, tools and support for areas of performance that need improvement (such as staff stress, quality of teamworking, or climates of psychological safety). The preceding chapters have much material for such developmental support. When people see swift, supportive action following their completion of questionnaires, it helps to meet their needs for autonomy/control, belonging and competence or contribution. It also renews their faith in the value of such surveys.

Swift feedback for learning

It is important to provide summary feedback to those completing questionnaires, quickly, clearly and helpfully, to support learning and so that they do not feel their work of completing questionnaires has just disappeared into a void or that, by the time they receive the feedback, it is no longer relevant.

Change over time

It is often helpful to repeat the same measures over time to determine the extent to which developmental interventions have enabled improvement or whether there is no change, or worse, deterioration. In the NHS in England, prior to the pandemic, there had been a steady increase in levels of staff stress over a five-year period, with a further large increase during the first year of the pandemic. Such trends provide important information about the need for change that offer more compelling evidence than one-off snapshots.

Joy and pride at work: Northumbria Healthcare NHS Foundation Trust

Annie Laverty, Chief Experience Officer, Northumbria Healthcare NHS Foundation Trust works to strengthen board accountability and ensure visibility and momentum for their trust-wide patient and staff experience programme.

She writes: 'It was a new role for me, and for Northumbria, and is the only one of its kind in the NHS. I've been lucky to have the time and freedom to design a comprehensive measurement programme that allows the organisation to use feedback to truly understand what matters to patients, staff and families. This means we can quickly improve where we need to, as well as continuing to do the things that make a positive difference.

There is a wealth of evidence that supports the link between staff well-being and the quality of care that patients receive. We also know about the association between staff burnout and patient safety and neglect. Having board-level responsibility – and therefore the influence to improve the experience of both patients and staff, in an integrated way – is very meaningful work for me. I also get to do this in an organisation that has demonstrated a long-standing and ongoing commitment to this work.

Drawing on the lessons from our patient experience programme, I reviewed the literature on workforce engagement and identified eight domains of staff experience that warranted particular attention and reflected the fundamental needs of staff. These included psychological safety, autonomy and choice, and health and well-being, as outlined in the Institute of Healthcare Improvement's Joy in Work framework. We then developed measures for each domain and launched our staff experience programme in December 2018.

The year that followed proved to be a very successful one. Our local measurement of staff experience, and the 2019 NHS Staff Survey results, both demonstrated that it is possible to improve joy and pride at work, within a relatively short period of time. But this work takes organisational readiness, dedicated leadership time and attention, with skills development and investment.'

*https://www.health.org.uk/news-and-comment/
blogs/supporting-staff-wellbeing-during-covid-19-a-
northumbrian-experience/*

Chapter 1

Measuring compassionate leadership

Compassionate leadership can be measured using the following items, based on the four dimensions of compassion: attending, understanding, empathising and helping. These can be used by team members or could be adapted as a self-report measure for leaders.

This person

Attending

... listens carefully to others when exploring problems

... pays close attention to you when listening

... is very attentive when you are telling them about difficulties

... gives you their full attention when you are describing challenges you face

Understanding

... is helpful in understanding the reasons for difficulties we face

... does not impose their understanding of the cause of difficulties we face

... takes time to understand carefully the causes of problems

... works together with us to come to an understanding of problems

Empathising

... is genuinely warm and empathic

... is emotionally in touch with others' feelings when they are upset

... is sensitive to what others are feeling

... genuinely cares about others' difficulties

Helping

... helps people practically with problems they face

... takes effective action to help others with the problems they face

... deals effectively with problems in order to help others

... is genuinely committed to making a difference in helping others

Response scale
Never = 1, Rarely = 2, Frequently = 3, Almost always = 4, Always = 5.

Scoring
- Calculate an overall score by averaging item responses across all 16 items.

- Form four subscale scores (Attending, Understanding, Empathising and Helping) by averaging item responses for each subscale.

- For a team of ten people, merely average across all ten to get scores.

A shorter scale capturing the same core dimensions:

This person …

… gives you their full attention when you are describing challenges you face

… works together with us to come to an understanding of problems

… genuinely cares about others' difficulties

… takes effective action to help others with the problems they face

Response scale
Never = 1, Rarely = 2, Frequently = 3, Almost always = 4, Always = 5.

Scoring
Calculate an overall score by averaging item responses across all four items.

Chapter 2

Measuring strain or burnout

A standard measure of strain or burnout is the work-related burnout scale from the Copenhagen Burnout Inventory (used in the General Medical Council Training Survey), with the following seven items:

1. Is your work emotionally exhausting?

2. Do you feel burnt out because of your work?

3. Does your work frustrate you?

4. Do you feel worn out at the end of the working day?

5. Are you exhausted in the morning at the thought of another day at work?

6. Do you feel that every working hour is tiring for you?

7. Do you have enough energy for family and friends during leisure time?

Response scale
First three questions: To a very high degree = 100, To a high degree = 75, Somewhat = 50, To a low degree = 25, To a very low degree = 0.

Last four questions: Always = 100, Often = 75, Sometimes = 50, Seldom = 25, Never/Almost never = 0, with a reversed score for the last question.

Scoring
An overall score is calculated by averaging item responses across all seven items.

If less than three questions have been answered, the respondent is classified as a non-responder.

Interpretation
Scores of 50 to 74 are considered 'Moderate burnout', 75–99 are 'High burnout', and a score of 100 is considered 'Severe burnout'.

Chapter 3

Measuring compassionate care

The Schwartz Center measure of Compassionate Care is a free measure where respondents are asked to what extent did their doctor (or other healthcare provider):

1. Express sensitivity, caring and compassion for your situation?

2. Strive to understand your emotional needs?

3. Consider the effect of your illness on you, your family and the people most important to you?

4. Listen attentively to you?

5. Convey information to you in a way that is understandable?

6. Gain your trust?

7. Always involve you in decisions about your treatment?

8. Comfortably discuss sensitive, emotional, or psychological issues?

9. Treat you as a person, not a disease?

10. Show respect for you, your family and those important to you?

11. Communicate results in a timely and sensitive manner?

12. Spend enough time with you?

For a downloadable version of the survey, see:
https://journals.plos.org/plosone/article?id=10.1371/journal.pone.0220911

Response scale
1 to 10, where 1 is 'Not at all successful' and 10 is 'Very successful'.

Scoring
An overall score is calculated by averaging item responses across all 12 items.

Chapter 4

Measuring compassion within organisational culture

The Culture Assessment Tool (CAT) – a copyrighted instrument developed by Michael West, with support from AffinaOD (*https://www.affinaod.com*) and The King's Fund (*https://www.kingsfund.org.uk*), assesses the extent to which the culture of an organisation is characterised by compassion: between staff and patients, between staff, and between managers (or leaders) and staff. One of the constituent scales measures compassion at the organisational level by assessing the behaviour of leaders and managers, but ideally this will be used to assess the behaviour of all staff. The other scales are:

- Values

- Vision

- Goals and performance

- Learning, innovation and quality

- Support

- Teamworking

- Collective leadership

The compassion scale is described here. This contains two subscales, one focusing on managers and leaders, the other focusing on the behaviour of colleagues.

The Culture Assessment Tool	Score (1-5)*
The following statements relate to levels of support provided by managers and leaders in your workplace. How strongly do you agree or disagree with the following statements?	
Support 1. Managers and leaders encourage warm, supportive relationships among staff	
2. Managers and leaders recognise and celebrate good performance	
3. Managers and leaders deal effectively with problems that get in the way of our work	
4. My manager listens carefully to staff to find out how to support them effectively	
5. My manager is very compassionate towards staff when they face problems	
6. My manager is highly empathic in their dealings with members of staff	
The following statements relate to levels of compassion shown to and demonstrated by people in your workplace. How strongly do you agree or disagree with the following statements?	
Compassion 7. People here are very compassionate towards colleagues when they face problems	
8. People here give good support to colleagues who are distressed	
9. People here are very compassionate in the way they behave towards patients/service users	
10. People here take effective action to help patients/service users in distress	

Response scale
Strongly disagree = 1, Disagree = 2, Somewhat agree = 3, Agree = 4, Strongly agree = 5.

Scoring
Calculate an overall score for compassionate management/leadership by averaging item responses across the first six items, and an overall score for compassionate culture by averaging item responses across the last four items.

Chapter 5

Measuring effective teamworking

The Affina Team Performance Inventory (ATPI)

The ATPI is a copyrighted comprehensive online assessment tool for measuring a team's potential to deliver effective performance. The ATPI's design is based on research into what we know about high performing teams.

The Affina Real Team Profile Plus (ARTP+)

The ARTP+ is an online assessment tool for measuring team effectiveness. The ARTP+ measures the seven structural features that are essential for 'real teams'.

The Affina Team Journey

The Affina Team Journey is an online team assessment and development tool for team leaders and HR/OD leads to use with their teams. It improves performance by giving teams a structured, evidence-based experience.

Details about how to access these instruments and training in using them is available from AffinaOD:
https://www.affinaod.com/

Measuring psychological safety within teams

The Fearless Organization Scan, based on Amy Edmondson's work, maps how team members perceive the level of psychological safety. The open-access, simple and helpful online survey is administered, scored and interpreted automatically. On completion, respondents receive a free report via email.
https://fearlessorganization.com/

Chapter 6

Measuring Direction, Alignment and Commitment

Access the Center for Creative Leadership (CCL) questionnaire for assessing Direction, Alignment and Commitment via this link: *https://www.ccl.org/insights-research/direction-alignment-and-commitment-assessment/*

Instructions
On a scale of 1-5, indicate the extent to which each of the following statements describes the way things stand right now in your group/team/ organisation. The terms we, our, everyone, and people in the statements refer to members of the group.

Direction

1. We agree on what we should be aiming to accomplish together.

2. We have a clear vision of what the group needs to achieve in the future.

3. We have group goals that guide our key decisions.

4. Our work is united by a common direction.

Alignment

5. Our work is aligned across the group.

6. Although individuals take on different tasks in the group, our combined work fits together.

7. People who perform different roles or functions in the group coordinate their work effectively.

8. The work of each individual is well coordinated with the work of others.

Commitment

9. People in the group are committed to the group.

10. People give the effort needed for the group to succeed.

11. People are dedicated to this group even when we face setbacks.

12. We trust one another to accomplish the work of the group.

Response scale
Not descriptive = 1, Slightly descriptive = 2, Moderately descriptive = 3, Greatly descriptive = 4, Completely descriptive = 5.

Scoring

- Calculate an overall score by averaging item responses across all 12 items.

- Form three subscale scores (Direction, Alignment and Commitment) by averaging item responses for each subscale.

- For a team of ten people, average across all ten to get scores.

Interpretation

The CCL website and associated book suggest taking action when a total score for one outcome is noticeably lower than the total score for the other outcomes; when a total score for one outcome is less than 16; and when two to three of the statements used to assess an outcome are rated as 3 or lower by a majority of group members. The excellent little book Direction, Alignment, Commitment: Achieving Better Results through Leadership, Second Edition provides a wealth of practical information.

Assessing the ABC of core work needs

The self-determination theory website (*https://www.selfdeterminationtheory.org /basic-psychological-needs-scale/*) provides a free online and very helpful tool for assessing the ABC of core work needs, the Basic Psychological Need Satisfaction at Work Scale (Deci & Ryan, 2000). The copyrighted instrument is free for use by researchers but cannot be used commercially without written permission from those administering the website.

Respondents are asked to indicate how true each of the following 21 statements is for them at work:

1. I feel like I can make a lot of inputs to deciding how my job gets done.

2. I really like the people I work with.

3. I do not feel very competent when I am at work.

4. People at work tell me I am good at what I do.

5. I feel pressured at work.

6. I get along with people at work.

7. I pretty much keep to myself when I am at work.

8. I am free to express my ideas and opinions on the job.

9. I consider the people I work with to be my friends.

10. I have been able to learn interesting new skills on my job.

11. When I am at work, I have to do what I am told.

12. Most days I feel a sense of accomplishment from working.

13. My feelings are taken into consideration at work.

14. On my job I do not get much of a chance to show how capable I am.

15. People at work care about me.

16. There are not many people at work that I am close to.

17. I feel like I can pretty much be myself at work.

18. The people I work with do not seem to like me much.

19. When I am working I often do not feel very capable.

20. There is not much opportunity for me to decide for myself how to go about my work.

21. People at work are pretty friendly towards me.

Response scale
1 to 7. Not at all = 1, Somewhat true = 3, True= 5, Very true = 7.

Scoring
- Form three subscale scores (see below) by averaging item responses for each subscale, after reverse scoring the items that are worded in a negative direction.

- Any item that has (R) after it in the code below should be reverse scored by subtracting the person's response from 8. The subscales are:

Autonomy: 1, 5(R), 8, 11(R), 13, 17, 20(R)
Competence: 3(R), 4, 10, 12, 14(R), 19(R)
Relatedness: 2, 6, 7(R), 9, 15, 16(R), 18(R), 21

For more information see:
Deci, E. L., & Ryan, R. M. (2000). The "what" and "why" of goal pursuits: Human needs and the self-determination of behavior. *Psychological Inquiry, 11*, 227-268.
Deci, E. L., Ryan, R. M., Gagné, M., Leone, D. R., Usunov, J., & Kornazheva, B. P. (2001). Need satisfaction, motivation, and well-being in the work organizations of a former Eastern Bloc country. *Personality and Social Psychology Bulletin, 27*(8), 930-942.
Ilardi, B. C., Leone, D., Kasser, R., & Ryan, R. M. (1993). Employee and supervisor ratings of motivation: Main effects and discrepancies associated with job satisfaction and adjustment in a factory setting. *Journal of Applied Social Psychology, 23*, 1789-1805.
Kasser, T., Davey, J., & Ryan, R. M. (1992). Motivation, dependability, and employee supervisor discrepancies in psychiatric vocational rehabilitation settings. *Rehabilitation Psychology, 37*, 175-187.

Chapter 7

Measuring valuing diversity and procedural justice

A measure of valuing diversity

a. Managing diversity helps my organisation to be more effective.

b. My organisation has classes, workshops and seminars on diversity.

c. My organisation puts a lot of effort into diversity management.

d. My organisation values diversity.

Response scale
Strongly disagree = 1, Disagree = 2, Somewhat agree = 3,
Agree = 4, Strongly agree = 5.

Scoring
Calculate an overall score for valuing diversity by averaging item responses across all four items.

A measure of procedural justice

a. Consistent rules and procedures are used when making decisions in this organisation.

b. Procedures used in this organisation are free from bias.

c. Procedures in this organisation use just and fair standards.

d. Accurate information is used for making decisions.

e. We can get feedback about decisions made in this organisation.

Response scale
Strongly disagree = 1, Disagree = 2, Somewhat agree = 3,
Agree = 4, Strongly agree = 5.

Scoring
Calculate an overall score for procedural justice by averaging item responses across all five items.

Chapter 8

Measuring collective leadership

Collective leadership – the health and social care systems of all four UK nations have a commitment to developing collective as well as compassionate and inclusive leadership. This questionnaire has already been used successfully (in terms of reliability and validity) in NHS organisations. Either the complete measure or a shortened four item version (with just those items marked with an asterisk) can be used.

1. Leaders here prioritise overall patient/service user care, not just their own work area.*

2. Leaders across different departments work together to ensure high-quality overall patient/service user care.

3. Leaders here go out of their way to help each other across different departments to provide high-quality care.

4. Everyone in this organisation is expected to act as a leader in ensuring high-quality care.*

5. Team leaders encourage everyone to lead changes in order to improve the work we do.

6. We all play a leadership role in our teams in this organisation.*

7. We all listen to each other's views so we can best lead this organisation.*

8. Leadership in teams is shared rather than the responsibility of only one person.

Response scale
Strongly disagree = 1, Disagree = 2, Somewhat agree = 3, Agree = 4, Strongly agree = 5.

Scoring
Calculate an overall score for collective leadership by averaging item responses across all eight items (or, in the case of using the shortened version, all four items).

Chapter 9

Assessing compassionate partnership working across boundaries

Michael West and AffinaOD have developed a multi-dimensional survey to assess partnership working across boundaries. This examines nine dimensions listed below (along with examples of items from the questionnaire):

Shared vision and values

1. There is a clear, shared vision for our work in the partnership.
2. We have taken the time to carefully agree a set of partnership values to guide our work together.

Roles and teamworking

1. Partnership members are committed to achieving the partnership's goals.
2. There is good leadership in this partnership.

Frequent positive contact

1. We meet regularly to review our objectives and our progress.
2. There is a lot of face-to-face interaction between key people in the partnership.

Long-term commitment

1. There is a strong sense that we are in this partnership for the long term.
2. We plan a long way ahead together, not just for the short term.

Conflict management

1. We identify potential conflicts between us quickly and openly.
2. Conflict does not tend to linger in the partnership.

Mutual support

1. We are strongly focused on how we can help each other in this partnership.
2. Members of the partnership do not just focus on what they can get out of it for their organisations.

Trust

1. Those in the partnership act with integrity in their dealings with each other.
2. We can rely on members of this partnership to do what they commit to.

Innovation

1. The way the organisations in the partnership work together is readily changed in order to achieve the vision.
2. The methods we use to achieve the vision are often discussed.

Compassion

1. People in the partnership are very compassionate towards each other when they face problems.
2. People in the partnership are quick to help each other when they are under pressure.

This tool is subject to copyright (Michael West and AffinaOD). For more information see: *https://www.affinaod.com/* or contact Dr Thomas West, Lecturer of Leadership in Healthcare and Occupational Psychology within Health Sciences at the University of Southampton (T.H.R.West@southampton.ac.uk).

Chapter 10

Measuring team innovation and positivity

Team innovation

An eight-item measure that can be used for assessing team innovation in teams, groups, departments, or organisations.

1. This team is always moving toward the development of new answers.

2. Assistance in developing new ideas is readily available.

3. This team is open and responsive to change.

4. People in this team are always searching for fresh, new ways of looking at problems.

5. In this team we take the time needed to develop new ideas.

6. People in the team co-operate to help develop and apply new ideas.

7. Members of the team provide and share resources to help in the application of new ideas.

8. Team members provide practical support for new ideas and their application.

Response scale
Strongly disagree = 1, Disagree = 2, Somewhat agree = 3,
Agree = 4, Strongly agree = 5.

Scoring
Calculate an overall score for team innovation by averaging item responses across all 8 items.

Team positivity

This 12-item measure provides a simple measure of the affective climate in a team, group, department or organisation.

1. Team members willingly provide support for each other.

2. Team members complain about the contribution of other team members.

3. Team members celebrate the team's achievements.

4. Team members are cynical about the team's work.

5. Team members celebrate each other's achievements.

6. Team members express doubts about the team's ability to succeed.

7. Team members are enthusiastic about the team's vision.

8. Team members dwell on failures and difficulties.

9. Team members encourage each other to succeed.

10. Team members talk about the obstacles they see at work.

11. Team members joke and laugh together.

12. Team members talk about their wish to leave the team.

Response scale
Strongly disagree = 1, Disagree = 2, Somewhat agree = 3,
Agree = 4, Strongly agree = 5.

Scoring
- Sum the totals across all team members for answers to the positive items (1, 3, 5, 7, 9, 11) and divide by six (the number of items).

- Sum the totals across all team members for answers to the negative items (2, 4, 6, 8, 10, 12) and divide by six (the number of items).

- Divide these two figures by the number of people who completed the questionnaire and you can then use this information to assess the climate for positivity in your team.

Average scores for each of the two dimensions will be between 1 and 5.

Interpretation
The overall ratio of reported positive to negative features in your team indicates the likely health and effectiveness of your team now and in the future.

- An average positivity score of four and above suggests your team is generally highly positive and likely to be optimistic, effective, innovative, and cohesive.

- An average positivity score of 3 or below suggests low levels of optimism, cohesion and efficacy, and this will affect team performance and team member health and well-being negatively.

- An average negativity score of 3 or above suggests a high degree of cynicism and pessimism and an expectation of team failure. This will have a negative impact on team member health and well-being as well as on team performance.

The Team Positivity tool was developed by Michael West. You may also wish to use other evidence-based diagnostic tools such as the AffinaOD Real Team Profile+ or the AffinaOD Team Performance Inventory (*https://www.affinaod.com*).

Chapter 11

Measuring self-compassion

Kristin Neff offers a very helpful and free questionnaire to assess self-compassion with scores on dimensions of self-kindness, self-judgment, common humanity, isolation, mindfulness, over-identification and an overall score. For full details of how to use the questionnaire and receive an online interpretation go to:
https://self-compassion.org/test-how-self-compassionate-you-are/

1. I'm disapproving and judgmental about my own flaws and inadequacies.

2. When I'm feeling down, I tend to obsess and fixate on everything that's wrong.

3. When things are going badly for me, I see the difficulties as part of life that everyone goes through.

4. When I think about my inadequacies, it tends to make me feel more separate and cut off from the rest of the world.

5. I try to be loving towards myself when I'm feeling emotional pain.

6. When I fail at something important to me, I become consumed by feelings of inadequacy.

7. When I'm down and out, I remind myself that there are lots of other people in the world feeling like I am.

8. When times are really difficult, I tend to be tough on myself.

9. When something upsets me, I try to keep my emotions in balance.

10. When I feel inadequate in some way, I try to remind myself that feelings of inadequacy are shared by most people.

11. I'm intolerant and impatient towards those aspects of my personality I don't like.

12. When I'm going through a very hard time, I give myself the caring and tenderness I need.

13. When I'm feeling down, I tend to feel like most other people are probably happier than I am.

14. When something painful happens, I try to take a balanced view of the situation.

15. I try to see my failings as part of the human condition.

16. When I see aspects of myself that I don't like, I get down on myself.

17. When I fail at something important to me, I try to keep things in perspective.

18. When I'm really struggling, I tend to feel like other people must be having an easier time of it.

19. I'm kind to myself when I'm experiencing suffering.

20. When something upsets me, I get carried away with my feelings.

21. I can be a bit cold-hearted towards myself when I'm experiencing suffering.

22. When I'm feeling down, I try to approach my feelings with curiosity and openness.

23. I'm tolerant of my own flaws and inadequacies.

24. When something painful happens, I tend to blow the incident out of proportion.

25. When I fail at something that's important to me, I tend to feel alone in my failure.

26. I try to be understanding and patient towards those aspects of my personality I don't like.

Kristen Neff also provides a range of questionnaires on self-compassion that researchers can use, including the self-compassion scale, scales for youths, self-compassion short forms, and a measure of state self-compassion (self-compassion in the moment).
https://self-compassion.org/self-compassion-scales-for-researchers/

References

Chapter 1

1. Gilbert, P., & Choden. (2013). *Mindful compassion*. London: Robinson.

2. Cole-King, A., & Gilbert, P. (2011). Compassionate care: the theory and the reality. *Journal of Holistic Healthcare, 8*(3), 29-37.

3. Gilbert, P. (Ed.). (2017). *Compassion: concepts, research and applications*. London: Routledge.

4. de Zulueta, P. C. (2016). Developing compassionate leadership in healthcare: an integrative review. *Journal of Healthcare Leadership, 8,* 1-10.

5. Brown, B., Crawford, P., Gilbert, P., Gilbert, J., & Gale, C. (2014). Practical compassions: repertoires of practice and compassion talk in acute mental healthcare. *Sociology of Health & Illness, 36*(3), 383-399.

6. Lama, D. (2012). *The compassionate life*. Simon and Schuster.

7. Feldman, C. (2016). *Compassion: Listening to the cries of the world*. Boulder, Colorado: Shambhala Publications.

8. Feldman, C., & Kuyken, W. (2011). Compassion in the landscape of suffering. *Contemporary Buddhism, 12*(1), 143-155.

9. Brach, T. (2012). Mindful presence: A foundation for compassion and wisdom. In C. K. Germer & R. D. Siegel (Eds.), *Wisdom and compassion in psychotherapy: Deepening mindfulness in clinical practice.* (pp. 35–47). Guilford: The Guilford Press.

10. Rynes, S. L., Bartunek, J. M., Dutton, J. E., & Margolis, J. D. (2012). Care and compassion through an organizational lens: Opening up new possibilities. *Academy of Management Review, 37*(4), 503-523.

11. Atkins, P. W. B., & Parker, S. K. (2012). Understanding individual compassion in organizations: The role of appraisals and psychological flexibility. *Academy of Management Review, 37*(4), 524–546.

12. Dixon-Woods, M., Baker, R., Charles, K., Dawson, J., Jerzembek, G., Martin, G., McCarthy, I., McKee, L., Minion, J., Ozieranski, P., Willars, J., Wilkie, P., & West, M. (2014). Culture and behaviour in the English National Health Service: overview of lessons from a large multimethod study. *BMJ Quality and Safety, 23*(2), 106-115.

13. Dickinson, H., Ham, C., Snelling, I., & Spurgeon, P. (2013). *Are we there yet? Models of medical leadership and their effectiveness: An exploratory study.* Birmingham: NIHR Service Delivery and Organisation Programme.

14. West, M. A., Topakas, A., & Dawson, J. F. (2014). Climate and culture for healthcare performance. In B. Schneider & K. M. Barbera (Eds.). *The Oxford handbook of organizational climate and culture.* (pp. 335-359). Oxford: Oxford University Press.

15. Greguras, G. J., & Diefendorff, J. M. (2009). Different fits satisfy different needs: Linking person-environment fit to employee commitment and performance using self-determination theory. *Journal of Applied Psychology, 94*(2), 465-477.

16. Kline, N. (2002). *Time to think: Listening to ignite the human mind.* London: Cassell.

17. West, M. A., Armit, K., Loewenthal, L., Eckert, R., West, T., & Lee, A. (2015). *Leadership and leadership development in healthcare.* London: FMLM and The King's Fund/Brussels: Center for Creative Leadership.

18. West, M. A., Dawson, J. F., Admasachew, L., & Topakas, A. (2011). NHS staff management and health service quality: *Results from the NHS Staff Survey and related data.* Report to the Department of Health and Social Care. *https://assets.publishing.service.gov.uk/government/uploads/system/uploads/attachment_data/file/215455/dh_129656.pdf*

19. Gilbert, P. (2010). *The compassionate mind (compassion focused therapy).* London: Constable.

20. Lilius, J. M., Kanov, J., Dutton, J. E., Worline, M. C., & Maitlis, S. (2011). Compassion revealed: What we know about compassion at work (and where we need to know more). In K. S. Cameron & G. M. Spreitzer (Eds.), *The Oxford handbook of positive organizational scholarship.* (pp. 273-287). New York: Oxford University Press.

21. Worline, M. C., & Boik, S. (2006). Leadership lessons from Sarah: Values based leadership as everyday practice. In K. Cameron & E. Hess (Eds.), *Leading with values: Positivity, virtue, and high performance.* (pp. 108-131). Cambridge: Cambridge University Press.

22. Hatfield, E., Cacioppo, J. T., & Rapson, L. R. (1992). Primitive emotional contagion. In M. S. Clark (Ed.), *Review of personality and social psychology: Volume 14. Emotion and social behavior* (pp. 151–177). Newbury Park, CA: Sage.

23. Totterdell, P. (2000). Catching moods and hitting runs: mood linkage and subjective performance in professional sport teams. *Journal of Applied Psychology, 85*(6), 848.

24. Totterdell, P., Kellett, S., Teuchmann, K., & Briner, R. B. (1998). Evidence of mood linkage in work groups. *Journal of Personality and Social Psychology, 74*(6), 1504-1515.

25. Cherulnik, P. D., Donley, K. A., Wiewel, T. S. R., & Miller, S. R. (2001). Charisma is contagious: The effect of leaders' charisma on observers' affect. *Journal of Applied Social Psychology, 31*(10), 2149-2159.

26. George, J. M. (1990). Personality, affect, and behavior in groups. *Journal of Applied Psychology, 75*(2), 107-116.

27. George, J. M. (1995). Leader positive mood and group performance: The case of customer service. *Journal of Applied Social Psychology, 25*(9), 778-794.

28. Dutton, J. E., Workman, K. M., & Hardin, A. E. (2014). Compassion at work. *Annual Reviews of Organizational Psychology and Organizational Behavior, 1*(1), 277-304.

29. West, M. A., Eckert, R., Collins, B., & Chowla, R. (2017). *Caring to change: How compassionate leadership can stimulate innovation in healthcare.* London: The King's Fund.

30. Edmondson, A. C., & Harvey, J. F., (2017). *Extreme teaming: Lessons in complex, cross-sector leadership.* Bingley, UK: Emerald Publishing.

31. Edmondson, A. C., & Lei, Z. (2014). Psychological safety: The history, renaissance, and future of an interpersonal construct. *Annual Reviews of Organizational Psychology and Organizational Behavior, 1*(1), 23-43.

32. West, M. A., Lyubovnikova, J., Eckert, R., & Denis, J. L. (2014). Collective leadership for cultures of high-quality healthcare. *Journal of Organizational Effectiveness: People and Performance, 1*(3), 240–260.

33. Lyubovnikova, J., West, M. A., Dawson, J. F., & Carter, M. R. (2015). 24-Karat or fool's gold? Consequences of real team and co-acting group membership in healthcare organizations. *European Journal of Work and Organizational Psychology, 24*(6), 929-950.

34. West, M. A., & Chowla, R. (2017). Compassionate leadership for compassionate healthcare. In Gilbert, P. (Ed.). *Compassion: concepts, research and applications* (pp. 237-257). London: Routledge.

Chapter 2

1. Health Foundation, The King's Fund, Nuffield Trust. (2018). *The healthcare workforce in England: make or break?* Retrieved August 21, 2020, from *https://www.kingsfund.org.uk/publications/health-care-workforce-england*

2. Beech, J., Bottery, S., Charlesworth, A., Evans, H., Gershlick, B., Hemmings, N., Imison, C., Kahtan, P., McKenna, H., Murray, R., & Palmer, B. (2019). *Closing the gap: key areas for action on the health and care workforce.* The Health Foundation, The King's Fund, Nuffield Trust. Retrieved May 8, 2020, from *https://www.kingsfund.org.uk/sites/default/files/2019-06/closing-the-gap-full-report-2019.pdf*

3. Department of Health. (2019). *Health and social care Northern Ireland quarterly workforce bulletin June 2019.* Retrieved August 21, 2020, from *https://www.health-ni.gov.uk/sites/default/files/publications/health/hscwb-key-facts-june-2019.pdf*

4. West, M., & Coia, D. (2019). *Caring for doctors, caring for patients. How to transform UK healthcare environments to support doctors and medical students to care for patients.* General Medical Council. Retrieved March 19, 2021, from *https://www.gmc-uk.org/-/media/documents/caring-for-doctors-caring-for-patients_pdf-80706341.pdf*

5. NHS National Services Scotland, Information Services Division. (2019). *NHS Scotland workforce: quarter ending 30 June 2019.* *https://www.isdscotland.org/Health-Topics/Workforce/Publications/2019-09-03/2019-09-03-Workforce-Summary.pdf*

6. National Audit Office. (2020). *The NHS nursing workforce.* Retrieved March 19, 2021, from *https://www.nao.org.uk/wp-content/uploads/2020/03/The-NHS-nursing-workforce-Summary.pdf*

7. NHS Education for Scotland. (2020). *NHS Scotland workforce: quarter ending 31 December 2019.* Retrieved September 3, 2020, from *https://www.isdscotland.org/Health-Topics/Workforce/NES-Publication/2020-03-03/2020-03-03-NHSScotland-Workforce-Summary.pdf*

8. Royal College of Nursing Wales. (2019). *The nursing workforce in Wales 2019.* Retrieved August 21, 2020, from *https://www.rcn.org.uk/-/media/royal-college-of-nursing/documents/publications/2019/october/007-907.pdf?la=en*

9. Department of Health. (2020). *Northern Ireland health and social care (HSC) workforce vacancies March 2020.* Retrieved August 25, 2020, from *https://www.health-ni.gov.uk/publications/northern-ireland-health-and-social-care-hsc-workforce-vacancies-september-2020*

10. NHS Digital. (2020). *NHS workforce statistics April 2020.* Retrieved August 21, 2020, from *https://digital.nhs.uk/data-and-information/publications/statistical/nhs-workforce-statistics/april-2020*

11. Institute of Health Visiting. (2020). *Health visiting in England: state of health visiting in England.* Retrieved September 3, 2020, from *https://ihv.org.uk/wp-content/uploads/2020/02/State-of-Health-Visiting-survey-FINAL-VERSION-18.2.20.pdf* (accessed on 3 September 2020).

12. Maybin, J., Charles, A., & Honeyman, M. (2016). *Understanding quality in district nursing services: learning from patients, carers and staff.* The King's Fund. Retrieved September 3, 2020, from *https://www.kingsfund.org.uk/publications/quality-district-nursing*

13. Skills for Care. (2020). *The size and structure of the adult social care sector and workforce in England, 2020.* Retrieved September 3, 2020, from *https://www.skillsforcare.org.uk/adult-social-care-workforce-data/Workforce-intelligence/publications/national-information/The-size-and-structure-of-the-adult-social-care-sector-and-workforce-in-England.aspx*

14. Royal College of Nursing. (2020). *The UK nursing labour market review 2019.* Retrieved August 24, 2020, from *https://www.rcn.org.uk/professional-development/publications/rcn-the-uk-nursing-labour-market-review-2019-uk-pub-009135*

15. Office for National Statistics. (2018). *Sickness absence falls to the lowest rate on record.* Retrieved March 19, 2021, from *https://www.ons.gov.uk/employmentandlabourmarket/peopleinwork/employmentandemployeetypes/articles/sicknessabsencefallstothelowestratein24years/2018-07-30*

16. Committee for Finance and Personnel. (2015). *Report on sickness absence in the Northern Ireland public sector, volume one.* The Stationery Office. Retrieved September 2, 2020, from *www.niassembly.gov.uk/globalassets/documents/reports/finance/report-on-sickness-absence-vol1.pdf*

17. Welsh Government. (2019). *Sickness absence in the NHS in Wales, quarter ended 31 March 2019.* Retrieved September 3, 2020, from *https://gov.wales/sites/default/files/statistics-and-research/2019-08/sickness-absence-nhs-wales-quarter-ended-31-march-2019-549.pdf*

18. NHS National Services Scotland, Information Services Division. (2019). *NHS Scotland workforce: quarter ending 30 June 2019. https://www.isdscotland.org/Health-Topics/Workforce/ Publications/2019-09- 03/2019-09-03-Workforce-Summary.pdf*

19. NHS England. (2019). *NHS Staff Survey 2019: detailed spreadsheets.* Survey Coordination Centre. Retrieved August 20, 2020, from *https://www.nhsstaffsurveys.com/Page/1106/Past-Results/Staff-Survey-2019-Detailed-Spreadsheets/*

20. Moberly, T. (2018). *Sickness absence rates across the NHS.* BMJ. Retrieved October 19, 2019, from *https://www.bmj.com/content/361/ bmj.k2210*

21. NHS England. (2018). *NHS Staff Survey 2018: detailed spreadsheets.* Survey Coordination Centre. Retrieved October 30, 2019, from *https://www.nhsstaffsurveys.com/Page/1101/Past-Results/Staff-Survey-2018-Detailed-Spreadsheets/* Additional analysis conducted on data provided by NHS England.

22. NHS Wales. (2018). *NHS Wales Staff Survey 2018: National report. https://gov.wales/sites/default/files/publications/2019-02/nhs-wales-staff-survey-2018-national-report.pdf.* Additional analysis conducted on data provided by NHS Wales.

23. Mitchell, K., & Vayalumkal, J. (2017). Sickness presenteeism: The prevalence of coming to work while ill among paediatric resident physicians in Canada. *Paediatrics & Child Health, 22*(2),84-88.

24. Aysun, K., & Bayram, Ð. (2017). Determining the level and cost of sickness presenteeism among hospital staff in Turkey. *International Journal of Occupational Safety and Ergonomics, 23*(4),501-509.

25. McIlroy, R. (2019). *RCN Employment Survey 2019.* Royal College of Nursing. Retrieved August 19, 2020, from *https://www.rcn.org.uk/ professional-development/publications/pub-007927*

26. West, M., Bailey, S., & Williams, E. (2020). *The courage of compassion: Supporting nurses and midwives to deliver high quality care.* London: The King's Fund.

27. Buchan, J., Charlesworth, A., Gershlick, B., & Seccombe, I. (2019). *A critical moment: NHS staffing trends, retention and attrition.* Health Foundation. Retrieved May 8, 2020, from *https://www.health.org. uk/sites/default/files/upload/publications/2019/A%20Critical%20 Moment_1.pdf*

28. Borneo, A., Dalrymple, A., Hadden, C., Johnson, A., Kiely, S., Knape, J., Oakley, P., Oorthuysen-Dunne, J., & Turnbull, L. (2020). *Building a better future for nursing RCN members have their say.* Royal College of Nursing. Retrieved August 24, 2020, from *https://www.rcn.org.uk/professional-development/publications/rcn-builiding-a-better-future-covid-pub-009366*

29. Royal College of Midwives. (2016). *Why midwives leave – revisited.* Retrieved August 21, 2020, from *https://cdn.ps.emap.com/wp-content/uploads/sites/3/2016/10/Why-Midwives-Leave.pdf*

30. Nursing and Midwifery Council. (2020). *Leavers' survey 2019: why do people leave the NMC register?* Retrieved September 3, 2020, from *https://www.nmc.org.uk/globalassets/sitedocuments/nmc-register/march-2020/nmc-leavers-survey-2019.pdf*

31. Quality Health. (2015). *HSC staff survey - regional report.* Department of Health. *https://www.health-ni.gov.uk/publications/2015-hsc-staff-survey-regional-report*

32. Gibson, J., Sutton, M., Spooner, S., & Checkland, K. (2017). *Ninth national GP worklife survey.* Manchester Centre for Health Economics, Policy Research Unit in Commissioning and the Healthcare System. *https://prucomm.ac.uk/assets/uploads/Ninth-National-GP-Worklife-Survey.pdf*

33. Royal College of General Practitioners Scotland. (2019). *From the frontline: The changing landscape of Scottish general practice.* *https://allcatsrgrey.org.uk/wp/download/primary_care/RCGP-scotland-frontline-june-2019.pdf*

34. Wall, T. D., Bolden, R. I., Borrill, C. S., Carter, A. J., Golya, D. A., Hardy, G. E., Haynes, C. E., Rick, J. E., Shapiro, D. A., & West, M. A. (1997). Minor psychiatric disorder in NHS trust staff: Occupational and gender differences. *British Journal of Psychiatry, 171*(6), 519-523.

35. General Medical Council. (2019). *National training surveys 2019.* Retrieved October 30, 2019, from *https://www.gmc-uk.org/-/media/documents/national-training-surveys-initial-findings-report-2019_pdf-84390391.pdf*

36. Doty, M. M., Tikkanen, R., Shah, A., & Schneider, E. C. (2019). Primary care physicians' role in coordinating medical and health-related social needs in eleven countries, *Health Affairs, 39*(1), 115-123.

37. Health and Safety Executive. (2019). *Statistics – industries*. Retrieved October 29, 2019, from *https://www.hse.gov.uk/statistics/industry/index.htm*

38. West, M., & Dawson, J. F. (2012). *Employee engagement and NHS performance*. The King's Fund. Retrieved September 3, 2020, from *www.kingsfund.org.uk/sites/default/files/employee-engagement-nhs-performance-west-dawson-leadership-review2012-paper.pdf*

39. West, M., & Dawson, J. (2018). *Employee engagement, sickness absence and agency spend in NHS trusts*. NHS England. Retrieved September 3, 2020, from *www.england.nhs.uk/wp-content/uploads/2018/03/wres-engagement-absence-agency-spend.pdf*

40. Schnall, P., Dobson, M., & Landsbergis, P. (2017). Work, stress, and cardiovascular disease. In Cooper, C. L., & Quick, J. C. (Eds.). *The handbook of stress and health: a guide to research and practice.* (pp 99–124). New Jersey: John Wiley & Sons.

41. Roche, A., Kostadinov, V., Fischer, J. (2017). Stress and addiction. In Cooper, C. L., & Quick, J. C. (Eds.). *The handbook of stress and health: a guide to research and practice.* (pp 252–279). New Jersey: John Wiley & Sons.

42. Krantz, D., McCeney, M. (2002). Effects of psychological and social factors on organic disease: A critical assessment of research on coronary heart disease. *Annual Review of Psychology, 53*(1), 341-369.

43. Levy, R., Cain, K., Jarrett, M., & Heitkemper, M. (1997). The relationship between daily life stress and gastrointestinal symptoms in women with irritable bowel syndrome. *Journal of Behavioral Medicine, 20*(2), 177-193.

44. Heitkemper, M., Jarrett, M., Levy, R., Cain, K., Burr, R., Feld, A., Barney, P., & Weisman, P. (2004). Self-management for women with irritable bowel syndrome. *Clinical Gastroenterology and Hepatology, 2*(7), 585-596.

45. Cohen, S., & Herbert, T. (1996). Health Psychology: Psychological factors and physical disease from the perspective of human psychoneuroimmunology. *Annual Review of Psychology, 47*(1), 113-142.

46. American Psychological Association. (2018). *Stress effects on the body*. Retrieved October 30, 2019, from *https://www.apa.org/topics/stress/body*

47. Mental Health Foundation. (2018) *Stress: are we coping? https://www.mentalhealth.org.uk/publications/stress-are-we-coping*

48. Goh, J., Pfeffer, J., Zenios, S., & Rajpal, S. (2015). Workplace stressors & health outcomes: Health policy for the workplace. *Behavioral Science & Policy, 1*(1), 43-52.

49. British Medical Association. (2018). *Fatigue and sleep deprivation – the impact of different working patterns on doctors. https://www.bma.org. uk/media/1074/bma_fatigue-sleep-deprivation-briefing-jan2017.pdf*

50. Salminen, S. (2010). Shift work and extended working hours as risk factors for occupational injury. *The Ergonomics Open Journal, 3*(1), 14-18.

51. Firth-Cozens, J. (2001). Cultures for improving patient safety through learning: the role of teamwork. *BMJ Quality and Safety in Health Care, 10*(Suppl. 2), ii26-ii31.

52. Trzeciak, S., Mazzarelli, A., & Booker, C. (2019). *Compassionomics: The revolutionary scientific evidence that caring makes a difference.* Pensacola, FL: Studer Group.

53. West, C. P., Tan, A. D., Habermann, T. M., Sloan, J. A., & Shanafelt, T. D. (2009). Association of resident fatigue and distress with perceived medical errors. *JAMA, 302*(12), 1294-1300.

54. Shanafelt, T. D., Bradley, K. A., Wipf, J. E., & Back, A. L. (2002). Burnout and self-reported patient care in an internal medicine residency program. *Annals of Internal Medicine, 136*(5), 358-367.

55. Shanafelt, T. D., Balch, C. M., Bechamps, G., Russell, T., Dyrbye, L., Satele, D., Collicott, P., Novotny, P. J., Sloan, J., & Freischlag, J. (2010). Burnout and medical errors among American surgeons. *Annals of Surgery, 251*(6), 995-1000.

56. Maslach, C., & Leiter, M. P. (2013). The truth about burnout: *How organizations cause personal stress and what to do about it.* New York: John Wiley & Sons.

57. Welp, A., Meier, L. L., & Manser, T. (2015). Emotional exhaustion and workload predict clinician-rated and objective patient safety. *Frontiers in Psychology, 5,* 1573.

58. Aiken, L. H., Sermeus, W., den Heede, K. V., Sloane, D. M., Busse, R., McKee, M., Bruyneel, L., Rafferty, A. M., Griffiths, P., Moreno-Casbas, M. T., Tishelman, C., Scott, A., Brzostek, T., Kinnunen, J., Schwendimann, R., Heinen, M., Zikos, D., & Kutney-Lee, A. (2012). Patient safety, satisfaction, and quality of hospital care: cross sectional surveys of nurses and patients in 12 countries in Europe and the United States. *British Medical Journal, 344.*

59. Marangozov, R., Huxley, C., Manzoni, C., & Pike, G. (2017). *Royal College of Nursing employment survey 2017.* Institute for Employment Studies. Retrieved September 3, 2020, from *https://www.rcn.org.uk/ professional-development/publications/pdf-007076*

60. Royal College of Midwives. (2017). *The gathering storm: England's midwifery workforce challenges.* Retrieved September 3, 2020, from *https://www.rcm.org.uk/media/2374/the-gathering-storm-england-s-midwifery-workforce-challenges.pdf*

61. Royal College of Midwives. (2016). *Why midwives leave - revisited.* Retrieved March 19, 2021, from *https://cdn.ps.emap.com/wp-content/uploads/sites/3/2016/10/Why-Midwives-Leave.pdf*

62. Sonnentag, S., Venz, L., & Casper, A. (2017). Advances in recovery research: What have we learned? What should be done next? *Journal of Occupational Health Psychology, 22*(3), 365-380.

63. Johnson, J., Hall, L. H., Berzins, K., Baker, J., Melling, K., & Thompson, C. (2018). Mental healthcare staff well-being and burnout: A narrative review of trends, causes, implications, and recommendations for future interventions. *International Journal of Mental Health Nursing, 27*(1), 20–32.

64. Kinman, G., Teoh, K., & Harriss, A. (2020). *The mental health and well-being of nurses and midwives in the United Kingdom.* The Society of Occupational Medicine. Retrieved September 3, 2020, from *https://www.som.org.uk/sites/som.org.uk/files/The_Mental_Health_and_Wellbeing_of_Nurses_and_Midwives_in_the_United_Kingdom.pdf*

65. Sheen, K., Spiby, H., & Slade, P. (2016). The experience and impact of traumatic perinatal event experiences in midwives: A qualitative investigation. *International Journal of Nursing Studies, 53,* 61–72.

66. Rushton, C. (2017). Moral distress and building resilience. *Johns Hopkins Nursing.* Retrieved August 5, 2020, from *https://magazine.nursing.jhu.edu/2017/02/moral-distress-and-building-resilience*

67. Whittaker, B. A., Gillum, D. R., & Kelly, J. M. (2018). Burnout, moral distress, and job turnover in critical care nurses. *International Journal of Studies in Nursing, 3*(3), 108-121.

68. Duxbury, J. A., Wright, K., Bradley, D., & Barnes, P. (2010). Administration of medication in the acute mental health ward: perspective of nurses and patients. *International Journal of Mental Health Nursing, 19*(1), 53–61.

69. Robertson, J. H., & Thomson, A. M. (2016). An exploration of the effects of clinical negligence litigation on the practice of midwives in England: A phenomenological study. *Midwifery, 33,* 55–63.

70. Royal College of Nursing. (2020). Personal protective equipment: *Use and availability during the COVID-19 pandemic.* Retrieved August 21, 2020, from *https://www.rcn.org.uk/professional-development/ publications/rcn-ppe-survey-covid-19-uk-pub-009235*

71. Royal College of Nursing. (2020). *Second personal protective equipment survey of UK nursing staff report: Use and availability of PPE during the COVID-19 pandemic.* Retrieved August 21, 2020, from *https://www.rcn.org.uk/professional-development/publications/rcn-second-ppe-survey-covid-19-pub009269*

72. Royal College of Nursing. (2020). *The UK nursing labour market review 2019.* Retrieved August 24, 2020, from *https://www.rcn.org.uk/ professional-development/publications/rcn-the-uk-nursing-labour-market-review-2019-uk-pub-009135*

73. Darbyshire, P., Thompson, D. R., & Watson, R. (2019). Nursing's future? Eat young. Spit out. Repeat. Endlessly. *Journal of Nursing Management, 27*(7), 1337–1340.

74. Wilson, J. L. (2016). An exploration of bullying behaviours in nursing: a review of the literature. *British Journal of Nursing, 25*(6), 303–306.

75. Williams, D. R., & Mohammed, S. A. (2009). Discrimination and racial disparities in health: Evidence and needed research. *Journal of Behavioral Medicine, 32*(1), 20-47.

76. General Medical Council. (2019). *National training surveys 2019.* Retrieved October 30, 2019, from *https://www.gmc-uk.org/-/media/ documents/national-training-surveys-initial-findings-report-2019_pdf-84390391.pdf*

77. Punshon, G., Maclaine, K., Radford, M., Trevatt, P., Shanley, O., & Leary, A. (2019). Nursing pay by gender distribution in the UK – does the glass escalator still exist? *International Journal of Nursing Studies, 93,* 21–29.

78. Kristensen, T. S., Borritz, M., Villadsen, E., & Christensen, K. B. (2005). The Copenhagen burnout inventory: A new tool for the assessment of burnout. *Work & Stress, 19*(3), 192-207.

Chapter 3

1. Trzeciak, S., & Mazzarelli, A. (2019). *Compassionomics: The revolutionary scientific evidence that caring makes a difference.* Pensacola, FL: Studer Group.

2. Holt-Lunstad, J., Smith, T. B., & Layton, J. B. (2010). Social relationships and mortality risk: A meta-analytic review. *PLoS Medicine, 7*(7), e1000316.

3. Holt-Lunstad, J., Smith, T. B., Baker, M., Harris, T., & Stephenson, D. (2015). Loneliness and social isolation as risk factors for mortality: A meta-analytic review. *Perspectives on psychological science, 10*(2), 227-237.

4. Rico-Uribe, L. A., Caballero, F. F., Martín-María, N., Cabello, M., Ayuso-Mateos, J. L., & Miret, M. (2018). Association of loneliness with all-cause mortality: A meta-analysis. *PLoS One, 13*(1), e0190033.

5. Perissinotto, C. M., Cenzer, I. S., & Covinsky, K. E. (2012). Loneliness in older persons: A predictor of functional decline and death. *Archives of Internal Medicine, 172*(14), 1078-1083.

6. Singer, C. (2018). Health effects of social isolation and loneliness. *Journal of Aging Life Care, 28*(1), 4-8.

7. Berkman, L. F., Leo-Summers, L., & Horwitz, R. I. (1992). Emotional support and survival after myocardial infarction: A prospective, population-based study of the elderly. *Annals of Internal Medicine, 117*(12), 1003-1009.

8. Cohen, S., Janicki-Deverts, D., Turner, R. B., & Doyle, W. J. (2015). Does hugging provide stress-buffering social support? A study of susceptibility to upper respiratory infection and illness. *Psychological Science, 26*(2), 135-147.

9. Fuentes, J., Armijo-Olivo, S., Funabashi, M., Miciak, M., Dick, B., Warren, S., Rashiq, S., Magee, D. J., & Gross, D. P. (2014). Enhanced therapeutic alliance modulates pain intensity and muscle pain sensitivity in patients with chronic low back pain: An experimental controlled study. *Physical Therapy, 94*(4), 477-489.

10. Dibbelt, S., Schaidhammer, M., Fleischer, C., & Greitemann, B. (2009). Patient–doctor interaction in rehabilitation: The relationship between perceived interaction quality and long-term treatment results. *Patient Education and Counseling, 76*(3), 328-335.

11. Egbert, L. D., Battit, G. E., Turndorf, H., & Beecher, H. K. (1963). The value of the preoperative visit by an anesthetist: A study of doctor-patient rapport. *JAMA, 185*(7), 553-555.

12. Egbert, L. D., Battit, G. E., Welch, C. E., & Bartlett, M. K. (1964). Reduction of postoperative pain by encouragement and instruction of patients: A study of doctor-patient rapport. *New England Journal of Medicine, 270*(16), 825-827.

13. Pereira, L., Figueiredo-Braga, M., & Carvalho, I. P. (2016). Preoperative anxiety in ambulatory surgery: The impact of an empathic patient-centered approach on psychological and clinical outcomes. *Patient Education and Counseling, 99*(5), 733-738.

14. Mumford, E., Schlesinger, H. J., & Glass, G. V. (1982). The effect of psychological intervention on recovery from surgery and heart attacks: An analysis of the literature. *American Journal of Public Health, 72*(2), 141-151.

15. Hojat, M., Louis, D. Z., Markham, F. W., Wender, R., Rabinowitz, C., & Gonnella, J. S. (2011). Physicians' empathy and clinical outcomes for diabetic patients. *Academic Medicine, 86*(3), 359-364.

16. Del Canale, S., Louis, D. Z., Maio, V., Wang, X., Rossi, G., Hojat, M., & Gonnella, J. S. (2012). The relationship between physician empathy and disease complications: An empirical study of primary care physicians and their diabetic patients in Parma, Italy. *Academic Medicine, 87*(9), 1243-1249.

17. Beach, M. C., Keruly, J., & Moore, R. D. (2006). Is the quality of the patient-provider relationship associated with better adherence and health outcomes for patients with HIV? *Journal of General Internal Medicine, 21*(6), 661-665.

18. Flickinger, T. E., Saha, S., Roter, D., Korthuis, P. T., Sharp, V., Cohn, J., Eggly, S., Moore, R. D., & Beach, M. C. (2016). Clinician empathy is associated with differences in patient–clinician communication behaviors and higher medication self-efficacy in HIV care. *Patient Education and Counseling, 99*(2), 220-226.

19. Temel, J. S., Greer, J. A., Muzikansky, A., Gallagher, E. R., Admane, S., Jackson, V. A., Dahlin, C. M., Blinderman, C. D., Jacobsen, J., Pirl, W. F., & Billings, J. A. (2010). Early palliative care for patients with metastatic non–small-cell lung cancer. *New England Journal of Medicine, 363*(8), 733-742.

20. Neumann, M., Wirtz, M., Bollschweiler, E., Mercer, S. W., Warm, M., Wolf, J., & Pfaff, H. (2007). Determinants and patient-reported long-term outcomes of physician empathy in oncology: A structural equation modelling approach. *Patient Education and Counseling, 69*(1-3), 63-75.

21. Mercer, S. W., Neumann, M., Wirtz, M., Fitzpatrick, B., & Vojt, G. (2008). General practitioner empathy, patient enablement, and patient-reported outcomes in primary care in an area of high socio-economic deprivation in Scotland — A pilot prospective study using structural equation modeling. *Patient Education and Counseling, 73*(2), 240-245.

22. Verheul, W., Sanders, A., & Bensing, J. (2010). The effects of physicians' affect-oriented communication style and raising expectations on analogue patients' anxiety, affect and expectancies. *Patient Education and Counseling, 80*(3), 300-306.

23. Barsade, S. G., & O'Neill, O. A. (2014). What's love got to do with it? A longitudinal study of the culture of companionate love and employee and client outcomes in a long-term care setting. *Administrative Science Quarterly, 59*(4), 551–598.

24. Kirby, J. N., Tellegen, C. L., & Steindl, S. R. (2017). A meta-analysis of compassion-based interventions: Current state of knowledge and future directions. *Behavior Therapy, 48*(6), 778-792.

25. Wen, L. S., & Tucker, S. (2015). What do people want from their health care? A qualitative study. *Journal of Participatory Medicine, 7*, e10.

26. Menendez, M. E., Chen, N. C., Mudgal, C. S., Jupiter, J. B., & Ring, D. (2015). Physician empathy as a driver of hand surgery patient satisfaction. *The Journal of Hand Surgery, 40*(9), 1860-1865.

27. Davis, L. (2013, November 13). Dignity Health survey finds majority of Americans rate kindness as top factor in quality health care. *Dignity Health. https://www.dignityhealth.org/about-us/press-center/press-releases/majority-of-americans-rate-kindness*

28. Slawson, P. F., & Guggenheim, F. G. (1984). Psychiatric malpractice: A review of the national loss experience. *The American Journal of Psychiatry, 141*(8), 979-981.

29. Lieberman, J. A. (1985). *The litigious society.* New York: Basic Books.

30. Friedman, L. M. (1985). *Total justice.* New York: Russell Sage Foundation.

31. Eisenberg, H. (1973). New light on the costliest malpractice mistakes. *Med Econ, 16*, 146-150.

32. Hicks, R. G. (1973). Ounces of prevention. I. *New York State Journal of Medicine, 73*(18), 2268-2269.

33. Vincent, C., Phillips, A., & Young, M. (1994). Why do people sue doctors? A study of patients and relatives taking legal action. *The Lancet, 343*(8913), 1609-1613.

34. Gilbert, P. (2010). The compassionate mind (compassion focussed therapy). London: Constable.

35. Weiss, R., Vittinghoff, E., Fang, M. C., Cimino, J. E., Chasteen, K. A., Arnold, R. M., Auerbach, A. D., & Anderson, W. G. (2017). Associations of physician empathy with patient anxiety and ratings of communication in hospital admission encounters. *Journal of Hospital Medicine, 12*(10), 805-810.

36. Goldstein, P., Weissman-Fogel, I., & Shamay-Tsoory, S. G. (2017). The role of touch in regulating inter-partner physiological coupling during empathy for pain. *Scientific Reports, 7*(1), 1-12.

37. Kiecolt-Glaser, J. K., Loving, T. J., Stowell, J. R., Malarkey, W. B., Lemeshow, S., Dickinson, S. L., & Glaser, R. (2005). Hostile marital interactions, proinflammatory cytokine production, and wound healing. *Archives of General Psychiatry, 62*(12), 1377-1384.

38. Zolnierek, K. B., & Dimatteo, M. R. (2009). Physician communication and patient adherence to treatment: A meta-analysis. *Medical Care, 47*(8), 826–834.

39. Mercer, S. W., Jani, B. D., Maxwell, M., Wong, S. Y., & Watt, G. C. (2012). Patient enablement requires physician empathy: A cross-sectional study of general practice consultations in areas of high and low socioeconomic deprivation in Scotland. *BMC Family Practice, 13*(1), 6.

40. Kerse, N., Buetow, S., Mainous, A. G., Young, G., Coster, G., & Arroll, B. (2004). Physician-patient relationship and medication compliance: A primary care investigation. *The Annals of Family Medicine, 2*(5), 455-461.

41. Ratanawongsa, N., Karter, A. J., Parker, M. M., Lyles, C. R., Heisler, M., Moffet, H. H., Adler, N., Warton, E. M., & Schillinger, D. (2013). Communication and medication refill adherence: The diabetes study of Northern California. *JAMA Internal Medicine, 173*(3), 210-218.

42. Kahn K. L., Schneider, E. C., Malin, J. L., Adams, J. L., & Epstein, A. M. (2007). Patient centered experiences in breast cancer: Predicting long-term adherence to tamoxifen use. *Medical Care, 45*(5), 431–439.

43. Klimecki, O. M., Leiberg, S., Ricard, M., & Singer, T. (2014). Differential pattern of functional brain plasticity after compassion and empathy training. *Social Cognitive and Affective Neuroscience, 9*(6), 873-879.

44. Klimecki, O. M., Leiberg, S., Lamm, C., & Singer, T. (2013). Functional neural plasticity and associated changes in positive affect after compassion training. *Cerebral Cortex, 23*(7), 1552-1561.

45. Kemper, K. J., & Shaltout, H. A. (2011). Non-verbal communication of compassion: measuring psychophysiologic effects. *BMC Complementary and Alternative Medicine, 11*(1), 132.

46. Shaltout, H. A., Tooze, J. A., Rosenberger, E., & Kemper, K. J. (2012). Time, touch, and compassion: Effects on autonomic nervous system and well-being. *Explore, 8*(3), 177-184.

47. Maben, J., Taylor, C., Dawson, J., Leamy, M., McCarthy, I., Reynolds, E., Ross, S., Shuldham, C., Bennett, L., & Foot, C. (2018). A realist informed mixed-methods evaluation of Schwartz Center Rounds® in England. *Health Services and Delivery Research, 6*(37), 1-260.

48. Neumann, M., Edelhäuser, F., Tauschel, D., Fischer, M. R., Wirtz, M., Woopen, C., Haramati, A., & Scheffer, C. (2011). Empathy decline and its reasons: A systematic review of studies with medical students and residents. *Academic Medicine, 86*(8), 996-1009.

49. Kelm, Z., Womer, J., Walter, J. K., & Feudtner, C. (2014). Interventions to cultivate physician empathy: A systematic review. *BMC Medical Education, 14*(1), 1-11.

50. Kelley, J. M., Kraft-Todd, G., Schapira, L., Kossowsky, J., & Riess, H. (2014). The influence of the patient-clinician relationship on healthcare outcomes: A systematic review and meta-analysis of randomized controlled trials. *PLoS One, 9*(4), e94207.

51. Trzeciak, S., Gaughan, J. P., Bosire, J., & Mazzarelli, A. J. (2016). Association between Medicare summary star ratings for patient experience and clinical outcomes in US hospitals. *Journal of Patient Experience, 3*(1), 6-9.

52. Bertakis, K. D., & Azari, R. (2011). Patient-centered care is associated with decreased health care utilization. *The Journal of the American Board of Family Medicine, 24*(3), 229-239.

53. Stewart, M., Brown, J. B., Donner, A., McWhinney, I., Oates, J., & Weston, W. (1995). *The impact of patient-centred care on patient outcomes in family practice (final report).* Canada: Center for Studies in Family Medicine, University of Western Ontario.

54. Redelmeier, D. A., Molin, J. P., & Tibshirani, R. J. (1995). A randomised trial of compassionate care for the homeless in an emergency department. *The Lancet, 345*(8958), 1131-1134.

55. Andel, C., Davidow, S. L., Hollander, M., & Moreno, D. A. (2012). The economics of health care quality and medical errors. *Journal of Health Care Finance, 39*(1), 39-50.

56. Yau, C. W. H., Leigh, B., Liberati, E., Punch, D., Dixon-Woods, & M., Draycott, T. (2020). Clinical negligence costs: Taking action to safeguard NHS sustainability. *BMJ, 368.*

57. West, C. P., Tan, A. D., Habermann, T. M., Sloan, J. A., & Shanafelt, T. D. (2009). Association of resident fatigue and distress with perceived medical errors. *JAMA, 302*(12), 1294-1300.

58. West, C. P., Huschka, M. M., Novotny, P. J., Sloan, J. A., Kolars, J. C., Habermann, T. M., & Shanafelt, T.D. (2006). Association of perceived medical errors with resident distress and empathy: A prospective longitudinal study. *JAMA, 296*(9), 1071-1078.

59. Shanafelt, T. D., Balch, C. M., Bechamps, G., Russell, T., Dyrbye, L., Satele, D., Collicott, P., Novotny, P. J., Sloan, J., & Freischlag, J. (2010). Burnout and medical errors among American surgeons. *Annals of Surgery, 251*(6), 995-1000.

60. Welp, A., Meier, L. L., & Manser, T. (2015). Emotional exhaustion and workload predict clinician-rated and objective patient safety. *Frontiers in Psychology, 5,* 1573.

61. Dasan, S., Gohil, P., Cornelius, V., & Taylor, C. (2015). Prevalence, causes and consequences of compassion satisfaction and compassion fatigue in emergency care: A mixed-methods study of UK NHS consultants. *Emergency Medicine Journal, 32*(8), 588-594.

62. Riess, H., Kelley, J. M., Bailey, R. W., Dunn, E. J., & Phillips, M. (2012). Empathy training for resident physicians: A randomized controlled trial of a neuroscience-informed curriculum. *Journal of General Internal Medicine, 27*(10), 1280-1286.

63. Darley, J. M., & Batson, C. D. (1973). "From Jerusalem to Jericho": A study of situational and dispositional variables in helping behavior. *Journal of Personality and Social Psychology, 27*(1), 100-108.

64. Fogarty, L. A., Curbow, B. A., Wingard, J. R., McDonnell, K., & Somerfield, M. R. (1999). Can 40 seconds of compassion reduce patient anxiety? *Journal of Clinical Oncology, 17*(1), 371-379.

65. Roter, D. L., Hall, J. A., Kern, D. E., Barker, L. R., Cole, K. A., & Roca, R. P. (1995). Improving physicians' interviewing skills and reducing patients' emotional distress: A randomized clinical trial. *Archives of Internal Medicine, 155*(17), 1877-1884.

66. Bylund, C. L., & Makoul, G. (2005). Examining empathy in medical encounters: An observational study using the empathic communication coding system. *Health Communication, 18*(2), 123-140.

67. Van Osch, M., Sep, M., van Vliet, L. M., van Dulmen, S., & Bensing, J. M. (2014). Reducing patients' anxiety and uncertainty, and improving recall in bad news consultations. *Health Psychology, 33*(11), 1382-1390.

68. Sep, M. S., Van Osch, M., Van Vliet, L. M., Smets, E. M., & Bensing, J. M. (2014). The power of clinicians' affective communication: How reassurance about non-abandonment can reduce patients' physiological arousal and increase information recall in bad news consultations. An experimental study using analogue patients. *Patient Education and Counseling, 95*(1), 45-52.

69. Dempsey, C. (2017). The antidote to suffering: *How compassionate connected care can improve safety, quality, and experience.* Ohio, United States: McGraw Hill Professional.

70. Mogilner, C., Chance, Z., & Norton, M. I. (2012). Giving time gives you time. *Psychological Science, 23*(10), 1233-1238.

71. Brown, B. (2008). I thought it was just me (but it isn't): *Making the journey from "what will people think?" to "I am enough".* Avery.

72. Grandey, A. A. (2003). When "the show must go on": Surface acting and deep acting as determinants of emotional exhaustion and peer-rated service delivery. *Academy of Management Journal, 46*(1), 86-96.

73. Fredrickson, B. L., Cohn, M. A., Coffey, K. A., Pek, J., & Finkel, S. M. (2008). Open hearts build lives: Positive emotions, induced through loving-kindness meditation, build consequential personal resources. *Journal of Personality and Social Psychology, 95*(5), 1045-1062.

74. Ricard, M. (2007, February). *Habits of Happiness* [Video]. TED Conferences. *https://www.ted.com/talks/matthieu_ricard_the_habits_of_happiness?language=en*

75. Goleman, D., & Davidson, R. J. (2017). Altered traits: *Science reveals how meditation changes your mind, brain, and body.* London: Penguin.

76. Lutz, A., Greischar, L. L., Rawlings, N. B., Ricard, M., & Davidson, R. J. (2004). Long-term meditators self-induce high-amplitude gamma synchrony during mental practice. *Proceedings of the National Academy of Sciences, 101*(46), 16369-16373.

77. Weng, H. Y., Fox, A. S., Shackman, A. J., Stodola, D. E., Caldwell, J. Z., Olson, M. C., Rogers, G. M., & Davidson, R. J. (2013). Compassion training alters altruism and neural responses to suffering. *Psychological Science, 24*(7), 1171-1180.

78. Teding van Berkhout, E., & Malouff, J. M. (2016). The efficacy of empathy training: A meta-analysis of randomized controlled trials. *Journal of Counseling Psychology, 63*(1), 32-41.

79. Satterfield, J. M., & Hughes, E. (2007). Emotion skills training for medical students: A systematic review. *Medical Education, 41*(10), 935-941.

80. Batt-Rawden, S. A., Chisolm, M. S., Anton, B., & Flickinger, T. E. (2013). Teaching empathy to medical students: An updated, systematic review. *Academic Medicine, 88*(8), 1171-1177.

81. Razavi, D., Delvaux, N., Marchal, S., Durieux, J. F., Farvacques, C., Dubus, L., & Hogenraad, R. (2002). Does training increase the use of more emotionally laden words by nurses when talking with cancer patients? A randomised study. *British Journal of Cancer, 87*(1), 1-7.

82. Gholamzadeh, S., Khastavaneh, M., Khademian, Z., & Ghadakpour, S. (2018). The effects of empathy skills training on nursing students' empathy and attitudes toward elderly people. *BMC Medical Education, 18*(1), 198.

83. Wu, L. M., Chin, C. C., & Chen, C. H. (2009). Evaluation of a caring education program for Taiwanese nursing students: A quasi-experiment with before and after comparison. *Nurse Education Today, 29*(8), 873-878.

84. Bas-Sarmiento, P., Fernández-Gutiérrez, M., Baena-Baños, M., & Romero-Sánchez, J. M. (2017). Efficacy of empathy training in nursing students: A quasi-experimental study. *Nurse Education Today, 59*, 59-65.

85. Chadwick, K. (2014, April 9). Study confirms impact of clinician-patient relationship on health outcomes. Massachusetts General Hospital. *https://www.sciencedaily.com/releases/2014/04/140409204427.htm*

86. Schumann, K., Zaki, J., & Dweck, C. S. (2014). Addressing the empathy deficit: Beliefs about the malleability of empathy predict effortful responses when empathy is challenging. *Journal of Personality and Social Psychology, 107*(3), 475-493.

87. Weinstein, N., & Ryan, R. M. (2010). When helping helps: Autonomous motivation for prosocial behavior and its influence on well-being for the helper and recipient. *Journal of Personality and Social Psychology, 98*(2), 222-244.

88. West, M., & Coia, D. D. (2019). *Caring for doctors, caring for patients.* General Medical Council. *https://www.gmc-uk.org/-/media/documents/ caring-for-doctors-caring-for-patients_pdf-80706341.pdf*

89. Shanafelt, T. D., Hasan, O., Dyrbye, L. N., Sinsky, C., Satele, D., Sloan, J., & West, C. P. (2015). Changes in burnout and satisfaction with work-life balance in physicians and the general US working population between 2011 and 2014. *Mayo Clinic Proceedings, 90*(12), 1600-1613.

90. Peckham, C. (2018). *Medscape national physician burnout & depression report 2018.* Medscape. *https://www.medscape.com/slideshow/2018-lifestyle-burnout-depression-6009235*

91. Tawfik, D. S., Profit, J., Morgenthaler, T. I., Satele, D. V., Sinsky, C. A., Dyrbye, L. N., Tutty, M. A., West, C. P., & Shanafelt, T. D. (2018). Physician burnout, well-being, and work unit safety grades in relationship to reported medical errors. *Mayo Clinic Proceedings, 93*(11), 1571-1580.

92. Wilkinson, H., Whittington, R., Perry, L., & Eames, C. (2017). Examining the relationship between burnout and empathy in healthcare professionals: A systematic review. *Burnout Research, 6*, 18-29.

93. Thomas, M. R., Dyrbye, L. N., Huntington, J. L., Lawson, K. L., Novotny, P. J., Sloan, J. A., & Shanafelt, T. D. (2007). How do distress and well-being relate to medical student empathy? A multicenter study. *Journal of General Internal Medicine, 22*(2), 177-183.

94. Gleichgerrcht, E., & Decety, J. (2013). Empathy in clinical practice: How individual dispositions, gender, and experience moderate empathic concern, burnout, and emotional distress in physicians. *PloS one, 8*(4), e61526.

95. Krasner, M. S., Epstein, R. M., Beckman, H., Suchman, A. L., Chapman, B., Mooney, C. J., & Quill, T. E. (2009). Association of an educational program in mindful communication with burnout, empathy, and attitudes among primary care physicians. *JAMA, 302*(12), 1284-1293.

96. Mascaro, J. S., Kelley, S., Darcher, A., Negi, L. T., Worthman, C., Miller, A., & Raison, C. (2018). Meditation buffers medical student compassion from the deleterious effects of depression. *The Journal of Positive Psychology, 13*(2), 133-142.

97. McKee, A., & Wiens, K. (2017, May 11). Prevent burnout by making compassion a habit. *Harvard Business Review. https://hbr.org/2017/05/ prevent-burnout-by-making-compassion-a-habit*

98. Wright, S. M., Kern, D. E., Kolodner, K., Howard, D. M., & Brancati, F. L. (1998). Attributes of excellent attending-physician role models. *New England Journal of Medicine, 339*(27), 1986-1993.

99. Rodriguez, A. M., Lown, B. A. (2019) Measuring compassionate healthcare with the 12-item Schwartz Center compassionate care scale. *PLoS One, 14*(9), e0220911.

Chapter 4

1. Salas, E., Rosen, M. A., & King, H. (2007). Managing teams managing crises: principles of teamwork to improve patient safety in the emergency room and beyond. *Theoretical Issues in Ergonomics Science, 8*(5), 381-394.

2. Wall, T. D., Bolden, R. I., Borrill, C. S., Carter, A. J., Golya, D. A., Hardy, G. E., Haynes, C. E., Rick, J. E., Shapiro, D. A., & West, M. A. (1997). Minor psychiatric disorder in NHS trust staff: occupational and gender differences. *The British Journal of Psychiatry, 171*(6), 519-523.

3. West, M. A., Bailey, S., & Williams, E. (2020). *The courage of compassion: Supporting nurses and midwives to deliver care across our communities.* The King's Fund.

4. Dixon-Woods, M., Baker, R., Charles, K., Dawson, J., Jerzembek, G., Martin, G., McCarthy, I., McKee, L., Minion, J., Ozieranski, P., Willars, J., Wilkie, P., & West, M. (2014). Culture and behaviour in the English National Health Service: Overview of lessons from a large multimethod study, *British Medical Journal Quality and Safety, 23*(2), 106-115.

5. Schneider, B., & Barbera K. M. (Eds.) (2014). *The Oxford Handbook of Organizational Climate and Culture.* Oxford: Oxford University Press.

6. Amos, E. A., & Weathington, B. L. (2008). An analysis of the relation between employee-organization value congruence and employee attitudes. *The Journal of Psychology, 142*(6), 615-632.

7. Schneider, B., González-Romá, V., Ostroff, C., & West, M. A. (2017). Organizational climate and culture: Reflections on the history of the constructs in the Journal of Applied Psychology. *Journal of Applied Psychology, 102*(3), 468-482.

8. Kelly, J. (2007). Barriers to achieving patient-centered care in Ireland. *Dimensions of Critical Care Nursing, 26*(1), 29-34.

9. Gilbert, P. (2009). *The Compassionate Mind.* London: Constable Robinson.

10. Gilbert, P., & Choden. (2013). *Mindful compassion.* London: Robinson.

11. Cole-King, A. & Gilbert, P. (2011). Compassionate care: The theory and the reality. *Journal of Holistic Healthcare, 8*(3), 29-37.

12. de Zulueta, P. (2013). Compassion in 21st century medicine: Is it sustainable? *Clinical Ethics, 8*(4), 119-128.

13. de Zulueta, P. C. (2016). Developing compassionate leadership in healthcare: An integrative review. *Journal of Healthcare Leadership, 8,* 1-10.

14. Mannion, R. (2014). Enabling compassionate health care: Perils, prospects and perspectives. *International Journal of Health Policy & Management, 2*(3), 115-117.

15. West, M., & Coia, D. D. (2019). *Caring for doctors, caring for patients. How to transform UK healthcare environments to support doctors and medical students to care for patients.* General Medical Council. *https://www.gmc-uk.org/-/media/documents/caring-for-doctors-caring-for-patients_pdf-80706341.pdf*

16. Hatfield, E., Cacioppo, J. T., & Rapson, L. R. (1992). Primitive emotional contagion. In M. S. Clark (Ed.), *Review of personality and social psychology: Volume 14. Emotion and Social Behavior.* (pp. 151–177). Newbury Park, CA: Sage.

17. Totterdell, P. (2000). Catching moods and hitting runs: Mood linkage and subjective performance in professional sport teams. *Journal of Applied Psychology, 85*(6), 848-859.

18. Totterdell, P., Kellett, S., Teuchmann, K., & Briner, R. B. (1998). Evidence of mood linkage in work groups. *Journal of Personality and Social Psychology, 74*(6), 1504-1515.

19. Cherulnik, P. D., Donley, K. A., Wiewel, T. S. R., & Miller, S. R. (2001). Charisma is contagious: The effect of leaders' charisma on observers' affect. *Journal of Applied Social Psychology, 31*(10), 2149-2159.

20. George, J. M. (1990). Personality, affect, and behavior in groups. *Journal of Applied Psychology, 75*(2), 107-116.

21. George, J. M. (1995). Leader positive mood and group performance: The case of customer service. *Journal of Applied Social Psychology, 25*(9), 778-794.

22. Kanov, J. M., Maitlis, S., Worline, M. C., Dutton, J. E., Frost, P. J., & Lilius, J. M. (2004). Compassion in organizational life. *American Behavioral Scientist, 47*(6), 808-827.

23. Dutton, J. E., Worline, M. C., Frost, P. J., & Lilius, J. (2006). Explaining compassion organizing. *Administrative Science Quarterly, 51*(1), 59-96.

24. Lilius, J. M., Kanov, J, Dutton, J. E., Worline, M. C., & Maitlis, S. (2011). Compassion revealed: What we know about compassion at work (and where we need to know more). In K. S. Cameron, & G. M. Spreitzer (Eds.), *The Oxford handbook of positive organizational scholarship.* (pp. 273-288). New York: Oxford University Press.

25. Dutton, J. E., Workman, K. M., & Hardin, A. E. (2014). Compassion at work. *Annual Reviews of Organizational Psychology and Organizational Behaviour, 1*(1), 277-304.

26. West, M. A., Dawson, J. F., Admasachew, L., & Topakas, A. (2011). NHS staff management and health service quality: *Results from the NHS Staff Survey and related data.* Report to the Department of Health, available at: *https://assets.publishing.service.gov.uk/government/uploads/system/uploads/attachment_data/file/215455/dh_129656.pdf*

27. Lilius, J. M., Worline, M. C., Maitlis, S., Kanov, J. M., Dutton, J. E., & Frost, P. (2008). The contours and consequences of compassion at work. *Journal of Organizational Behavior, 29*(2), 193-218.

28. Fredrickson, B. (2013). Love 2.0: *How our supreme emotion affects everything we feel, think, do, and become.* New York: Hudson Street Press.

29. Worline, M., & Dutton, J. E. (2017). *Awakening compassion at work: The quiet power that elevates people and organizations.* San Francisco: Berrett-Koehler Publishers.

30. Curry, O. S., Rowland, L. A., Van Lissa, C. J., Zlotowitz, S., McAlaney, J., & Whitehouse, H. (2018). Happy to help? A systematic review and meta-analysis of the effects of performing acts of kindness on the well-being of the actor. *Journal of Experimental Social Psychology, 76,* 320-329.

31. Fredrickson, B. L. (2006). *Unpacking positive emotions: Investigating the seeds of human flourishing. The Journal of Positive Psychology, 1*(2), 57-59.

32. Lawrence, T. B., & Maitlis, S. (2012). Care and possibility: Enacting an ethic of care through narrative practice. *Academy of Management Review, 37*(4), 641-663.

33. Nelson, S. K., Layous, K., Cole, S. W., & Lyubomirsky, S. (2016). Do unto others or treat yourself? The effects of prosocial and self-focused behavior on psychological flourishing. *Emotion, 16*(6), 850–861.

34. Porath, C., & Pearson, C. (2009). How toxic colleagues corrode performance. *Harvard Business Review, 87*(4).

35. Richardson, J. & West, M. A. (2009) Dream teams: A positive psychology of team working. In A. Lindley, S. Harrington, & N. Page, (Eds.) *Oxford handbook of positive psychology and work.* (pp. 235-250). New York: Oxford University Press.

36. West, M. A. (2012). *Effective teamwork: Practical lessons from organizational research* (3rd ed.). Oxford: Blackwell Publishing.

37. West, M.A., Topakas, A., & Dawson, J.F. (2014). Climate and culture for healthcare performance. In B. Schneider & K. M. Barbera (Eds.), *The Oxford Handbook of Organizational Climate and Culture.* (pp. 335-359). Oxford: Oxford University Press.

38. Eckert, R., West, M. A., Altman, D., Steward, K., & Pasmore, B. (2014). *Delivering a collective leadership strategy for health care.* Center for Creative Leadership/The King's Fund.

Chapter 5

1. Baumeister, R. F., & Leary, M. R. (1995). The need to belong: desire for interpersonal attachments as a fundamental human motivation. *Psychological bulletin, 117*(3), 497-529.

2. Bliese, P. D., Edwards, J. R., & Sonnentag, S. (2017). Stress and well-being at work: a century of empirical trends reflecting theoretical and societal influences. *The Journal of Applied Psychology, 102*(3), 389–402.

3. Porath, C., & Pearson, C. (2009). How toxic colleagues corrode performance. *Harvard Business Review, 87*(4).

4. West, M. A., & Markiewicz, L. (2016). Effective team work in healthcare. In E. Ferlie, K. Montgomery, & R. Pedersen (Eds.), *The Oxford handbook of healthcare management.* (pp. 231-252). Oxford: Oxford University Press.

5. West, M. A., & Lyubovnikova, J. (2012). Real teams or pseudo teams? The changing landscape needs a better map. *Industrial and Organizational Psychology, 5*(1), 25–28.

6. West, M. A. (2012). Effective teamwork: *Practical lessons from organisational research* (3rd ed.). Oxford: Blackwell Publishing.

7. Edmondson, A. C. (2012). Teaming: *How organisations learn, innovate, and compete in the knowledge economy.* San Francisco: Jossey-Bass.

8. Lyubovnikova, J., West, M. A., Dawson, J. F., & Carter, M. R. (2015). 24-karat or fool's gold? Consequences of real team and co-acting group membership in healthcare organisations. *European Journal of Work and Organisational Psychology, 24*(6), 929–950.

9. West, M. A., & Lyubovnikova, J. R. (2013). Illusions of team working in healthcare. *Journal of Health Organization and Management, 27*(1), 134-142.

10. NHS England. (2019). *NHS Staff Survey results 2019: detailed spreadsheets.* Survey Coordination Centre. Retrieved August 5, 2020, from *https://www.nhsstaffsurveys.com/Page/1106/Past-Results/Staff-Survey-2019-Detailed-Spreadsheets/*

11. Edmondson, A. C., & Lei, Z. (2014). Psychological safety: The history, renaissance, and future of an interpersonal construct. *Annual Review of Organizational Psychology and Organizational Behavior, 1*(1), 23–43.

12. West, M. A., Lyubovnikova, J., Eckert, R., & Denis, J. L. (2014). Collective leadership for cultures of high-quality healthcare. *Journal of Organizational Effectiveness: People and Performance, 1*(3), 240–260.

13. Hughes, A. M., Gregory, M. E., Joseph, D. L., Sonesh, S. C., Marlow, S. L., Lacerenza, C. N., Benishek, L. E., King, H. B., & Salas, E. (2016). Saving lives: a meta-analysis of team training in healthcare. *Journal of Applied Psychology, 101*(9), 1266-1304.

14. Borrill, C., West, M. A., Shapiro, D., & Rees, A. (2000). Team working and effectiveness in health care. *British Journal of Healthcare Management, 6*(8), 364–371.

15. West, M., & Coia, D. (2019). *Caring for doctors, caring for patients. How to transform UK healthcare environments to support doctors and medical students to care for patients.* General Medical Council. *https://www.gmc-uk.org/-/media/documents/caring-for-doctors-caring-for-patients_pdf-80706341.pdf*

16. Borrill, C. S., Carletta, J., Carter, A. J., Dawson, J., Garrod, S., Rees, A., Richards, A., Shapiro, D., & West, M. A. (2000). *The effectiveness of health care teams in the National Health Service.* Birmingham: Aston Centre for Health Service Organisation Research.

17. Poulton, B. C., & West, M. A. (1993). Effective multidisciplinary teamwork in primary healthcare. *Journal of Advanced Nursing, 18*(6), 918–925.

18. Tannenbaum, S. I., & Cerasoli, C. P. (2013). Do team and individual debriefs enhance performance? A meta-analysis. *Human Factors, 55*(1), 231-245.

19. Carter, A. J., & West, M. A. (1999). Sharing the burden - teamwork in healthcare settings. In J. Firth-Cozens & R. Payne (Eds.), *Stress in health professionals.* (pp. 191-202). Chichester: John Wiley & Sons, Ltd.

20. Richter, A. W., Dawson, J. F., & West, M. A. (2011). The effectiveness of teams in organisations: A meta-analysis. *The International Journal of Human Resource Management, 22*(13), 2749-2769.

21. Buttigieg, S., West, M. A., & Dawson, J. F. (2011). Well-structured teams and the buffering of hospital employees from stress. *Health Services Management Research, 24*(4), 203–212.

22. Firth-Cozens, J. (2001). Cultures for improving patient safety through learning: The role of teamwork. *Quality in Health Care, 10*(Suppl. 2), ii26–ii31.

23. Richardson, J., West, M. A., & Cuthbertson, B. H. (2010). Team working in intensive care: Current evidence and future endeavors. *Current Opinion in Critical Care, 16*(6), 643-648.

24. Nembhard, I. M., & Edmondson, A. C. (2006). Make it safe: The effects of leader inclusiveness and professional status on psychological safe and improvement efforts in healthcare teams. *Journal of Organizational Behavior, 27*(7), 941-966.

25. Lewis, P. J., & Tully, M. P. (2009). Uncomfortable prescribing decisions in hospitals: The impact of teamwork. *Journal of the Royal Society of Medicine, 102*(11), 481–488.

26. Fay, D., Borrill, C. S., Amir, Z., & West, M. A. (2006). Getting the most out of multidisciplinary teams: A multi-sample study on team innovation in healthcare. *Journal of Occupational and Organizational Psychology, 79*(4), 553-567.

27. Jansson, A., Isaccsson, A., & Lindhom, L. H. (1992). Organization of healthcare teams and the population's contacts with primary care. *Scandinavian Journal of Primary Health Care, 10*(4), 257-265.

28. West, M. A., Borrill, C. S., Dawson, J., Scully, J., Carter, M., Anelay, S., Patterson, M., & Waring, J. (2002). The link between the management of employees and patient mortality in acute hospitals. *The International Journal of Human Resource Management, 13*(8), 1299-1310.

29. West, M. A., Dawson, J. F., Admasachew, L., & Topakas, A. (2011). NHS staff management and health service quality: *Results from the NHS Staff Survey and related data.* Report to the Department of Health. *https://assets.publishing.service.gov.uk/government/uploads/system/ uploads/attachment_data/file/215455/dh_129656.pdf*

30. Lyubovnikova, J., West, M. A., Dawson, J. F., & Carter, M. R. (2015). 24-karat or fool's gold? Consequences of real team and co-acting group membership in healthcare organisations. *European Journal of Work and Organisational Psychology, 24*(6), 929-950.

31. Sommers, L. S., Marton, K. I., Barbaccia, J. C., & Randolph, J. (2000). Physician, nurse, and social worker collaboration in primary care for chronically ill seniors. *Archives of Internal Medicine, 160*(12), 1825-1833.

32. West, M. A. (1990). The social psychology of innovation in groups. In M. A. West & J. L. Farr (Eds.), *Innovation and creativity at work: Psychological and organisational strategies.* (pp. 309-333). Chichester: John Wiley & Sons, Ltd.

33. Lyubovnikova, J., & West, M. A. (2013). Why teamwork matters: Enabling healthcare team effectiveness for the delivery of high-quality patient care. In E. Salas, S. I. Tannembaum, D. Cohen, & G. Latham (Eds.), *Developing and enhancing teamwork in organisations.* (pp. 331-372). San Francisco: Jossey Bass.

34. Hewstone, M., & Swart, H. (2011). FiftyÐodd years of interÐgroup contact: From hypothesis to integrated theory. *British Journal of Social Psychology, 50*(3), 374-386.

35. Van Knippenberg, D., Dawson, J. F., West, M. A., & Homan, A. C. (2011). Diversity faultlines, shared objectives, and top management team performance. *Human Relations, 64*(3), 307-336.

36. Locke, E. A., & Latham, G. P. (Eds.). (2013). *New developments in goal setting and task performance.* London: Routledge.

37. Soderfjall, S., & Svensson, C. (2020). *A little book on goals.* Umea, Sweden: Amazon.

38. Schippers, M. C., West, M. A., & Dawson, J. F. (2015). Team reflexivity and innovation: The moderating role of team context. *Journal of Management, 41*(3), 769–788.

39. West, M. A. (1996). Reflexivity and work group effectiveness: A conceptual integration. In. M.A. West (Ed.), *The handbook of work group psychology.* (pp. 555-579). Chichester: John Wiley & Sons, Ltd.

40. West, M. A. (2000). Reflexivity, revolution, and innovation in work teams. In M. M. Beyerlein, D. A. Johnson, & S. T. Beyerlein (Eds.), *Product development teams.* (pp. 1-29). Stamford, Connecticut: JAI Press.

41. Schippers, M. C., Edmondson, A. C., & West, M. A. (2020). Team reflexivity. In L. Argote & J. M. Levine (Eds.), *The Oxford handbook of group and organisational learning.* (pp. 175-193). Oxford: Oxford University Press.

42. Berwick, D. (2013). A promise to learn – a commitment to act: *Improving the safety of patients in England.* London: Department of Health and Social Care.

43. West, M. A., Borrill, C. S., Dawson, J. F., Brodbeck, F., Shapiro, D. A., & Haward, B. (2003). Leadership clarity and team innovation in healthcare. *The Leadership Quarterly, 14*(4-5), 393-410.

44. Liu, D., Chen, X. P., & Yao, X. (2011). From autonomy to creativity: A multilevel investigation of the mediating role of harmonious passion. *Journal of Applied Psychology, 96*(2), 294-309.

45. Somech, A. (2006). The effects of leadership style and team process on performance and innovation in functionally heterogeneous teams. *Journal of Management, 32*(1), 132-157.

46. Hirst, G., Van Knippenberg, D., Chen, C. H., & Sacramento, C. A. (2011). How does bureaucracy impact individual creativity? A cross-level investigation of team contextual influences on goal orientation–creativity relationships. *Academy of Management Journal, 54*(3), 624-641.

47. Kiesler, S., & Sproull, L. (1992). Group decision making and communication technology. *Organizational Behavior and Human Decision Processes, 52*(1), 96–123.

48. Kiesler, S., & Cummings, J. N. (2002). What do we know about proximity and distance in work groups? A legacy of research. In P. Hinds & S. Kiesler (Eds.), *Distributed work.* (pp. 57–82). Cambridge, MA: MIT Press.

49. Axtell, C. M., Fleck, S. J., & Turner, N. (2004). Virtual teams: Collaborating across distance. In C.L. Cooper & I.T. Robertson (Eds.), *International review of industrial and organizational psychology: Volume 19.* (pp. 205–248). Chichester: John Wiley & Sons, Ltd.

50. Gluesing, J. C., Alcordo, T. C., Baba, M. L., Britt, D., Wagner, K. H., McKether, W., Monplaisir, L., Ratner, H. H., & Riopelle, K. (2003). The development of global virtual teams. In C. B. Gibson & S. G. Cohen (Eds.), *Virtual teams that work: Creating conditions for virtual team effectiveness.* (pp. 353–380). San Francisco: Jossey-Bass.

51. Paulus, P. B. (2000). Groups, teams and creativity: The creative potential of idea- generating groups. *Applied Psychology: An International Review, 49*(2), 237–262.

52. Tjosvold, D. (1991). *Team organisation: An enduring competitive advantage.* Chichester: John Wiley & Sons, Ltd.

53. Tjosvold, D. (1998). Cooperative and competitive goal approaches to conflict: Accomplishments and challenges. *Applied Psychology: An International Review, 47*(3), 285–342.

54. De Dreu, C. K. W., & De Vries, N. K. (1997). Minority dissent in organisations. In C.K.W. De Dreu & E. Van De Vliert (Eds.), *Using conflict in organisations.* (pp. 72–86). London: Sage.

55. Gallo, A. (2017). *HBR Guide to Dealing with Conflict (HBR Guide Series)*. Harvard: Harvard Business Review Press.

56. Van Knippenberg, D., van Ginkel, W. P., & Homan, A. C. (2013). Diversity mindsets and the performance of diverse teams. *Organizational Behavior and Human Decision Processes, 121*(2), 183-193.

57. Johnson, S., Osborn, D. P., Araya, R., Wearn, E., Paul, M., Stafford, M., & Anderson, E. (2012). Morale in the English mental health workforce: Questionnaire survey. *The British Journal of Psychiatry, 201*(3), 239-246.

58. Carter, M. R., & Tourangeau, A. E. (2012). Staying in nursing: What factors determine whether nurses intend to remain employed? *Journal of Advanced Nursing, 68*(7), 1589-1600.

59. West, M. A., Bailey, S., & Williams, E. (2020). *The courage of compassion: Supporting nurses and midwives to deliver care across our community*. London: The King's Fund.

60. Sousa, M., & van Dierendonck, D. (2017). Servant leadership and the effect of the interaction between humility, action, and hierarchical power on follower engagement. *Journal of Business Ethics, 141*(1), 13-25.

Chapter 6

1. McCauley, C., & Fick-Cooper, L. (2020). *Direction, alignment, commitment: Achieving better results through leadership.* Greensboro, NC: Center for Creative Leadership.

2. West, M. A., Lyubovnikova, J., Eckert, R., & Denis, J. L. (2014). Collective leadership for cultures of high quality health care. *Journal of Organisational Effectiveness: People and Performance, 1*(3), 240-260.

3. McCauley, C. (2011). *Making leadership happen.* Greensboro, NC: Center for Creative Leadership.

4. Dixon-Woods, M., Baker, R., Charles, K., Dawson, J., Jerzembek, G., Martin, G., McCarthy, I., McKee, L., Minion, J., Ozieranski, P., Willars, J., Wilkie, P., & West, M. (2013). Culture and behaviour in the English National Health Service: Overview of lessons from a large multimethod study. *British Medical Journal Quality and Safety, 23*(2), 106-115.

5. Avolio, B. J., & Gardner, W. L. (2005). Authentic leadership development: Getting to the root of positive forms of leadership. *The Leadership Quarterly, 16*(3), 315–338.

6. Brown, M. E., & Trevino, L. K. (2009). Leader-follower value congruence: Are socialized charismatic leaders better able to achieve it? *Journal of Applied Psychology, 94*(2), 478-490.

7. Schein, E. (2004). *Organizational Culture and Leadership* (3rd ed.). San Francisco, CA: Jossey Bass.

8. West, M. A. (2013), Creating a culture of high-quality care in health services. *Global Economics and Management Review, 18*(2), 40-44.

9. Ham, C. (2014). *Reforming the NHS from within. Beyond hierarchy, inspection and markets.* The King's Fund. *https://www.kingsfund.org. uk/sites/files/kf/field/field_publication_file/reforming-the-nhs-from-within-kingsfund-jun14.pdf*

10. Soderfjall, S., & Svensson, C. (2020). *A little book on goals.* Umea, Sweden: Amazon.

11. Locke, E. A., & Latham, G. P. (2013). *New developments in goal setting and task performance.* East Sussex: Routledge.

12. Wageman, R., Nunes, D. A., Burruss, J. A., & Hackman, J. R. (2008). *Senior leadership teams: What it takes to make them great.* Boston, MA: Harvard Business School Press.

13. West, M. A., Dawson, J. F., Admasachew, L., & Topakas, A. (2011). *NHS staff management and health service quality: Results from the NHS Staff Survey and related data.* Report to the Department of Health. *https://assets.publishing.service.gov.uk/government/uploads/system/uploads/attachment_data/file/215455/dh_129656.pdf*

14. Schneider, B., White, S. S., & Paul, M. C. (1998). Linking service climate and customer perceptions of service quality: Tests of a causal model. *Journal of Applied Psychology, 83*(2), 150-163.

15. Schneider, B., Ehrhart, M. G., Mayer, D. M., Saltz, J. L., & Niles-Jolly, K. (2005). Understanding organization-customer links in service settings. *Academy of Management Journal, 48*(6), 1017-1032.

16. Schneider, B., & Barbera, K. M. (2014). Introduction: the Oxford handbook of organizational climate and culture. In B. Schneider & K. M. Barbera (Eds.), *The Oxford handbook of organizational climate and culture.* (pp. 3-20). Oxford: Oxford University Press.

17. Yagil, D. (2014). Service quality. In B. Schneider & K. M. Barbera (Eds.), *The Oxford handbook of organizational climate and culture.* (pp. 297-316). Oxford: Oxford University Press.

18. West M. A., & Dawson, J. F. (2011). *NHS staff management and health service quality.* Department of Health and Social Care. *https://assets.publishing.service.gov.uk/government/uploads/system/uploads/attachment_data/file/215454/dh_129658.pdf*

19. Wong, C. A., & Cummings, G. G. (2007), The relationship between nursing leadership and patient outcomes: A systematic review. *Journal of Nursing Management, 15*(5), 508-521.

20. Carter, A. J., & West, M. A. (1999). Sharing the burden: Teamwork in health care settings. In J. Firth-Cozens & R. Payne (Eds.), *Stress in health professionals: Psychological causes and interventions.* (pp. 191-202). Chichester: Wiley.

21. Mickan, M. S., & Rodger, S. A. (2005). Effective health care teams: A model of six characteristics developed from shared perceptions. *Journal of Interprofessional Care, 19*(4), 358-370.

22. West, M. A., Borrill, C. S., Dawson, J., Scully, J., Carter, M., Anelay, S., Patterson, M., & Waring, J. (2002). The link between the management of employees and patient mortality in acute hospitals. *The International Journal of Human Resource Management, 13*(8), 1299-1310.

23. West, M. A., Guthrie, J. P., Dawson, J. F., Borrill, C. A., & Carter, M. (2006). Reducing patient mortality in hospitals: The role of human resource management. *Journal of Organizational Behavior, 27*(7), 983-1002.

24. West, M., & Dawson, J. (2012). *Employee engagement and NHS performance*. The King's Fund.

25. Bakker, A. B. (2011). An evidence-based model of work engagement. *Current Directions in Psychological Science, 20*(4), 265-269.

26. Bakker, A. B., Schaufeli, W. B., Leiter, M. P., & Taris, T. W. (2008). Work engagement: An emerging concept in occupational health psychology. *Work and Stress, 22*(3), 187-200.

27. Bakker, A. B., van Emmerik, H., & Euwema, M. C. (2006). Crossover of burnout and engagement in work teams. *Work and Occupations, 33*(4), 464-489.

28. Schaufeli, W. B., & Bakker, A. B. (2004). Job demands, job resources and their relationship with burnout and engagement: A multi-sample study. *Journal of Organizational Behavior, 25*(3), 293-315.

29. West, M. A., Topakas, A., & Dawson, J. F. (2014). Climate and culture for health care performance. In B. Schneider & Barbera, K. M. (Eds.), *The Oxford handbook of organizational climate and culture.* (pp. 335-359). Oxford: Oxford University Press.

30. Bono, J. E., Glomb, T. M., Shen, W., Kim, E., & Koch, A. J. (2013). Building positive resources: Effects of positive events and positive reflection on work stress and health. *Academy of Management Journal, 55*(6), 1601-1627.

31. West, M., & Coia, D. D. (2019). *Caring for doctors, caring for patients.* General Medical Council.

32. West, M., Bailey, S., & Williams, E. (2020). *The courage of compassion: Supporting nurses and midwives to deliver high quality care.* London: The King's Fund/RCN Foundation.

33. Macey, W. H., Schneider, B., Barbera, K. M., & Young, S. A. (2009). Employee engagement: Tools for analysis, practice and competitive advantage. Chichester: Wiley.

34. Norman, S. M., Avolio, B. J., & Luthans, F. (2010). The impact of positivity and transparency on trust in leaders and their perceived effectiveness. *The Leadership Quarterly, 21*(3), 350-364.

35. Graen, G. B., & Uhl-Bien, M. (1995), Relationship-based approach to leadership: Development of leader-member exchange (LMX) theory of leadership over 25 years: Applying a multi-level multi-domain perspective. *The Leadership Quarterly, 6*(2), 219-247.

36. Soderfjall, S. (2019). *A little book on leadership.* Umea, Sweden: Amazon.

37. Stone, D. N., Deci, E. L., & Ryan, R. M. (2009). Beyond talk: Creating autonomous motivation through self-determination theory. *Journal of General Management, 34*(3), 75-91.

38. Holt-Lunstad, J., Smith, T. B., Baker, M., Harris, T., & Stephenson, D. (2015). Loneliness and social isolation as risk factors for mortality: A meta-analytic review. *Perspectives on Psychological Science, 10*(2), 227-237.

39. West, M. A., Bailey, S., & Williams, E. (2020). *The courage of compassion: Supporting nurses and midwives to deliver care across our communities.* The King's Fund.

Chapter 7

1. Guillaume, Y. R. F., Dawson, J. F., Woods, S. A., Sacramento, C. A., & West, M. A. (2013). Getting diversity at work to work: What we know and what we still don't know. *Journal of Occupational and Organizational Psychology, 86*(2), 123-141.

2. Guillaume, Y. R. F., Dawson, J. F., Priola, V., Sacramento, C. A., Woods, S. A., Higson, H. E., Budhwar, P. S., & West, M. A. (2014). Managing diversity in organizations: An integrative model and agenda for future research. *European Journal of Work and Organizational Psychology, 23*(5), 783-802.

3. Guillaume, Y. R. F., Dawson, J. F., Otaye-Ebede, L., Woods, S. A., West, M. A. (2017). Harnessing demographic differences in organizations: What moderates the effects of workplace diversity? *Journal of Organizational Behavior, 38*(2), 276-303.

4. Lyubovnikova, J., West, M. (2013). Why teamwork matters: Enabling health care team effectiveness for the delivery of high quality patient care. In E. Salas, S. Tannembaum, D. Cohen & G. Latham (Eds.), *Developing and enhancing teamwork in organizations.* (pp. 331-372). San Francisco: Jossey Bass.

5. West, M. A., & Markiewicz, L. (2016). Effective team work in health care. In E. Ferlie, K. Montgomery & R. Pedersen (Eds.), The Oxford handbook of health care management. (pp. 231-252). Oxford: Oxford University Press.

6. West, M. A., Borrill C. S., Dawson, J. F., Brodbeck, F., Shapiro, D. A., & Haward, B. (2003). Leadership clarity and team innovation in health care. *The Leadership Quarterly, 14*(4-5), 393-410.

7. NHS Constitution for England. (2012). Department of Health and Social Care. *https://www.gov.uk/government/publications/the-nhs-constitution-for-england*

8. West, M., & Coia, D. (2019). *Caring for doctors, caring for patients.* General Medical Council.

9. West, M. A., Bailey, S., & Williams, E. (2020). *The courage of compassion: Supporting nurses and midwives to deliver high quality care.* The King's Fund.

10. Maguire, A. (2016). *Illustrating equality vs equity* [Image]. Interaction Institute for Social Change. *https://interactioninstitute.org/illustrating-equality-vs-equity/*

11. King, E. B., Dawson, J. F., West, M. A., Gilrane, V. L., Peddie, C. I., & Bastin, L. (2011). Why organizational and community diversity matter: Representativeness and the emergence of incivility and organizational performance. *Academy of Management Journal, 54*(6), 1103-1118.

12. Mumford, M. D. (Ed.). (2011). *Handbook of organizational creativity.* San Diego: Academic Press Inc.

13. De Dreu, C. K. W. (1997). Productive conflict: The importance of conflict management and conflict issue. In C. K. W. de Dreu & E. van de Vliert (Eds.), *Using conflict in organizations.* (pp. 9-22). London: Sage.

14. West, M. A., Hirst, G., Richter, A., & Shipton, H. (2004). Twelve steps to heaven: Successfully managing change through developing innovative teams. *European Journal of Work and Organizational Psychology, 13*(2), 269-299.

15. Cornelis, I., Van Hiel, A., & De Cremer, D. (2011). Birds of a feather: Leader-follower similarity and procedural fairness effects on cooperation. *European Journal of Work and Organizational Psychology, 20*(3), 388-415.

16. Graen, G. B., & Uhl-Bien, M. (1995). Relationship-based approach to leadership: Development of leader-member exchange (LMX) theory of leadership over 25 years: Applying a multi-level multi-domain perspective. *Leadership Quarterly, 6*(2), 219-247.

17. King, E. B., Botsford, W., Hebl, M. R., Kazama, S., Dawson, J. F., & Perkins, A. (2012). Benevolent sexism at work: Gender differences in the distribution of challenging developmental experiences. *Journal of Management, 38*(6), 1835-1866.

18. Pelled, L. H., Eisenhardt, K. M., & Xin, K. R. (1999). Exploring the black box: An analysis of work group diversity, conflict, and performance. *Administrative Science Quarterly, 44*(1), 1-28.

19. Gallo, A. (2017). *HBR guide to dealing with conflict (HBR guide series).* Boston, Massachusetts: Harvard Business Review Press.

20. Tjosvold, D. (1991). *Team organization: An enduring competitive advantage.* Chichester: Wiley.

21. Watson, W. E., Kumar, K., & Michaelsen, L. K. (1993). Cultural diversity's impact on interaction process and performance: Comparing homogenous and diverse task groups. *Academy of Management Journal, 36*(3), 590-602.

22. Nadeem, S. (2020). *Being an inclusion ally.* London: Care Quality Commission.

23. West M. A., Dawson, J. F., & Kaur, M. (2015). *Making the difference: Diversity and inclusion in the NHS.* The King's Fund.

24. Avery, D. R., McKay, P. F., & Wilson, D. C. (2008). What are the odds? How demographic similarity affects the prevalence of perceived employment discrimination. *Journal of Applied Psychology, 93*(2), 235-249.

25. Avery, D. R., McKay, P. F., Tonidandel, S., Volpone, S. D., & Morris, M. A. (2012). Is there method to the madness? Examining how racioethnic matching influences retail store productivity. *Personnel Psychology, 65*(1), 167-199.

26. Downey, S. N., van der Werff, L., Thomas, K. M., & Plaut, V. C. (2015). The role of diversity practices and inclusion in promoting trust and employee engagement. *Journal of Applied Social Psychology, 45*(1), 35-44.

27. Williams, D. R., & Mohammed, S. A. (2013). Racism and health I: Pathways and scientific evidence. *American Behavioral Scientist, 57*(8), 1152-1173.

28. Byrne, B., Alexander, C., Khan, O., Nazroo, J., & Shankley, W. (2020). *Ethnicity, race and inequality in the UK: state of the nation.* Bristol: Policy Press.

29. Bezrukova, K., Spell, C. S., Perry, J. L., & Jehn, K. A. (2016). A meta-analytical integration of over 40 years of research on diversity training evaluation. *Psychological Bulletin, 142*(11), 1227-1274.

30. Bezrukova, K., Jehn, K. A., & Spell, C. S. (2012). Reviewing diversity training: Where we have been and where we should go. *Academy of Management Learning & Education, 11*(2), 207-227.

31. Groggins, A., & Ryan, A. M. (2013). Embracing uniqueness: The underpinnings of a positive climate for diversity. *Journal of Occupational and Organizational Psychology, 86*(2), 264-282.

32. Dixon-Woods, M., Baker, R., Charles, K., Dawson, J., Jerzembek, G., Martin, G., McCarthy, I., McKee, L., Minion, J., Ozieranski, P., Willars, J., Wilkie, P., & West, M. (2014). Culture and behaviour in the English National Health Service: Overview of lessons from a large multimethod study. *British Medical Journal Quality and Safety, 23*(2), 106-115.

33. Triana, M. D. C., & Garcia, M. F. (2009). Valuing diversity: A groupÐvalue approach to understanding the importance of organizational efforts to support diversity. *Journal of Organizational Behavior, 30*(7), 941-962.

34. Naumann, S. E., & Bennett, N. (2000). A case for procedural justice climate: Development and test of a multilevel model. *Academy of Management Journal, 43*(5), 881-889.

35. Colquitt, J. A. (2001). On the dimensionality of organizational justice: A construct validation of a measure. *Journal of Applied Psychology, 86*(3), 386-400.

36. NHS Workforce Race Equality Standard. (2019). *NHS workforce race equality standard. 2019 data analysis report for NHS Trusts.* NHS. Retrieved March 23, 2021, from *https://www.england.nhs.uk/wp-content/uploads/2020/01/wres-2019-data-report.pdf*

37. NHS Digital. (2018). *NHS workforce statistics - June 2018 - including supplementary analysis on pay by ethnicity.* Retrieved August 21, 2020, from *https://digital.nhs.uk/data-and-information/publications/statistical/nhs-workforce-statistics/june-2018*

38. Lindsey, A. P., Avery, D. R., Dawson, J. F., & King, E. B. (2017). Investigating why and for whom management ethnic representativeness influences interpersonal mistreatment in the workplace. *Journal of Applied Psychology, 102*(11), 1545-1563.

Chapter 8

1. Curtis, E. A., Beirne, M., Cullen, J. G., Northway, N., & Corrigan, S. (Eds.). (2021). *Distributed leadership in nursing and healthcare: Theory, evidence and development.* London: Open University Press.

2. West, M. A., Lyubovnikova, J., Eckert, R., & Denis, J. L. (2014). Collective leadership for cultures of high-quality healthcare. *Journal of Organizational Effectiveness: People and Performance, 1*(3), 240-260.

3. McAuliffe, E., De Brún, A., Ward, M., O'Shea, M., Cunningham, U., O'Donovan, R., McGinley, S., Fitzsimons, J., Corrigan, S., & McDonald, N. (2017). Collective leadership and safety cultures (Co-Lead): protocol for a mixed-methods pilot evaluation of the impact of a co-designed collective leadership intervention on team performance and safety culture in a hospital group in Ireland. *BMJ Open, 7*(11), e017569.

4. Eckert, R., West, M. A., Altman, D., Steward, K., & Pasmore, B. (2014). *Delivering a collective leadership strategy.* London: Center for Creative Leadership/The King's Fund.

5. West, M. A., Steward, K., Eckert, R. & Pasmore, B. (2014). *Developing a collective leadership strategy for health care.* London: Center for Creative Leadership/The King's Fund.

6. Woods, S. & West, M. A. (2019). *The psychology of work and organizations* (3rd edition). London: Cengage.

7. Bakker, A. B. (2011). An evidence-based model of work engagement. *Current Directions in Psychological Science, 20*(4), 265-269.

8. West, M., & Dawson, J. (2012). *Employee engagement and NHS performance.* The King's Fund. *https://www.kingsfund.org.uk/sites/default/files/employee-engagement-nhs-performance-west-dawson-leadership-review2012-paper.pdf*

9. Dawson, J. (2018). *Links between NHS staff experience and patient satisfaction: Analysis of surveys from 2014 and 2015.* London: NHS England.

10. West, M. A., Armit, K., Loewenthal, L., Eckert, R., West, T., & Lee, A. (2015). *Leadership and leadership development in health care.* London: Faculty of Medical Leadership and Management and The King's Fund, Brussels: Center for Creative Leadership.

11. National Advisory Group on the Safety of Patients in England. (2013). *A promise to learn - a commitment to act.* Department of Health and Social Care.

12. West, M. A., Topakas, A., & Dawson, J. F. (2014). Climate and culture for health care performance. In B. Schneider & K. M. Barbera (Eds.), The Oxford handbook of organizational climate and culture. (pp. 335-359). Oxford: Oxford University Press.

13. De Brun, A., Anjara, S., Cunningham, U., Khurshid, Z., MacDonald, S., O'Donovan, R., Rogers, L., & McAuliffe, E. The collective leadership for safety culture (Co-Lead) team intervention to promote teamwork and patient safety. *International Journal of Environmental Research and Public Health, 17*(22), 8673.

14. McCauley, C. (2011). *Making leadership happen.* Greensboro, NC: Center for Creative Leadership.

15. Aime, F., Humphrey, S., DeRue, D. S., & Paul, J. B. (2014). The riddle of heterarchy: Power transitions in cross-functional teams. *Academy of Management Journal, 57*(2), 327-352.

16. D'Innocenzo, L., Mathieu, J. E., & Kukenberger, M. R. (2016). A meta-analysis of different forms of shared leadership—team performance relations. *Journal of Management, 42*(7), 1964-1991.

17. Carson, J. B., Tesluk, P. E., & Marrone, J. A. (2007). Shared leadership in teams: An investigation of antecedent conditions and performance. *Academy of Management Journal, 50*(5), 1217-1234.

18. McCauley, C., & Fick-Cooper, L. (2020). *Direction, alignment, commitment: Achieving better results through leadership.* Greensboro, NC: Center for Creative Leadership.

19. Browning, H. W., Torain, D. J., & Patterson, T. E. (2011). *Collaborative health care leadership.* Greensboro, NC: Center for Creative Leadership.

20. Ham, C., Baker, G. R., Docherty, J., Hockey, P., Lobley, K., Tugendhat, L., & Walshe, K. (2011). *The future of leadership and management in the NHS: No more heroes.* London: The King's Fund.

21. Ham, C. (2014). *Reforming the NHS from within. Beyond hierarchy, inspection and markets.* The King's Fund. *https://www.kingsfund.org.uk/sites/default/files/field/field_publication_file/reforming-the-nhs-from-within-kingsfund-jun14.pdf*

22. Chassin, M. R., & Loeb, J. M. (2013). High-reliability health care: Getting there from here. *Millbank Quarterly, 91*(3), 459-490.

23. Dixon-Woods, M. (2019). How to improve healthcare improvement - an essay by Mary Dixon-Woods. *British Medical Journal, 367,* I5514.

24. Liberati, E. G., Tarrant, C., Willars, J., Draycott, T., Winter, C., Kuberska, K., Paton, A., Marjanovic, S., Leach, B., Lichten, C., Hocking, L., Ball, S., & Dixon-Woods, M. (2020). Seven features of safety in maternity units: A framework based on multisite ethnography and stakeholder consultation. *BMJ Quality & Safety.*

25. Lyubovnikova, J., West, T. H., Dawson, J. F., & West, M. A. (2018). Examining the indirect effects of perceived organizational support for teamwork training on acute health care team productivity and innovation: The role of shared objectives. *Group & Organization Management, 43*(3), 382-413.

26. Lyubovnikova, J., West, M. A., Dawson, J. F., & Carter, M. R. (2015). 24-karat or fool's gold? Consequences of real team and co-acting group membership in healthcare organizations. *European Journal of Work and Organizational Psychology, 24*(6), 929-950.

27. West, M. A. & Lyubovnikova, J. R. (2013). Illusions of team working in health care. *Journal of Health Organization and Management, 27*(1), 134-142.

28. West, M. A., & Markiewicz, L. (2016). Effective team working in health care. In E. Ferlie, K. Montogomery & A. R. Pedersen (Eds.), The Oxford handbook of health care management. (pp. 231-252). Oxford University Press.

See also:

1. Bolden, R. (2011). Distributed leadership in organizations: A review of theory and research. *International Journal of Management Reviews, 13*(3), 251–269.

2. Denis, J. L., Langley, A., & Sergi, V. (2012). Leadership in the plural. *Academy of Management Annals, 6*(1), 1-73.

3. Fitzgerald, L., Ferlie, E., McGivern, J. & Buchanan, D. (2013). Distributed leadership patterns and service improvement: Evidence and argument from English healthcare. *The Leadership Quarterly, 24*(1), 227-239.

Chapter 9

1. Baumeister R. F., & Leary, M. R. (1995). The need to belong: Desire for interpersonal attachments as a fundamental human motivation. *Psychological Bulletin, 117*(3), 497-529.

2. Batson, C. D., Turk, C. L., Shaw, L. L., & Klein, T. R. (1995). Information function of empathic emotion: Learning that we value the other's welfare. *Journal of Personality and Social Psychology, 68*(2), 300–313.

3. Brown, S. L., Nesse, R. M., Vinokur, A. D., & Smith, D. M. (2003). Providing social support may be more beneficial than receiving it results from a prospective study of mortality. *Psychological Science, 14*(4), 320–327.

4. Worthington, E. L., & Scherer, M. (2004). Forgiveness is an emotion-focused coping strategy that can reduce health risks and promote health resilience: Theory, review, and hypotheses. *Psychology & Health, 19*(3), 385–405.

5. Porath, C., & Pearson, C. (2009). How toxic colleagues corrode performance. *Harvard Business Review, 87*(4).

6. Hewstone, M., & Swart, H. (2011). Fifty-odd years of inter-group contact: From hypothesis to integrated theory. *British Journal of Social Psychology, 50*(3), 374–386.

7. Lawrence, T. B., & Maitlis, S. (2012). Care and possibility: Enacting an ethic of care through narrative practice. *Academy of Management Review, 37*(4), 641–663.

8. Hulks, S., Walsh, N., Powell, M., Ham, C., & Alderwick, H. (2017). *Leading across the health and care system.* London: The King's Fund.

9. West, M. A., & Chowla, R. (2017). Compassionate leadership for compassionate health care. In P. Gilbert (Ed.), *Compassion: Concepts, research and applications.* (pp. 237-257). London: Routledge.

10. Senge, P., Hamilton, H., & Kania, J. (2014). The dawn of system leadership. *Stanford Social Innovation Review, 13*(1), 27–30.

11. Gallo, A. (2017). *HBR guide to dealing with conflict (HBR guide series).* Harvard Business Review Press.

12. Kilmann Diagnostics. *Take the Thomas-Kilmann Instrument | Improve How You Resolve Conflict.* Retrieved April 19 2021, from *https://www.kilmanndiagnostics.com/overview-thomas-kilmann-conflict-mode-instrument-tki*

13. Hardin, G. (1968). The tragedy of the commons. *Science, 162*(3859), 1243–1248.

14. Timmins, N., & Ham, C. (2013). *The quest for integrated health and social care: A case study in Canterbury, New Zealand.* The King's Fund. *https://www.kingsfund.org.uk/publications/quest-integrated-health-and-social-care*

15. Schluter, P. J., Hamilton, G. J., Deely, J. M., & Ardagh, M. W. (2016). Impact of integrated health system changes, accelerated due to an earthquake, on emergency department attendances and acute admissions: A Bayesian change-point analysis. BMJ Open, 6(5).

16. Fillingham, D., & Weir, B. (2014). *System leadership: Lessons and learning from AQuA's integrated care discovery communities.* The King's Fund. Retrieved April 20, 2017, from *https://www.kingsfund.org.uk/publications/system-leadership*

17. Collins, B. (2016). *New care models.* London: The King's Fund.

18. Timmins, N. (2015). *The practice of system leadership: Being comfortable with chaos.* The King's Fund. Retrieved April 20, 2017, from *https://www.kingsfund.org.uk/publications/practice-system-leadership*

19. Addicott, R., Walsh, N., Ham, C., & Shortell, S. (2014). *Accountable care organisations in the United States and England: Testing, evaluating and learning what works.* The King's Fund. Retrieved April 20, 2017, from *https://www.kingsfund.org.uk/publications/accountable-care-organisations-united-states-and-england*

20. Collins, B. (2015). *Intentional whole health system redesign: Southcentral Foundation's 'Nuka' system of care.* London: The King's Fund.

21. Gilbert, P. (2010). *The Compassionate Mind: A new approach to life's challenges.* Oakland, CA: New Harbinger Publications.

22. Trzeciak, S., & Mazzarelli, A. (2019). *Compassionomics: The revolutionary scientific evidence that caring makes a difference.* Pensacola, FL: Studer Group.

Chapter 10

1. West, M., Eckert, R., Collins, B., & Chowla, R. (2017). *Caring to change. How compassionate leadership can stimulate innovation in health care.* London: The King's Fund.

2. Shalley, C. E., & Zhou, J. (2008). Organizational creativity research: a historical overview. In J. Zhou & C. E. Shalley (Eds.), *Handbook of organisational creativity.* (pp. 3–31). New York: Lawrence Erlbaum.

3. Amabile, T. M. (1996). *Creativity in context.* Boulder, CO: Westview.

4. Oldham, G. R., & Cummings, A. (1996). Employee creativity: Personal and contextual factors at work. *Academy of Management Journal, 39*(3), 607–634.

5. West, M. A., & Farr, J. L. (1990). Innovation at work. In M. A. West & J. L. Farr (Eds.), *Innovation and creativity at work: Psychological and organisational strategies.* (pp. 3–13). Chichester: John Wiley & Sons.

6. Hoppe, M. H. (2007). *Active listening: Improve your ability to listen and lead.* Greensboro, NC: Center for Creative Leadership.

7. Ting, S. & Scisco, P. (2012). *The CCL handbook of coaching: a guide for the leader coach* (Vol. 30). Hoboken, NJ: John Wiley & Sons.

8. Strauss, K., Griffin, M. A., & Rafferty, A. E. (2009). Proactivity directed toward the team and organization: The role of leadership, commitment and roleÐbreadth selfÐefficacy. *British Journal of Management, 20*(3), 279–291.

9. Hackett, G., & Betz, N. E. (1981). A self-efficacy approach to the career development of women. *Journal of Vocational Behavior, 18*(3), 326–339.

10. Bledow, R., Rosing, K., & Frese, M. (2013). A dynamic perspective on affect and creativity. *Academy of Management Journal, 56*(2), 432–450.

11. Fredrickson, B. L. (2004). The broaden-and-build theory of positive emotions. *Philosophical Transactions of the Royal Society B: Biological Sciences, 359*(1449), 1367–1378.

12. Worthington, E. L., & Scherer, M. (2004). Forgiveness is an emotion-focused coping strategy that can reduce health risks and promote health resilience: Theory, review, and hypotheses. *Psychology & Health, 19*(3), 385–405.

13. Brown, S. L., Nesse, R. M., Vinokur, A. D., & Smith, D. M. (2003). Providing social support may be more beneficial than receiving it: Results from a prospective study of mortality. *Psychological Science, 14*(4), 320–327.

14. Batson, C. D., Turk, C. L., Shaw, L. L., & Klein, T. R. (1995). Information function of empathic emotion: Learning that we value the other's welfare. *Journal of Personality and Social Psychology, 68*(2), 300–313.

15. West, M. A., & Richter, A. W. (2007). Climates and cultures for innovation and creativity at work. In C. Ford (Ed.), *Handbook of organisational creativity.* (pp. 211–237). London: Taylor & Francis.

16. Dutton, J. E., Workman, K. M., & Hardin, A. E. (2014). Compassion at work. *Annual Reviews of Organisational Psychology and Organisational Behaviour, 1*(1), 277–304.

17. West, M. A., Topakas, A., & Dawson, J. F. (2014). Climate and culture for health care performance. In B. Schneider, K. M. Barbera (Eds.), *The Oxford handbook of organisational climate and culture.* (pp. 335–359). Oxford: Oxford University Press.

18. West, M. A. (1989). Innovation among health care professionals. *Social Behaviour, 4,* 173–184.

19. Bunce, D., & West, M. A. (1996). Stress management and innovation interventions at work. *Human Relations, 49*(2), 209–232.

20. Bunce, D., & West, M. A. (1995). Changing work environments: Innovative coping responses to occupational stress. *Work and Stress, 8*(4), 319–331.

21. Borrill, C., West, M. A., Shapiro, D., & Rees, A. (2000). Team working and effectiveness in health care. *British Journal of Health Care, 6*(8), 364–371.

22. West, M. A., & Anderson, N. (1996). Innovation in top management teams. *Journal of Applied Psychology, 81*(6), 680–693.

23. West, M. A., & Anderson, N. (1992). Innovation, cultural values and the management of change in British hospitals. *Work and Stress, 6*(3), 293–310.

24. West, M., & Coia, D. D. (2019). Caring for doctors *Caring for patients*. London: General Medical Council.

25. West, M. A., Bailey, S., & Williams, E. (2020). *The courage of compassion: Supporting nurses and midwives to deliver care across our communities.* London: The King's Fund.

26. Worline, M. C., & Dutton, J. E. (2017). *Awakening compassion at work: The quiet power that elevates people and organizations.* New York City: McGraw-Hill Education.

27. Schneider, B., González-Romá, V., Osstroff, C., & West, M. A. (2017). Organizational climate and culture: Reflections on the history of the constructs in Journal of Applied Psychology. *Journal of Applied Psychology, 102*(3), 468–482.

28. Dixon-Woods, M., Baker, R., Charles, K., Dawson, J., Jerzembek, G., Martin, G., McCarthy, I., McKee, L., Minion, J., Ozieranski, P., Willars, J., Wilkie, P., & West, M. (2014). Culture and behaviour in the English National Health Service: Overview of lessons from a large multimethod study. *BMJ Quality & Safety, 23*(2), 106–115.

29. Wall, T. D., Bolden, R. I., Borrill, C. S., Carter, A. J., Golya, D. A., Hardy, G. E., Haynes, C. E., Rick, J. E., Shapiro, D. A., & West, M. A. (1997). Minor psychiatric disorder in NHS trust staff: Occupational and gender differences. *The British Journal of Psychiatry, 171*(6), 519–523.

30. West, M. A. (2013). Creating a culture of high-quality care in health services. *Global Economics and Management Review, 18*(2), 40–44.

31. Ham, C. (2014). *Reforming the NHS from within: Beyond hierarchy, inspection and markets.* The King's Fund. Retrieved March 21, 2017, from *https://www.kingsfund.org.uk/sites/default/files/field/field_publication_file/reforming-the-nhs-from-within-kingsfund-jun14.pdf*

32. West, M. A. (2012). *Effective teamwork: practical lessons from organisational research* (3rd ed.). Oxford: Blackwell Publishing.

33. Mehta, P., & Shenoy, S. (2011). *Infinite vision: How Aravind became the world's greatest business case for compassion.* Oakland, CA: Berrett-Koehler Publishers.

34. Shah, J., & Murty, L. S. (2004). Compassionate, high quality care at low cost: The Aravind model – in conversation with Dr G Venkataswamy and R D Thulasiraj. *IIMB Management Review, 16*(3), 31-43.

35. Govindarajan, V., & Ramamurti, R. (2013). Delivering world-class health care, affordably. *Harvard Business Review, 91*(11), 117-122.

36. Aravind Eye Care System. *Manufacturing (Aurolab) - Aravind Eye Care System.* Retrieved March 22, 2017, from *https://aravind.org/aurolab/*

37. Ou, A. Y., Waldman, D. A., & Peterson, S. J. (2015). Do humble CEOs matter? An examination of CEO humility and firm outcomes. *Journal of Management, 44*(3), 1147-1173.

38. West, M. A., & Markiewicz, L. (2016). Effective team work in health care. In E. Ferlie, K. Montgomery & R. Pedersen (Eds.), *The Oxford handbook of health care management.* (pp. 231–252). Oxford: Oxford University Press.

39. Edmondson, A. (1999). Psychological safety and learning behavior in work teams. *Administrative Science Quarterly, 44*(2), 350–383.

40. Hamel, G. (1996). Strategy as revolution. *Harvard Business Review, 74*(4), 69–82.

41. Simons, T., Pelled, L. H., & Smith, K. A. (1999). Making use of difference: Diversity, debate, and decision comprehensiveness in top management teams. *Academy of Management Journal, 42*(6), 662–673.

42. Milliken, F. J., & Martins, L. L. (1996). Searching for common threads: Understanding the multiple effects of diversity in organisational groups. *Academy of Management Review, 21*(2), 402–433.

43. Paulus, P. (2000). Groups, teams, and creativity: The creative potential of ideaÐgenerating groups. *Applied Psychology, 49*(2), 237–262.

44. Pearce III, J. A., & Ravlin, E. C. (1987). The design and activation of self-regulating work groups. *Human Relations, 40*(11), 751–782.

45. Porac, J. F., & Thomas, H. (1990). Taxonomic mental models in competitor definition. *Academy of Management Review, 15*(2), 224–240.

46. De Dreu, C. K. W. (1997). Productive conflict: The importance of conflict management and conflict issue. In C. K. W. De Dreu & E. Van De Vliert (Eds.), *Using conflict in organisations.* (pp. 9–22). London: Sage Publications.

47. Tjosvold, D. (1998). Cooperative and competitive goal approach to conflict: Accomplishments and challenges. *Applied Psychology, 47*(3), 285–313.

48. Gallo, A. (2017). *HBR guide to dealing with conflict (HBR guide series).* Harvard Business Review Press.

49. Dunbar, K. (1997). How scientists think: On-line creativity and conceptual change in science. In T. B. Ward, S. M. Smith & J. Vaid (Eds.), *Creative thought: An investigation of conceptual structures and processes.* (pp. 461–493). Washington, DC: American Psychological Association.

50. Dunbar, K. (1995). How scientists really reason: Scientific reasoning in real-world laboratories. In R. J. Sternberg & J. E. Davidson (Eds.), *The nature of insight.* (pp. 365–395). Cambridge, MA: MIT Press.

51. West, M. A. (2002). Sparkling fountains or stagnant ponds: An integrative model of creativity and innovation implementation in work groups. *Applied Psychology, 51*(3), 355–387.

52. Radjou, N., Prabhu, J., & Ahuja, S. (2012). *Jugaad innovation: Think frugal, be flexible, generate breakthrough growth.* Hoboken, NJ: John Wiley & Sons.

53. Davidson, L. (2015). *Do frugal innovations lead to frugal outcomes? A case study of healthcare in India* [Unpublished undergraduate dissertation]. University of Pennsylvania.

54. Davies, P. (2012). Could a passage to India be a way to get more surgical experience? *BMJ, 345*: e6637.

55. Smith, R. (2012, May 8). Can Devi Shetty make healthcare affordable across the globe? *The BMJ opinion. https://blogs.bmj. com/bmj/2012/05/08/richard-smith-can-devi-shetty-make-health-careaffordable-across-the-globe/*

56. Bibby, J. (2015, March 13). Unleashing the caring potential of families: Taking an innovation from India to the US. *The Health Foundation. https://www.health.org.uk/blogs/unleashing-the-caring-potential-of-families-taking-an-innovation-from-india-to-the-us*

57. Eisenhardt, K. M., & Martin, J. A. (2000). Dynamic capabilities: what are they? *Strategic Management Journal, 21*(10–11), 1105–1121.

58. Lyubovnikova, J., & West, M. A. (2013). Why teamwork matters: Enabling health care team effectiveness for the delivery of high quality patient care. In S. Salas, I. Tannembaum, D. Cohen & G. Latham (Eds.), *Developing and enhancing teamwork in organisations.* (pp. 331–372). San Francisco, CA: Jossey Bass.

59. Lyubovnikova, J., West, M. A., Dawson, J. F., & Carter, M. R. (2015). 24-karat or fool's gold? Consequences of real team and co-acting group membership in healthcare organisations. *European Journal of Work and Organisational Psychology, 24*(6), 929–950.

60. Carter, A. J. W., & West, M. A. (1999). Sharing the burden: Teamwork in health care settings. In J. Firth-Cozens & R. Payne (Eds.), *Stress in health professionals: Psychological causes and interventions.* (pp. 191–202). Chichester: Wiley.

61. Sacramento, C. A., Sophie Chang, M. W. S., & West, M. A. (2006). Team innovation through collaboration. In M. M. Beyerlein, S. T. Beyerlein & F. A. Kennedy (Eds.), *Innovation through collaboration.* (pp. 81–112). Bingley: Emerald Group Publishing.

62. Richter, A. W., West, M. A., Van Dick, R., & Dawson, J. F. (2006). Boundary spanners' identification, intergroup contact, and effective intergroup relations. *Academy of Management Journal, 49*(6), 1252–1269.

63. Cherulnik, P. D., Donley, K. A., Wiewel, T. S. R., & Miller, S. R. (2001). Charisma is contagious: The effect of leaders' charisma on observers' affect. *Journal of Applied Social Psychology, 31*(10), 2149–2159.

64. George, J. M. (1995). Leader positive mood and group performance: The case of customer service. *Journal of Applied Social Psychology, 25*(9), 778–794.

65. George, J. M. (1990). Personality, affect, and behavior in groups. *Journal of Applied Psychology, 75*(2), 107–116.

66. Amabile, T. M., Barsade, S. G., Mueller, J. S., & Staw, B. M. (2005). Affect and creativity at work. *Administrative Science Quarterly, 50*(3), 367–403.

67. Isen, A. M., & Baron, R. A. (1991). Positive affect as a factor in organisational-behavior. *Research in Organizational Behavior, 13*, 1–53.

68. Totterdell, P. (2000). Catching moods and hitting runs: mood linkage and subjective performance in professional sport teams. *Journal of Applied Psychology, 85*(6), 848–859.

69. Totterdell, P., Kellett, S., Teuchmann, K., & Briner, R. B. (1998). Evidence of mood linkage in work groups. *Journal of Personality and Social Psychology, 74*(6), 1504–1515.

70. Hatfield, E., Cacioppo, J. T., & Rapson, L. R. (1992). Primitive emotional contagion. In M. S. Clark (Ed.), *Review of personality and social psychology: Emotion and social behavior* (Vol. 14). (pp. 151–177). Newbury Park, CA: Sage Publications.

71. Lilius, J. M., Kanov, J., Dutton, J. E., Worline, M. C., & Maitlis, S. (2011). Compassion revealed: what we know about compassion at work (and where we need to know more). In K. Cameron & G. Spreitzer (Eds.), *The Oxford handbook of positive organizational scholarship.* (pp. 273–287). New York: Oxford University Press.

72. Dutton, J. E., Workman, K. M., & Hardin, A. E. (2014). Compassion at work. *Annual Reviews of Organisational Psychology and Organisational Behaviour, 1*(1), 277–304.

73. Hirst, G., Van Knippenberg, D., Chen, C. H., & Sacramento, C. A. (2011). How does bureaucracy impact individual creativity? A cross-level investigation of team contextual influences on goal orientation–creativity relationships. *Academy of Management Journal, 54*(3), 624–641.

74. Liu, D., Chen, X. P., & Yao, X. (2011). From autonomy to creativity: A multilevel investigation of the mediating role of harmonious passion. *Journal of Applied Psychology, 96*(2), 294–309.

75. Somech, A (2006). The effects of leadership style and team process on performance and innovation in functionally heterogeneous teams. *Journal of Management, 32*(1), 132–157.

76. West, M. A., Dawson, J. F., Admasachew, L., & Topakas, A. (2011). *NHS staff management and health service quality: Results from the NHS Staff Survey and related data.* Department of Health and Social Care. Retrieved March 21, 2017, from *https://assets.publishing.service.gov.uk/ government/uploads/system/uploads/attachment_data/file/215455/ dh_129656.pdf*

77. West, M. A. (2013). Creating a culture of high-quality care in health services. *Global Economics and Management Review, 18*(2), 40–44.

78. Mickan, S. M., & Rodger, S. A. (2005). Effective health care teams: A model of six characteristics developed from shared perceptions. *Journal of Interprofessional Care, 1*(4), 358–370.

79. Anderson, N. R., & West, M. A. (1998). Measuring climate for work group innovation: development and validation of the team climate. *Journal of Organisational Behavior: The International Journal of Industrial, Occupational and Organisational Psychology and Behavior, 19*(3), 235-258.

Chapter 11

1. Neff, K., & Germer, C. (2018). *The mindful self-compassion workbook: A proven way to accept yourself, build inner strength, and thrive.* New York: Guilford Publications.

2. Neff, K. (2011). *Self-compassion.* London: Hachette UK.

3. Brach, T. (2003). *Radical acceptance: Embracing your life with the heart of a Buddha.* New York: Bantam.

4. Brown, B. (2010). *The gifts of imperfection.* Center City, MN: Hazelden.

5. Salzberg, S. (2005). *The force of kindness: Change your life with love and compassion.* Boulder, CO: Sounds True.

6. Neff, K. D., Kirkpatrick, K. L., & Rude, S. S. (2007). Self-compassion and adaptive psychological functioning. *Journal of Research in Personality, 41*(1), 139-154.

7. Super, A. (2015). *A year of self-compassion: Finding care, connection and calm in our challenging times.* Market Harborough: Matador.

8. Silberstein-Tirch, L. (2019). *How to be nice to yourself: The everyday guide to self-compassion.* San Antonio, TX: Althea Press.

9. Peterson, C., & Seligman, M. E. (2004). *Character strengths and virtues: A handbook and classification* (Vol. 1). New York: Oxford University Press.

10. Brach, T. (2019). *Radical compassion: Learning to love yourself and your world with the practice of RAIN.* London: Random House.

11. Braun, S. (2017). Leader narcissism and outcomes in organizations: A review at multiple levels of analysis and implications for future research. *Frontiers in Psychology, 8*(773), 1-22.

12. Inwood, E., & Ferrari, M. (2018). Mechanisms of change in the relationship between selfÐcompassion, emotion regulation, and mental health: A systematic review. *Applied Psychology: Health and WellÐ Being, 10*(2), 215-235.

13. Breines, J. G., & Chen, S. (2012). Self-compassion increases self-improvement motivation. *Personality and Social Psychology Bulletin, 38*(9), 1133-1143.

14. Dweck, C. (2016). What having a "growth mindset" actually means. *Harvard Business Review, 13*, 213-226.

15. Raab, K. (2014). Mindfulness, self-compassion, and empathy among health care professionals: A review of the literature. *Journal of Health Care Chaplaincy, 20*(3), 95-108.

16. Wasylyshyn, K. M., & Masterpasqua, F. (2018). Developing self-compassion in leadership development coaching: A practice model and case study analysis. *International Coaching Psychology Review, 13*(1), 21-34.

Index

A

C

D

H

About the author

Photo credit: Rosa Hardy

Michael West CBE is a Senior Visiting Fellow at The King's Fund, London, Professor of Organisational Psychology at Lancaster University, Visiting Professor at University College, Dublin, and Emeritus Professor at Aston University, where he was formerly Executive Dean of Aston Business School.

He graduated from the University of Wales in 1973 and was awarded a PhD in 1977 for research on the psychology of meditation. He has authored, edited and co-edited 20 books and has published more than 200 articles in scientific and practitioner publications on teamwork, innovation, leadership, and culture, particularly in healthcare. He is a Fellow of many professional associations including the British Psychological Society, the American Psychological Association, the Academy of Social Sciences, the International Association of Applied Psychologists, and he is an Honorary Fellow of the Royal College of Physicians and Surgeons of Glasgow.

He led the NHS England Policy Research Programme into cultures of quality and safety. He also led the design and implementation of the NHS Staff Survey. He assisted in developing the national framework in England, *Developing People, Improving Care (2016)* and the *Collective Leadership Strategy for Health and Social Care (2017*) in Northern Ireland. He is supporting Health Education and Improvement Wales's ten-year strategy for developing compassionate leadership across all of health and social care. Michael co-chaired, with Dame Denise Coia, the two-year inquiry on behalf of the UK General Medical Council into the mental health and well-being of doctors, *Caring for Doctors, Caring for Patients (2019)*. He also led the review for The King's Fund, commissioned by the Royal College of Nursing Foundation, into the mental health and well-being of nurses and midwives across the UK, *The Courage of Compassion: Supporting Nurses and Midwives to Deliver High Quality Care (2020)*.

Michael was appointed a CBE in the Queen's Birthday Honours List 2020 for services to compassion and innovation in healthcare.

Among his other books are:

West, M. A. (2012). *Effective teamwork: Practical lessons from organizational research* (3rd ed.). Oxford: Blackwell Publishing.

West, M. A. (Ed.). (2016). *The psychology of meditation: Research and practice.* Oxford: Oxford University Press.

Woods, S. & West, M. A. (2019). *The psychology of work and organizations* (3rd ed.). London: Cengage.

About the Swirling Leaf Press

The Swirling Leaf Press, compassionately led by Rachna Chowla, is an independent publisher that collaborates with non-fiction writers, especially poets, to help share their writing with others. The Press publishes work, that in some way, reinforces the awareness of love, truth and beauty. Where appropriate, we work pro bono to ensure our books are accessible and affordable to all, and that our authors retain the copyright of their work and their royalties. Working with a talented group of friends (copy-editors, designers and illustrators) we ensure that enlightened design and complementary illustrations make our books beautiful, inside and out, and that the author's words are given space to point to the love, truth and beauty in the content.

About this book

Each of our books has a unique story and if you are curious to know how this one came about, please visit our website: *www.swirlingleafpress.com*

Warm thanks to the people who helped this book find her wings: *Michael West*, the author, who it was a joy to work with, *Mash Chudasama*, our designer from *www.mash-design.com*, for his infinite patience and zen-like design, and *Veronica Fajardo*, our copy-editor, for her diligence, care and eye for detail.

Printed in Great Britain
by Amazon

86456157R00194